Books by Carl Jonas

BEACHHEAD ON THE WIND

SNOWSLIDE

JEFFERSON SELLECK

Jefferson Selleck

Jefferson Selleck

by

CARL JONAS

Little, Brown and Company · Boston

1952

For permission to use a parody of "M–O–T–H–E–R" (lyric by Howard
Johnson, music by Theodore Morse) the author thanks Leo Feist, Inc.

*Published simultaneously
in Canada by McClelland and Stewart Limited*

PRINTED IN THE UNITED STATES OF AMERICA
BY H. WOLFF, NEW YORK

To
Tukey

A Word from the Publishers

Fortunately Dr. John C. Crocker, in a very real sense, was already Jeff Selleck's editor long before we, the publishers, even knew of this book's existence. It was Dr. Crocker who suggested the book in the first place. And he and Jeff talked about it together frequently during the time of its composition.

Dr. Crocker was born in Gateway City, the setting of Jeff Selleck's life and story. In this Middlewestern town, ninety thousand persons at the time of their birth and some two hundred thousand today, the two men grew up, attended grade and high school together and also the State University. Through the next thirty-odd years they saw each other daily, played together and worked together too in the various civic enterprises to which they devoted their efforts.

And finally, during Jeff Selleck's illness, which is the specific period of this book, Dr. Crocker was Jeff's counselor as well as his physician.

Introduction by Dr. John C. Crocker

The task of editing Jeff Selleck's memoirs has been both a pleasant and a troubling one for me. Pleasant because it has recalled to my mind so many incidents which I had forgotten. And troubling because it is the story of my generation and my walk of life as much as it is that of Jeff's. Has there been meaning to a man's life in the last fifty years? This cannot but be a troubling question.

In this task I have followed a policy of saying as little as possible, leaving it to Jeff for the most part, filling in gaps mostly and even then, as far as possible, letting others fill in those gaps for me. After all this is Jeff's book.

This has been my conclusion.

In this book of Jeff's it seems to me that he says almost everything that there is to say about him. The only exception I would make to this is that he does not say anywhere what he physically looked like, and his appearance was impressive.

The following description is given by Tom Selleck, Jeff's son, and will serve.

Father stood about six feet two with his shoes off. He weighed around two hundred and fifty pounds, but he carried himself so well that he was always thought of as a big man, not a fat man.

Father had a square-faced honest look of homespun integrity, earnestness of aspect. His hair was blond. His eyes were blue. His complexion was pink. For that matter he was pink all over.

Father, one must face it, dressed badly. His suits always seemed to have a texture which was a little heavier, a little more burlaplike than the next man's. He got them from a tailor named Sol Klein over whose door was this legend: "Through these portals walk the best-dressed men in the world . . . my customers." Mr. Klein also made suits for "Honest Bob" Brady, who was mayor of Gateway City for so many years. For working in the yard or off on picnics Father liked to wear a pongee play suit, the shirt tails out and the neck open. In the summertime he wore shoes with myriads of perforations on the toes and insteps because "my feet sweat."

In another place Tom Selleck has given another picture of Jeff, this one with practically no clothes.

Father liked exercise. He used to carry the idea of physical fitness almost to the point of fetish. At one time he had a punching bag mounted on the side wall of our garage and he would go out there, very much to Mother's embarrassment, wearing a gray sweat suit which looked like old winter underwear. However, when he did his exercises in the house, as he did every morning, he wore only his jockey shorts, and it was then that he really became pink all over. He had a set of chest weights. He had a set of springs for developing the biceps which came from Charles Atlas. He had a rowing machine. His favorite was an exerciser called the "Panther Push."

Father, in action, would put his knees on the knee rests, bridge himself forward, and grasp the handlebars. Then he would push forward against the tension of the springs. Forward slowly. Backward slowly. It was marvelous, he said, for the intestines. "Keeps them from getting sluggish." But in spite of this advantage he was never able to get Mother to try it although frequently he urged her.

*   *   *

Yet Jeff did have delicate sensibilities. He did not swear or tell off-color stories when there were ladies present. And he could not stand the sight of suffering.

In the late autumn of 1949 Jeff, as have so many of his contemporaries, suffered a coronary occlusion (the physician's illness at one time, now that of the man of business) which forced him into retirement. One resulting problem, among many others, was idleness, and Jeff never before had been idle.

He begins his book with an attempt to describe rapidly the historical times he has lived through, the frame for the portrait so to speak, but with him as with all of us, the frame seems to be as much a part of the picture as the paint and canvas.

Contents

Jefferson Selleck

Seven Worlds of T. J. Selleck

I HAVE always been interested in the subject of history although I have never had the time to pursue it. But as an indication of the turn of my mind I will list the publications our family subscribes to. We take *Life, Time, U. S. News and World Report,* the *Saturday Evening Post,* and the *Reader's Digest.* These for myself. And in addition, for Gertrude,[1] we subscribe to *Vogue, Harper's Bazaar, House Beautiful* and *Town and Country.* But to me these last are of no interest. We belong to the Book-of-the-Month Club, but it is of very little interest to me for, with the exception of the Mr. Glencannon stories in the *Post,* I read almost no fiction.

No, my interests are serious for the most part. And of these serious interests I find history the most compelling of them all, even though I have never had the time to study extensively in it. Mr. H. G. Wells's book, *The Outline of History,* several years old now, is one of the best books of my acquaintance.

But to come to my point more quickly. My point is that for several years now I have become increasingly aware that history is all around us. And that is one of my reasons for wanting to put all of this down here.

"Your kind of a disease," Doc Crocker said to me a while ago, "is in a sense a disease of collapse, and in a number of these diseases recovery depends to some extent upon understanding —

---

[1] Gertrude is Mrs. Selleck, Gertrude McCullough before her marriage.

not only understanding of the disease but of the forces which brought it on and of the world around you, where you have come from, where you are, and where you hope to be going."

Where you have come from, where you are, and where you hope to be going: these to me make up the meaning of history, and explain why it seems to me that history is all around us. I am not a professional historian in any sense of the word, but I think I can tell about where I have come from as well as the next man can — that is, tell about it from the way I saw it.

History, it seems to me, is all around me and always has been all around me also, for in counting things up it seems to me that at the age of fifty-five I have lived through at least seven distinct historical epochs. The world of my youth extended roughly from the turn of the century to the sinking of the *Lusitania*. Then came the world of World War I and after that the world of the 1920's, which has a subworld within it which is that of the Prohibition era. The world of the Depression followed immediately after that of the 1920's. Then came the world of Franklin Roosevelt, the devil take him. The world of World War II, I thought for a time, would be the last one, but even now another one, one of atomic fission, seems to be in the making. In describing the worlds which I have seen I will describe the two World Wars in one section for the things I have to say about one apply to the other also. The world prior to the First World War I will talk about much later on. The worlds between the two World Wars I will deal with in chronological order.

2

In 1919 when I returned to the United States from France, where I served with the Forty-second Division, better known as the Rainbow Division, I made my first trip to New York City where I saw the sights as any boy from the Middle West would naturally see them. Among the sights I saw was the Statue of Liberty, and I, with a party of sight-seers, went up inside of it.

As I remember there was a large space within the head of
Liberty in which our party assembled and looked out through
the eyes at New York Harbor. A guard was stationed at this point
and to this guard one of the ladies of our party said, "How does
one get into the wings, sir?"

The guard answered, "The wings? There ain't no wings. This
is Liberty, lady, not a gosh darn angel."

And this, to my mind, is what both wars have been about,
and it is also the lesson which they have taught us. Liberty,
lady, is not a gosh darn angel. And this was as true of the last
war as it was of the first one. For liberty you have to pay a price
and the big price, over and above war, seems to me to be change,
things changing all the time at two or three or four miles a
minute. I do not mean to say that I am against progress, but
sometimes I have wished that progress had not been quite so
progressive. Progress, Doc Crocker says, is not entirely uncon-
nected with coronary occlusions.

The price of liberty is progress, but after all it seems to me
to be as good a thing as anything else to lay your life down
for.

The First World War, to my mind, was not progress so much
in itself as a thing which touched it off, touched it off faster
than any of us had ever expected, for even against our wills it
seemed as though it was impossible to "keep us down on the
farm after we had seen Paree." And this last war has had almost
the same result to my mind. Not so much of progress happened
while it was going on either, but Lord the things which have
happened since it has ended. Every day it has seemed to me that
there has been some kind of change to cope with.

Where it was automobiles and radios after the first one, it's
jet-propelled aeroplanes and television sets now after this one.
Where it was trade unions and socialists after the first one it's
these new Labor Trusts [2] and Communists we now have to deal
with. And where it used to be Mr. Hull's reciprocal trade treaties

----

[2] Mr. Selleck means the C.I.O. mostly.

today it's the Marshall Plan and what not. Sam Zadina [3] has
said crudely, but aptly, "It used to be a matter of lifting up
the skirts, but now it's one of pulling the pants down mostly.
And those things for an old-timer get confusing."

Yes, these are the things which war and progress have brought
us, and while I believe implicitly in progress, sometimes I am
bewildered by this world which seems to have changed a good
deal faster than I have.

But if these things are the price, liberty is still, as I have said,
the thing they buy for us.

What is the good of liberty, one sometimes cannot help but
ask. Unfortunately I do not know except that it is a thing without which life, for me anyway, would be almost devoid of meaning. I am not exactly sure that Patrick Henry, so long ago, was
any smarter man than I am, but I am quite sure that he was expressing fundamental truth in his famous statement. And to those
who say that going to war has not brought liberty to us I can only
say that not going to war would have left us with a darn sight
less of it.

A wise old Frenchman whom I met in Paris when I had a pass
there in 1918 said to me, "Every man who lives has to see at
least two wars and, if he is unlucky, three of them."

It seems to me that possibly I am going to be one of the unlucky ones. Or possibly it is that my generation is an unlucky
one, for we have all seen two, and I cannot help but think that
despite that ex-haberdashery salesman who assures us that
"peace was never closer," [4] a third world war is now in the making. This being true, how does a man face the third war of his
lifetime?

During World War I the platoon sergeant over me was a man
named Thomas and he was probably the toughest man I have

---

[3] Sam Zadina was City Park Commissioner of Gateway City. He was
one of Mr. Selleck's best friends and he enters Mr. Selleck's story in numerous places.

[4] All of Mr. Selleck's dictations were made during the spring of 1950
when the war in Korea was not yet even thought of and when Mr. Truman
was saying that "peace was never closer."

ever known or ever shall know. He stood about five feet high, about five feet broad, and had cauliflower ears on both sides. Once upon a time in a bar I saw him deal with a sailor who was trying to start a fight. "Look here, Shorty," the sailor said to him, "don't get me started on you because I'll make a meal out of you if I do." Thomas answered, "That's all right, sailor, but just remember that while you're having a meal I'll be having myself a sandwich."

I am no expert on foreign affairs, but I would say that a man or a country with Thomas's attitude stays out of as much trouble as it gets into.[5]

3

These comments, as the reader can see, are for the most part random thoughts. I am not a professional writer, not even an amateur one for that matter. I mean that I only want to say here the things which I think are important.

After the First War came Prohibition, and it is about the Prohibition era that I want to speak now for a moment. And, bad as it was, there were a great many things about it which I am glad were included within my lifetime. The speak-easies, the bathtub gin, the gangsters: I do not regret that I knew them.

And while I am thinking about bathtub gin I think, as a matter of historical interest, I would like to say just how we made it. And in the first place I want to say that we never did make it in a bathtub. At least I never did, and no one I ever knew did, nor can I imagine why any man of sense ever would make it in a bathtub. What we used were gallon jugs which were ideal for the purpose.

A bathtub would be much too large for any kind of convenient home manufacture even supposing a home did possess a spare bath to use for this purpose. Then in addition consider the prob-

[5] As a past Commander of his Legion Post and as a holder of the Distinguished Service Cross some respect must be paid to Mr. Selleck's point of view in these matters.

lem of decanting the gin into bottles once the product has been completed. I doubt if the most efficient siphon known would be able to do the job without wasting at least a gallon. A washtub might conceivably be practical, but certainly not a bathtub.

Gallon jugs were the best thing. You filled the jug a third to a half, depending on how high a proof you desired, with grain alcohol which you obtained from the bootlegger who served you. And to this you added juniper extract which you could buy from your druggist and which was specially prepared for the purpose. There were directions on the little bottle, but mostly you mixed the juniper in to taste. And to that you added a little glycerine, but with the glycerine you had to be careful. Glycerine is a smoothing agent, but it must be remembered that what goes down smoothly can sometimes come up quickly also. When you had added the juniper and glycerine you filled the rest of the jug with distilled water and simply shook it. Then you labeled the jug "Gilbey's" or "Gordon's" or whatever brand name most struck your fancy.

This bathtub gin was an institution of the period, but the institution to which I look backward with especial fondness was not that one. The speak-easy is the institution about which I can become more sentimental. Illegal, corrupt, wrong, as the speakeasy most certainly was, there was still something about it, a kind of camaraderie, perhaps, which has vanished with it. For historical interest I have just described the making of bathtub gin. For historical interest also I will now describe the speak-easy as I knew it, for we had it in almost all of its varieties right here in Gateway City, as everywhere. We had everything, in fact, from the simple beer flat, usually in an apartment or private home where a man was simply trying to make an honest humble dollar, to the Hound and Hare Club which occupied a three-room suite in the Gateway Hotel where the Junior Chamber of Commerce offices now are. Between these two extremes were all manner of other places, Jack's Filling Station at Twentieth and Adams Streets, Mae's Place west of town outside the city limits, Jim's Place out of town also, where in addition to liquor there was gambling, or Club Reno which was very similar to a number of night clubs of the present moment. There were also the Italian Steak houses which served wine, and then a dozen or so low places along Railroad Avenue where needle-beer, ether beer that is, could be obtained, but no one went to those places except college boys and hobos.

Of them all I suppose Jack's Filling Station was as typical as any, and will serve as a good example. It was in a basement, and that underground feeling, first of all, gave it a fine illegal flavor which to some extent you already had before you got there, because on the way you would have passed through the gas house part of Gateway and gone by the great big dark gas tanks. The room was rectangular, the walls of it whitewashed brick. At one end was a bar. There were low booths around the walls. There were tables and chairs in the center, red checked tablecloths on the tables. On one side of the room was a low platform on which an orchestra could sit, for on some nights of the week the tables were pushed back for dancing. It was always clean and fairly orderly and very much like a hundred joints today except for the fact that a very fine class of people patronized it and that it was always noisier and friendlier than any places are or ever have been since Prohibition ended.

At Jack's we always drank gin rickeys and they cost us thirty-five cents or three for a dollar. Generally we got them three at a time in a tumbler, a drink known as a "three-in-one." A gin rickey, as everyone knows, is simply powdered sugar, gin, and lime juice. Usually that was what we drank there, but if we wanted whisky we usually bought it by the bottle, pint bottle that is, for the flat pint was designed expressly to be carried in the pocket, which was the way most liquor was carried in those days.

What was that whisky made out of?

Well, at Jack's, although it was labeled Scotch, Rye, or Bourbon, it was all the same and made out of potatoes.

Now there was one unique feature of Jack's, and this I would also like to mention. When you bought a pint from Jack he would

send his wife out to the shed behind which was where they kept
it. She was a short fat Italian woman with a very large bosom,
and that was where she kept your pint during her walk back
with it. There it would be, when she would come back in,
snuggled between her breasts, the liquor itself sometimes a little
warm from her body. "Mrs. Jack's milk," we used to call it.

Another historical item. The pint would cost you three dollars
and a half. They must have made an enormous profit.

Poor Jack, I see him occasionally today. With the end of Prohibition he was unable ever to stand up against legal competi-
tion. Today he is driving a truck for the city Park Department,
a job which Sam Zadina got him.

Jack's Filling Station was typical of the time, but now I would
like to describe the Hound and Hare, which was very special
and also the place I most frequently went to. In fact along with
Sam Zadina and others I helped to get it started. It was on the
third floor of the Gateway Hotel, a convenient place to go before
lunch or for a drink before going home in the evening to dinner.
It wasn't so much like a saloon. It was much more like a men's
club. And it was with the men's club idea in mind that all of
us put up the money to get it started. I don't mean to say that
we made any rules against women being there, but it was understood that no women ever would come except in the evenings
and then only with their husbands.

There were a number of us younger men who used to meet
at the Hound and Hare before the Carpe Diem Club luncheons,[6]
and since then the same group of us have formed a little lunch
club of our own which we call the Chowder and Marching
Society, one of the pleasantest associations of my lifetime. In
those days, though, we would meet for a drink, shoot poker dice
to see who picked up the check, and then go on downstairs in
the hotel for luncheon. However if you cared to you could have
the hotel room service bring up sandwiches or almost anything

[6] The Carpe Diem Club is a businessman's lunch club meeting on the
first and third Thursdays of the month. At one time Mr. Selleck was president of Carpe Diem.

you wanted. It was the only exclusive speak-easy in the city and you actually had to have cards to be admitted.

As I have said there were three rooms to the Hound and Hare, the bar being a very small one, in the room in the center. The walls of the rooms were painted a soft green color and for furniture we had overstuffed red leather armchairs and sofas. On the walls were colored prints of game birds. In one room for a while we had a stock ticker in operation. You could even place a bet on a horse up there if you cared to, for Sam Zadina had a cousin who was a bookie who hung out there.

I have described the Hound and Hare because I had an affection for it. But I have another reason in doing so also. It was at the Hound and Hare that I spent the last night of Prohibition and Gertrude was there with me. It was this last moment of Prohibition which I would now like to describe here.

It was completely out of sentiment that Gertrude and I went there on that last evening. The end of Prohibition we definitely sensed was going to be the end of something, and the Hound and Hare was the most suitable place we knew of in which to pay a last tribute to the era. A number of our friends must have felt the same way because the place was quite full when we got there.

It was crowded, as I have said, but it was also very quiet. People were drinking in an orderly way and speaking to each other in low voices. There was even a table of bridge as I remember. It was this way all evening until just before midnight when George, the bartender, came around and let us all order our last illegal drink. Then after he had served this last round he announced that it was on the house. Then he did something unprecedented in nature. He made himself a drink and came out from behind the bar to drink it. He announced that after midnight the Hound and Hare would forever close its doors to business. It was a sad announcement, and all of us felt its sadness. And as a matter of fact, all over the city, speak-easies would be closing up, some temporarily and some forever. They were all frightened, frightened to death of all the problems of becoming

legal. They all knew that in an honest business they just didn't
know how to compete with practiced merchants.

All of us in the room stood up to drink our last drink there and
George, standing in front of the bar which he had tended for
so long, proposed a toast which went as follows:

> May you live a thousand years,
> And may I live a thousand years less one day,
> For what care I for anything
> When my friends have passed away?

All of us drank to that and then all of us linked arms and sang
"Auld Lang Syne" just the way people do on New Year's Eve
except that on New Year's Eve people are always joyful and kissing each other while on this night which was the end of Prohibition all of us felt sad and doubtful of the future. It just
seemed as though that drink might be the last drink we would
all have together and some of us were crying during the singing.
And all of us sang with feeling:

> Should auld acquaintance be forgot
>   And never brought to mind? . . .
> We'll tak' a cup o' kindness yet
>   For auld lang syne.

It was a sad sad evening.

4

Why the 1920's were maligned for so long a time, really right
up to the present, I have no idea. As for me, when I think of the
"good old days" as often as not I think of the era of Calvin
Coolidge. And I think of it not without good reason.

First of all we enjoyed peace during the Harding and Coolidge
administrations, unparalleled national growth, prosperity, and
plenty. For example in 1929 A. T. & T. was selling at 335 and
General Motors at 396. I did not hold any A. T. & T. or General
Motors, but I would like to have, and I still feel the same way
about it. Westinghouse traded at 313, to name another. And

American investments abroad were valued at seven and a half billion dollars, which may not seem a high figure in the inflated values of the moment but which if you face it represented a tremendous business. People for a long time seemed to forget these things about the 1920's and seemed to remember only the tragic stock market crash or the unfortunate President Harding. What they do not seem to remember is that during the 1920's we came as close to realizing the great American dream as we ever have come.

The American dream, or at least my American dream, is simply the creation of a *status quo* of ever expanding markets, ever expanding production, opportunity, peace, freedom, and plenty for all men whosoever they may be. And perhaps this statement sounds naïve today, but there were a great many men who believed it in the mid-1920's I can assure you. There were a great many of us, in fact, who believed that we almost had achieved it. I suppose that that sounds naïve too, but, as I have said somewhere already, there used to be a kind of naïveté in the world which there isn't any more, and I for one am not happy that we have lost it.

To me those were great days, and they will always be great days to look back to. And because they were so great the Crash which brought them to an end seems doubly tragic. In fact it is my feeling that if the Crash could have been held off for a year it never would have been the Crash which we remember but simply a Wall Street Panic. Mr. Hoover was already at work correcting the abuses in our system . . . I won't deny that there were grave abuses . . . and in another year, I am sure, it would have been impossible for anything like what did happen to have happened.[7]

[7] Possibly it is difficult for a depression-bred generation to take Mr. Selleck seriously here, but in 1928 and later such ideas were not uncommon. Early in the Depression Andrew Mellon, then Secretary of the Treasury, made the following statement, "The nation will make steady progress in 1930. I see nothing in the present system that is either menacing or warrants pessimism." In 1931 Mr. Hoover said, "Whatever the immediate difficulties may be we know they are transitory in our lives and in the life of the nation."

But if the Depression need not have happened who is to blame then?

Mr. Hoover?

I would certainly say no, for to my mind Mr. Hoover has been one of the few great and surely consistent figures of the times we live in.

I blame a great many people. And among them, I am sorry to say, are a number of men of high finance and business who lacked the faith apparently which the times demanded. I suppose that today very few people recall the "Swope Plan" which Gerard Swope of the General Electric Company first proposed before the National Electrical Association in 1931 at the Hotel Commodore in New York City, a plan in which he virtually conceded the failure of the Capitalistic system. But Mr. Swope was not alone in loss of faith. Among the mighty there were enough others. It seems to me that Mr. Hoover alone kept the faith and saw that the panic of '29 was essentially no different, except in magnitude, from the panics of '21, '93, or '57.

Mr. Hoover alone, it seems to me, remembered our American birthright, and I am very glad to see that along with a re-evaluation of the 1920's has come a re-evaluation of Herbert Hoover also.

And to me the great irony of it all was that Hoover almost succeeded in conquering the Depression and probably would have succeeded had it not been for a few circumstances over which he had no control such as the fact that England, very inopportunely, went off the Gold Standard and, also unfortunately, our western farmers were suddenly assailed by unprecedented droughts and dust storms.

Ironically also the most successful programs of the New Deal were merely extensions of the Hoover program.

And despicably Mr. Hoover's reward was unparalleled vilification. He was called a fool and a man without sympathy or feeling, but he was the same man who had fed the Belgians and who said in those dark days, "No man with a spark of humanity can sit in my place without suffering from the picture of their [the people of this country] anxieties and hardships before him day and night."

However these are all matters which rightly belong in the next section of what I have to say, rather than this one. I am actually still talking about the 1920's and I want to conclude this matter with a description of how, for me, the 1920's ended.

My Father [8] was seventy years old in 1929 and it was at a birthday party which he gave for himself that for me the 1920's ended. At that time Father was still hale and hearty and active in his business and at that time I, as my brother Will is yet, was still in the firm of Selleck and Company. Father lived alone with a housekeeper then for Mother, of course, was no longer with us.

Father usually was not a man to pay much attention to his birthdays, but on this, his seventieth, he seemed to feel that it had special importance. Will and his wife were there, Gertrude and I; Caroline made a special trip for it from Kansas City. Only John, who lives in the East now, was not present. [9]

It was not a large dinner, just the six of us and Father's housekeeper who sat down at the table with us, for Father, being a very democratic man, detested the idea of servility of any kind in a servant, although he rather liked it in members of his family. The house was a small and somewhat ugly one which had come to him through the necessity of foreclosing on a mortgage in 1923, although he was really a very wealthy man and could have had a fine house if he had so desired. There was golden-oak woodwork in the living room and in the dining room a chandelier over the table with glass pendants from it which looked like old-fashioned horehound candy. For dinner we had

[8] This would be Mr. Luke Selleck (1859–1934), who came to Gateway City from Illinois in 1884. He was in the real estate business and Selleck and Company is still one of the most prominent real estate firms in the city. Mrs. Luke Selleck, Mary, died in 1925.

[9] Mr. Selleck was the youngest of five children who were born in this order: Will (1886), Luke (1888 and died in his twelfth year), Caroline (1889), John (1891), and Thomas Jefferson (1894), who is the subject of this volume.

fried chicken, boiled potatoes, peas and carrots; nothing to drink, of course, for Father did not believe in drinking.

Father's birthday, it so happened, was on October 24 and October 24, 1929, if you will recall, was the day on which a number of stocks listed on the New York Stock Exchange could find no buyers whatsoever. And so as we sat down to dinner we were all quite conscious of this evidence of a national economic stricture.

And Father, although he never traded in the market for he considered the market sinful, was as conscious as any of the rest of us of the disaster, and he must have been thinking about it deeply.

Before seating ourselves we stood behind our chairs as he gave the blessing.

"O Lord," he prayed, "look down upon this sinful nation and grant to it, in Thine infinite mercy, that its financial structure shall begin recovering on the morrow. I am not in the stock market, as Thou knowest, O Lord, but in the real estate business and have always been Thy servant. However, as Thou may not know, not being a man of business, the present market condition puts in sore straits all of Thy humble servants. O Lord, in Thine infinite mercy and wisdom, suggest to a few men of the caliber of Mr. J. P. Morgan, Mr. Thomas W. Lamont, or Mr. Richard Whitney and others that they with their infinite resources form a pool for bolstering up the market. And now bless this food to its intended use. Amen."

A most dramatic proof of the efficacy of prayer came on the next morning for Mr. Richard Whitney, floor operator for the Morgan Company entered the Stock Exchange and bid U. S. Steel at 205, which at the moment was trading at 193.

This was how, for me, the 1920's ended.

5

After God's, or Mr. Morgan's efforts to bolster the market failed, the action of the tragedy began in earnest, and we all lost faith and all went from the best of times to the worst of times with a rapidity which hardly can be imagined. And then to make folly complete in the next presidential election we put into office as our Chief Executive a Pied Piper whose only consistent policy seemed to be that of making the disaster of the moment a permanent condition. It was the end of straight thinking. We were all to live from then on in permanent confusion.

There are intemperate persons who would say that Franklin Roosevelt did it only through a lust for power, and who would say also that he had no intention of doing anything for any other reason. I never believed that. I was always of the more charitable school which considered him a gifted madman, for no one can deny that he was gifted.

But at any rate there we were bogged down in the deepest ruts of Depression and I shall never forget the Depression as I saw it in Gateway City.

Real estate, which was still at that time my business, was shot completely. Credit was either frozen or else there was none of it at all. Rents were down. Wages were down. The only thing which was up was unemployment. Gertrude and I were forced to resign our memberships in the Sleepy Hollow Country Club, as were most of our friends, and this was the only time we have ever been forced to do so.

I did not lose any money in the market for, out of respect to my Father's convictions, whatever money I had I had in farm mortgages, but these were really no more value to me than would have been a block of shares in Wildcat Mining, although I will say this in witness to Father's wisdom: those farms have paid off well, better than well, in these 1940's.[10] I was forced to foreclose those mortgages, but that only meant then that I had to maintain farms which could hardly pay their taxes. And in addition to everything else in and around Gateway we suffered from the dust storms. I do not mean that we had the real ones like

[10] Mr. Selleck's two farms paid him in 1949 in the neighborhood of $2000 on a valuation of something like $18,000. And this represents only a half share in the profits.

they had in Oklahoma, Kansas, and parts of Nebraska, but the
ones which did come to us were sufficiently shocking to disturb
one.

It is very hard to describe even a little dust storm to anyone
who has not gone through one. There would be periods of days
at a time when the sun at noon was only a red disk no bigger
than a penny, and daylight was always at least as dark as twilight. A housewife in Gateway could dust a table and then, with
doors and windows closed tightly all the while, in half an hour
be able to write her name on that table with her finger. I cannot
hope to describe the feeling of living for days in that continuous
red twilight or even the physical discomfort. But it was neither
of these matters which was the most appalling. The most appalling was the feeling that the wrath of God was upon one and not
only was the economic structure of the country crumbling but
the very land itself was blowing away and perhaps forever.

I had always enjoyed driving in the country around Gateway
heretofore. I had always found a sense of peace and security
in looking at the rolling green and growing country, but during
those years of the Depression that pleasure was denied me. In
an afternoon of driving you did not see a farmhouse or barn with
a fresh coat of paint on it — or any paint at all for that matter.
And not a mile outside of Gateway City I have actually seen
tumbleweed rolling across the highway. A daily sight was a
caravan of dusted-out farmers in their old and broken-down
trucks heading west for California. And the most awful sight of
all of those times I shall now describe to you.

It was an afternoon, late afternoon or early evening, in the
November of 1933, which for us was the worst year of the Depression. I had been out in the state, for it had been necessary
for me to tend personally to some business concerning the farms
of mine which I have mentioned. In this moment of late afternoon I was in my car heading back for Gateway.

The country around me looked big, bare, cold, and dead,
everything a drab brown color, and the fields made you think
that the country was simply going back to Great American

Prairie. The few and far between farmhouses hardly looked like habitations at all, and the windmills beside them seemed to lean with the wind behind them. The highway was a straight ribbon of concrete like a chalk line across the rolling hills and hummocks. I was at a point about twenty miles west of Gateway close to the Waubaunsee River, where I have frequently gone duck shooting, when the things which I am about to describe happened.

I topped a low ridge and saw down at the bridge across the Waubaunsee a collection of automobiles and trucks which at first suggested a wreck upon the highway, but as I approached I saw that what I was encountering was a road block. A rough barricade had been thrown across the entrance to the bridge, and sitting on a box in the middle of the highway was a farmer in a sheepskin coat holding a shotgun. There were some fifteen or twenty other farmers standing about and they too were carrying shotguns, and there were some others who were busy inspecting the cars and trucks which were drawn up there. The passenger cars were being passed through the barricade quickly, but the trucks for the most part were being detained. Just ahead of my car was a large truck filled with milk cans, and a group of farmers had taken off the tail gate of it, and they were busily pouring the milk out into the highway from which it ran off on either side to make mud down in the ditches.

This, as you have already guessed, was one of the farmers' strikes of the 1930's. They were destroying food in hopes of raising prices. I shall never forget how shocked I was at that moment. I shall never forget how awful it seemed to see milk, needed by children in Gateway, making mud on the roadside. I was frightened. I was not frightened for myself but for the land I lived in. When farmers, normally the most conservative of men, start destroying food you cannot help but know that times are desperate.

That was the way it was in the country, and in the city it was not any better, especially in some of the parts of the city I had to go into on Selleck and Company business, for we held

a great deal of cheap housing here and there about the city.
I saw the bread lines and the soup kitchens which everyone has
heard of. Down in South Gateway around the packing houses I
saw the lines of men waiting outside of the hiring offices where
actually there was no employment for them. When the hiring for
the day was over the lines would break up into little groups of
men, some of them angry, some of them hopeless looking. On the
edges of Gateway, and down by the city dumps, I saw the so-
called "Hoovervilles" which were shanty towns made up of
homemade houses and boxes which people lived in.

I have tried to speak of the various epochs through which I
have lived in the light of their influence on us and how they
changed our ways of thinking. To me the Depression seems to
have changed Americans more than either of the wars we have
passed through. It followed so closely after our time of greatest
triumph, and it turned our American Dream, at least for a time,
into an American Nightmare. Two wars perhaps destroyed our
faith in peace and security, but the Depression destroyed our
faith in money.

To me one of the most awful personal tragedies I saw happened on one of the farms which we had to foreclose on. I was
sent out to talk to the farmer, who wanted to pull out while we
wanted him to stay on as a tenant. At the farmhouse his wife
told me that he was in the barn. He was in the barn all right, for
he had hung himself from a rafter.

6

I firmly believe that the election of 1932 was the greatest
catastrophe of the time of which I am now speaking. I have
described the man as a Pied Piper, and that was exactly what
he was, for like the rats and children of Hamelin town in the
poem we were piped down the road to ruin by this gaudy figure.
He was a piper, and what a piper!

He was a man who never earned an honest dollar, never met
a pay roll, knew nothing about business. He was one of those

charming fellows, and, like a lot of charming fellows, had never
had to work very hard for any of the things he wanted. He was
a butterfly, and he diverted the glance from one of his failures
by flitting on to another. This is not my personal opinion alone.
I was fortunate enough to meet at a luncheon once a man who
had grown up with him and known him. "Franklin," the man
said — "why I wouldn't hire him as a ten-dollar law clerk." And
then he hastily amended himself saying, "Did I say ten-dollar?
I meant to say five-dollar."

Well, if you look at the basic F.D.R., and God knows we did
look at him long enough, what do you see there? You see an
invalid, a cripple, and a megalomania typical of the cripple.
Perhaps he was not mad actually, but he obviously had the seeds
of madness in him. "I hate wah," he said again and again and
again, but who, I ask you, was foremost in dragging us on toward
Pearl Harbor?

Finally in an analysis of the man one must remember his
aristocratic birth. Your aristocrat can rarely judge soundly outside of his limited sphere of reference. In regard to the common
man he tends either toward the fault of overcynicism or toward
that of oversentimentality. And it is the distinction of Franklin
Roosevelt that he managed to contain both faults in his single
person.

Now in the light of this brief analysis of the man we can go
into his administration and examine the devastating effects it
had upon us.

It started well enough with ringing words and phrases: "The
only thing we have to fear is fear itself"; "Plenty is at our door-
step, but the generous use of it languishes in the very sight of
supply." Whatever these words meant I have no idea, but when
he said them they sounded very stirring. He was the greatest
of American orators since William Jennings Bryan, and as with
Bryan it was sometimes difficult to know what he meant after
he had stopped speaking.

Things began with these fine phrases and a United States Senate investigation of banking. Well, possibly the investigation was

not instigated by the man for he was not yet in office when it
started, but at least it was instigated by a Democratic Congress.
It may even have been justified by events of the times, but the
way it was carried out showed that actually it was nothing more
nor less than an attempt to undermine the foundations of capitalistic practice. Respected men from respected banking houses
were dragged in one after another and held up to ridicule in one
way or another. Reputable men of finance and business were
pilloried without mercy. Mr. George Whitney of the Morgan
Bank, Mr. Donald Durant of Lee, Higginson and Company of
Boston, Charles E. Mitchell of the National City Bank, Rudolph
Spreckels of Kolster Radio Corporation, and many others were
questioned in a way which was insulting.

And now it is interesting to ask just what these men were
accused of for the whole thing took the form of an accusation.
Much was made out of such very common practices as Pools,
Syndicates, Price Pegging, Cut-ins, Preferred Lists, and so forth
which were in no way illegal but which, by malicious craftiness
on the part of the investigators, were made to appear as iniquities
beyond imagination. Actually there was nothing iniquitous about
them. They were simply practices known to everyone except
the naïve and the lambs come up for shearing.

The only result of this investigation was the only result which
might have been expected, a loss of faith on the part of the
common man in his established leaders. The man who knew
nothing of money then rushed to his bank to withdraw his savings; so bank runs were added in this manner, bank runs in unprecedented numbers, to the panic already rampant.

What it all amounted to was an assault on the whole philosophy
of business, a philosophy which was so simple and straight-
forward that actually a child could have understood it. In the
beginning there was enterprise which created earning. And earning created saving and from saving was derived investment. And
investment finished the cycle by again creating earning, the
whole thing becoming a never-ending spiral of continuous en-
richment. But you would have thought that that was a sin at

that moment. The fine words and ringing phrases were always there to delude you. For a while even we businessmen who should have known better believed them and were lambs bleating happily as the old black goat led us down to the slaughter. Six months later we knew better, but it was too late by that time to do much more than fight a defensive battle.

He closed all the banks as soon as he came into office which he had to do because I don't suppose that he ever did want complete ruin. He closed up the banks and then started the so-called "One Hundred Days" which changed America so completely and at the end of which we, who were sound citizens, knew pretty well what we were in for.

Occasionally I have tried to explain these things to Tom, my son, but he does not seem to be able to understand them. Perhaps none of his generation can fully understand them, and possibly this is why I am trying to set these things down here. The war, and the Service, seemed to straighten Tom out on a great many matters, but in these he still seems to retain a large blind spot. But to get on with what I was saying. . . .

There is neither time nor space here for me to deal with the whole of the Roosevelt era as it happened. And there is no need for me to do so either. The first six months . . . the first three, for that matter . . . are sufficient. We knew after that that we had been sold down the river.

At the end of this time we had gone off of the Gold Standard, and the Gold Standard had always been our anchor to windward.[11] We had the government right in the middle of business with the passing of the Securities Exchange Act, which although it did correct abuses that had to be corrected still contained limitations on business over which our forefathers would have shuddered. The government, by the end of the One Hundred Days, was not only in business but in agriculture also when in May the Agricultural Adjustment Act came into being, fixing farm prices, dictating acreages, paying men for not planting, and

[11] Mr. Selleck is wrong here. At the time he is mentioning the United States had been on the Gold Standard for less than fifty years.

killing little pigs to hold down production. In June we got the National Industrial Recovery Act, the forty-hour week, the recognition of labor unions and General Hugh Johnson, who had the manners and the intellect of an old-time master sergeant. After that the agencies began to multiply so rapidly that no man could keep track of them: the CCC, the CWA, the TVA, the PWA, the leaf rakers, the shovel leaners, the Brain Trusters, Rex Tugwell, Henry Wallace, Raymond Moley, and all the others, "Tommy the Cork" and so forth, plus an electorate so debauched as to feel that it was right and proper for them to get everything they could for nothing. I suppose that it is not strange that young people growing up under this kind of insanity find it difficult to recognize sanity when I tell it to them. I suppose that it is natural, but it is nonetheless alarming. And they ask me rather patiently, "Just what is it that you find so disturbing?"

What I find so disturbing and what to me characterizes it, its philosophy, and everything about it, is a kind of topsy-turvy upsidedownness contrary to all rational thinking. For example we, of my generation, had never before heard of curing hard times by taking it easy or of getting more by working less, which is what the philosophy of the forty-hour week argues. To my mind the man-productivity ratio has to increase, not diminish as it has been doing.

Another example, if another is necessary, was the New Deal idea of the relationship between productivity and wages. A man's wage, we had always believed, had something to do with the amount of goods he produced while he was working. But the Brain Trusters told us that this was unimportant and that our employees were already producing more per unit of time than they should be producing. Wages, the new thought told us, were only important for the amount of buying power . . . "Get that buying power" . . . which they created, and the trouble with the country was only that buying power had diminished because of a severe deflation which had knocked the buyer out of buying. To increase buying power, then, you were to hold wages up as high as you could and also hold up employment, and all of it was crystal clear except for one thing which was how, while you were doing this, did you keep from going bankrupt?

That was half the answer. The other half was what was called "pump priming," which actually meant tax business heavily and pour the money down the drain.

What all of this adds up to was that all our values, all the values which we had grown up with, were reversed completely. If you were poor you no longer practiced thrift. Instead you "spent your way out of a depression." You no longer conquered hard times through hard work and long hours. Instead you joined the WPA and leaned on the handle of a shovel. You were no longer the captain of your fate or of your soul. You filled out forms in triplicate and quadruplicate and hired an extra bookkeeper to keep them straight for you.

Pump priming was based upon the principle that water runs uphill, for this was the way it set about establishing a recovery in business. You gave money to the men in the shop or out of work completely on the theory that it would trickle slowly up to the men in the top office, and Mr. Hoover, who believed that water ran downhill, was laughed at for his contention. A little illustration from my own company will show who was right in this matter.

In 1933 in the Yaw-Et-Ag Manufacturing Company,[12] which was less than a year old at that time, we were as hard pressed, if not more so, as all the other businesses in Gateway. In fact we were so close to going out of business that it was a miracle that we did not. And it was only through the timely availability of ten thousand dollars from a source which I may not here divulge[13] that we did survive.

[12] The Yaw-Et-Ag Manufacturing Company, Mr. Selleck's business, was founded by him, Mr. Bert Bernstein, and Mr. Jake Brawn in 1932. Mr. Bernstein and Mr. Brawn are mentioned later on when Mr. Selleck describes the founding of the business. The name Yaw-Et-Ag, which sounds peculiar, is also explained at length in a later passage.

[13] However Mr. Selleck, further on, does divulge the source of this ten thousand dollars. Oddly it came from Miss Helen Flanagan, who was his secretary, and the sum, as he says later, must have represented her life savings.

But be that as it may, my point is this, that a contribution of ten thousand dollars at the bottom of the business, say to the machinists and shop foremen, would not have helped Yaw-Et-Ag very much, but this contribution being made at the topmost level not only pulled us through but put us on the paying basis on which we have operated ever since.

It was not the New Deal which pulled us through, I am saying. It was in spite of it that we survived, and in a measure I think that the same thing could be said of the whole country.[14]

(*Mr. Selleck does not seem to have been quite finished with his remarks here, but the record stops at this point, probably because he had come to the end of the tape on which he was recording at this moment and did not want to introduce a new one at the time. On the new tape he goes on, however, as though he actually had concluded the above.*)

With the exceptions of the periods of the immediate present and that of my boyhood and young manhood, both of which I'll get to later, I have here tried to sketch in briefly the times through which I have lived, the framework so to speak on which everything else has, and has had to have, been hung.

"This is Liberty, lady, not a gosh darn angel."

> *God Bless America,*
> *Land that I love*
> *Stand beside her and guide her*
> *Thru the night with a light from above.**

For me it has been a rather ghostly business reliving the times which Jeff has mentioned. Much of what he says I agree with and with much of it I disagree also. But all of it I lived through.

While Jeff is probably right, I do not remember Prohibition

[14] But in spite of Mr. Selleck's disapproval of the entire New Deal, he was not too proud to avail himself of government aids upon the farms he owned, the CCC and WPA soil erosion and conservation projects in particular.

ending in Gateway with the sharpness which Jeff describes although, because of the way laws are written, it really must have. But even if other things did not terminate so abruptly the Hound and Hare, as he says, did.

In the next section Jeff is no longer in the realm of history, but in the realm of himself and his illness. He described what I have already mentioned, how his book came into being.

How This Book Came to Be Written

CRXXS

I<small>T</small> IS a matter of curiosity but not of importance to anyone, except to me, how this book happened to be written . . . or to be dictated rather, for without the aid of a tape recorder I doubt if I could have done it, or even started it for that matter.

Why should a Middle Western small manufacturer suffering from a coronary occlusion . . . heart attack in English . . . in enforced retirement, idle and deviled for a want of occupation with which to fill his time, feel that he must set down his life story? There is nothing unusual about this man here. There is nothing to set him apart from a million or more men like him. These are not the War Diaries of Winston Churchill. These are not the revelations of Generals Eisenhower or Marshall. There is nothing unusual or dramatic, one soon finds out, about a man who finds in middle life that his physical system has gone on a sit-down strike on him.

It was a cold Sunday afternoon in mid-December. The occlusion had occurred in mid-November. The intervening time, for the most part, had been spent at Saint Luke's Hospital where I was taken almost within an hour of the attack. But on this Sunday afternoon in mid-December I was at home again and I had been there for almost a week already. While I had been in Saint Luke's the idea of going home had been a kind of goal and I had expected that once I did get home everything would be somehow different.

It had not been different at all. I had been confined to one floor of the house and mostly to my bedroom. I was regimented to a reducing diet, for Doc Crocker had decided that I was some twenty-five pounds too heavy. I was dependent upon Gertrude for my wants for the most part. I was not allowed to answer or use the telephone inasmuch as it was felt that the telephone had been one of the causes of my downfall. I was allowed to read, but reading loses its pleasure when it becomes a man's principal occupation. I was morose and steadily getting moroser.

So here is this middle-aged man that I am talking about on a Sunday afternoon in mid-December, a man who has wanted time for life always and who now, having it, cannot use it, a man who cannot play golf or go hunting or fishing or drink, except for the two one-ounce highballs a day allowed him, or pursue a hobby inasmuch as there is no hobby which can interest him very deeply. Here is this man on this Sunday afternoon sitting in the living room of his house for he has been allowed to come downstairs that day for the first time. He is wearing a bathrobe and pajamas and he is sitting in a wheel chair by the window which looks back from his house across the city. Here is this man, and what is he saying to himself as he sits there? He is saying silently, "Jesus God, I just can't stand it."

That man, of course, was me. And that moment was actually a lot better than a lot of the other moments, for Doc Crocker had come in for a social call, and Tom,[1] my son, was there, and they wheeled me into the back enclosed sun porch, off the living room, where they made me the first of the two drinks allowed me. Gertrude had gone out, for the Ecleses who were our next-door neighbors, were giving a cocktail party, and I liked her to get what relief she could from the everlasting job of ministering to my comfort. The moment, as I have said, was better than most moments, but still it was a bad one.

The three of us sat there in the sun porch and had our drinks together and watched the evening fall over Fleetwood,[2] every-

---

[1] Thomas Jefferson Selleck, Jr., lived in New York, but he made several trips back to Gateway the autumn of 1949 after Mr. Selleck's illness.

[2] Fleetwood, where the Sellecks lived, was on the western edge of Gate-

thing having that dead December twilight painted across it, not even any house lights on yet to raise the spirits.

We sat in silence for some time and then I, with all of it boiling up inside of me, burst out, "Look Doc, how long does all this go on?"

"All what go on?" he said in answer — the dull light reflected on his glasses making them into bright mirrors, I remember.

"All this sitting around and thinking," I said. "All this doing nothing. All this going round and round in circles."

He stood up, I remember, and went to the back windows and looked down at the evening over Fleetwood. Then he turned around and said, "Jeff,[3] did you ever think of trying to write your memoirs?"

When he said it the idea struck me as one of the silliest ideas which he could have come out with.

"Seriously, Jeff," he went on, "seriously, I mean it. Why don't you?"

"Why should I?" I asked him.

"Because you've lived," he said. "And what's more you've lived in the first half of the twentieth century, and that's something a lot of people who have written books have not done."

Now to me that was a very arresting moment.

"Have I lived," I said, "or have I existed?"

"If you try to write your memoirs," he said, "you might find out, Jeff."

It was arresting. It was almost frightening.

"Even if you've only existed," Doc went on, "they've been pretty hectic times and you ought to have something to say about what you've observed about them."

I said, "Who would ever want to read what I say?"

---

way City, their house on a ridge so that from the back it looked down on the rest of Fleetwood and Gateway City itself while on the front it looked westward onto farm lands which the newer subdivisions of the city were only beginning to encroach upon.

[3] Mr. Selleck was generally called "Jeff" by his friends. By persons of his parents' generation he was called "Jefferson" and by Mrs. Selleck "Jeffrey."

"You," he said slowly. "As for me I've always wanted to write my own memoirs, but I've never had the time to. You've got the time now. You might even find out something that would help you."

"What?" I said, although the idea was already beginning to excite me.

"Your kind of disease," he said, "is in a sense a disease of collapse, and in a number of these diseases recovery depends to some extent upon understanding — not only understanding of the disease but of the forces which brought it on and of the world around you, where you have come from, where you are, and where you hope to be going."

An obstacle occurred to me immediately.

"Look Doc," I said, "but I'm not a writer. I'm not dumb, but I'm not good with words either. I don't even spell right."

"You don't have to write or spell. Dictate things to Helen." [4]

"I couldn't dictate to Helen," I said, "Helen knows too much about me."

Then Tom, who had been silent all this time, interrupted. "Look Dad," he said, leaning forward and putting his drink down on the coffee table, "you don't have to dictate to Helen. If you would like to do this, I would like to give you a recording machine for Christmas."

It was such a simple solution that it was almost astounding.

"By God," I said, "but . . ."

"But what?" Tom said.

"Maybe you haven't lived," Doc Crocker said, "but sometime I'd like to read something about the people who have just existed."

On that basis I was able to get started.

I think that all of us have stories which we would just as soon get rid of, and in reading over the following I envied Jeff this opportunity which he takes advantage of here to brush aside the

[4] Helen Flanagan, Mr. Selleck's secretary mentioned in an earlier footnote.

matters of this nature. But curiously enough the untrue stories about him tell me just as much as does the true one.

Did Jeff or did he not say what he says he did not say to the deacon? Or did he or did he not set the fire in the South Gateway tenement? In spite of what he says I still think that he might have.

At any rate what he is trying to do in the following, for he told me so during its composition, is to again chart a course through the years, setting down moments as channel buoys through the historical sea he had already described for us. The Turn of the Century, 1914, 1918, and the 1930's are really not bad points of reference.

Three Untrue Stories
and One True One

As a means of dealing with myself I have already tried to describe the times through which I lived. As a further means of dealing with myself, I want to tell three untrue stories about myself which seemed to have dogged me for more years than I can remember. I am telling them because I want to get rid of them forever. I suppose that every man carries around a few such stories, and I suppose that I am luckier than most in having an opportunity here to correct them.

I have another reason in telling of these tales, for each one of them, it seems to me, gives me a chance, in passing, to comment on matters which may be of interest. The first untrue story concerns my childhood, the second my young manhood, the third a time shortly before I was married. Then there is a fourth story I want to tell which is a true one, and I want to tell it because I think that, as much as anything, it shows me the way I like to think of myself in my manhood.

Now it seems to me that there are two kinds of lies which are told about a man. The first kind of lie is one which a man inherits from someone else just as I, the youngest of five, inherited toys and outgrown garments from my older brothers. The second kind of lie is one which comes from nowhere. The thing never really happened, but someone wishes it had because to him it seems to suit you. Of the untrue stories I am about to tell the first is of the first kind, the other two of the second.

1

All of us in our family were brought up as Baptists. You would hardly know it now for I, since my marriage, have been Presbyterian. Brother Will Episcopalian, Caroline Christian Scientist, John nothing at all as far as you can notice, and brother Luke died too young to make his mind up.

But at any rate we were all brought up in the strictest kind of Baptist household. Father was a deacon at the old Second Baptist Church at Thirty-sixth and Van Buren Streets which all of us attended, the one which was pulled down a few years ago to be replaced by the new Second Baptist with the swimming pool and gymnasium in it.

As is well known, in the Baptist Church total immersion is the baptismal custom. But what is not so well known is that baptism does not take place with a child or an adult until he has reached an age of personal choice in regard to Christ, his Lord and Saviour. Infant baptism is contrary to church doctrine. An age of discretion must be reached although this age of discretion, in my case I must confess, was ten years old, which does not seem to me now to be quite old enough for a decision in such an important matter.

However at ten, as did most of the other children, I made my decision. Following the decision came a period of instruction by Dr. Pogue, who was our minister in those days. And following the instruction came an examination by the church deacons. The deacons decided upon the sincerity of the child although I have never heard of their deciding against one. It was at my examination by the deacons that I was supposed to have distinguished myself in the following manner.

Deacon Cluette, who was the oldest and most pious deacon of them all, according to the story asked me, "Jefferson, do you ever swear?"

And my answer, according to the story, was, "No sir, but I know all the words."

And this remark was considered so cute by the members of my family that it still sticks by me and is still told on all occasions on which the family gathers.

The truth of the matter is that I never made the remark at all. It was made, if it was ever made at all, by William, my oldest brother, who was much more the "cute" type than I was, for the story was told on him long before I ever came into the picture. It was passed on to brother Luke a year later when he came up for his baptism and he inherited the story and retained it even through the baptismal time of Caroline, who, being a girl, was not expected to know anything about swearing. But eventually Luke lost the story to John, who bequeathed it to me at last. It stuck on me inasmuch as I was the youngest.

It may seem strange to anyone who might happen to read this that at fifty-five years old it still rankles me to hear this story quoted, but it is still quoted, and it does make me angry. For I see no reason why such an untruth about me should have been conscientiously kept alive by seemingly religious people.

And aside from the fact that the story never really happened to me there are cogent reasons why it never could have happened. First of all I doubt very much whether at ten years old I did know all the words which I supposedly claimed to. In the second place I was not the kind of child who made cute sayings, and finally, if I had been, I would not any more have made a cute remark in front of Deacon Cluette than I would have in front of my father. Both of them were the sternest, most rigid, of old-time Baptists and made me think of men like Abraham, Elisha, or possibly even God the Father.

I was not one to make statements at all, but there were children in our congregation who did have the temerity to do so, and it may not be out of place to mention one of them now as a sort of leaven to the loaf I'm cooking. It concerns a boy named Emmet Pritchard who grew up later, unfortunately, to follow a career of passing bad checks and, to my last knowledge, was in Cook County Jail in Chicago. However, to describe Emmet's remark I have to describe a situation which came before it.

Every year Dr. Pogue, our minister, a month or two before
Easter gave a little talk to the whole Sunday School, of which,
of course, all of us were members. And the talk was always the
same one, and a part of the talk always was the following demonstration.

Dr. Pogue would hold up before us a bottle filled with clear
pure water, and this water, he told us, represented our pure and
unstained childish hearts. Then with an eye dropper he would add
tincture of iodine to the clear pure water, and it would quickly
become dark brown and ugly. The iodine, Dr. Pogue would explain, represented sin, which inevitably would similarly stain our
hearts to a similar ugly brownness. Then he would conclude the
demonstration by adding to the iodine-stained water a chemical,
I don't know what, which would precipitate away the foulness.
And the precipitating chemical, of course, represented our ac-
ceptance of Jesus as our personal Christ and Saviour. This was
the demonstration, and it was really quite a good one until Emmet, who had seen it several times already, spoiled it.

On the particular occasion of Emmet's remark Dr. Pogue
was holding up his bottle of pure clear water as always and saying, as always also, "What is this in this bottle, children? It is
something well known in every household and every child here
has had experience with it."

Of course the proper answer was "Water," but Emmet, before the proper answer could be given, called out, "Castor
oil."

I think it pleased almost everyone except Dr. Pogue that he
said that. But I suppose that Emmet's fate is that the story has
followed him for the rest of his life and is now, I imagine, being
told in Cook County Jail by his cellmates.

I said at the beginning that I had another purpose in telling
these stories than merely to deny them. And my purpose here
is to talk a little bit about the Baptists, who are well worth
mentioning in passing. It is fashionable today in some circles to
laugh at what is known as "the old-time religion," but I, for
one, am glad that it is included in my background. There was

something about the old Second Baptist Church which we. attended which seems to me to have almost vanished from today. It is hard to say exactly what that thing was but it was a thing which had both religious and historical meanings. It is hard to realize that Gateway City is less than one hundred years old, which means that some of the members of the old Second Baptist congregation had actually come out in covered wagons across what then was prairie. The wandering tribes of Israel were no strangers to them for they too, at least figuratively, had been led by a pillar of smoke by day and at night one of fire to the land which had been promised. I suppose that it is easy enough to laugh at God now, but I think that it is a fact that few of those old-timers would have come out at all that way without Him. Your pioneers were Baptists, Methodists, Lutherans, and not High Church Episcopalians.

It is now perhaps of value to describe the church building itself, which in those days was considered perfectly adequate for religion. It was a small and actually remarkably ugly building.

It was red brick, hexagonal in shape, with a brown painted wooden porch before it. Inside was the church itself and the basement below it. The Sunday School met there and church suppers were cooked in a kitchen in the back of that basement. Both the basement and the "auditorium," as we called the church proper, were painted with a chalky green paint which could rub off onto your overcoat or jacket. It was the color of billiard chalk and had the same sort of texture. At the forward end of the auditorium was an oak pulpit on an oak platform, and three massive oak chairs were behind the pulpit. The choir loft was above and behind the chairs and it was made of oak too, with a pipe organ in the center. There were thirty visible pipes, I know, for I don't know how many times I have killed time by counting. The organist sat with his back to the congregation, but he had a mirror focused on the pulpit so that, without turning around, he could get his signals from the preacher. In the left, or north, wall of the auditorium was the baptistry, a large niche ten or fifteen feet wide which contained a tank of water.

The back of the niche was painted with clouds and through the clouds a dove was flying.

This was about all there was to the church's physical setup, its plant as they call it now, but yet it seems to me that that old inadequate building contained something which today at the big new Fleetwood Presbyterian I sense a lack of. That thing simply was a sense of God. And I don't mean to say that there is any less of God among the Presbyterians than among the Baptists. It just seems to me that there is less of God in general in the whole world than there once was.

Now I do not pretend to be religious or know who or what God is, but I am quite sure that the long trend of the church from what we had once to something like a social service center is a wrong one. The primary thing about a church is what was once called "peace which passeth understanding," and it is a mistake to trade this for what the Y.M.C.A. can probably do better.

On Sunday mornings, all of us always went to both Bible School and church. On Sunday evenings we attended the B.Y.P.U., which was the Baptist Young People's Union. On Wednesday evenings Prayer Meeting was S.O.P. also. During the winter there were various church activities and socials, and in the summer a high point came with the annual Sunday School Picnic. It was usually held in July and usually held, in those days, in a grove of trees near a pasture at the north end of the city right at the end of the car line. The place was adjacent to an amusement park which was known as Sweeny's Garden, but never actually in Sweeny's Garden, for it was rumored that beer was sold there and that on Saturday nights there was also music there, and dancing. In those days we Baptists were neither drinkers nor dancers. And for all I know this may still be true, but for a number of years now I have been outside of Baptist churches.

During the morning of the day of the Sunday School Picnic the women and children of the congregation and a few of the men would all go to get things ready. Long wooden tables would have been set up there in the grove and benches alongside them. The women would be busy almost all of the morning getting the picnic lunch spread, and we children would be busy with games and sports provided for us. By noon most of the men of the church would have arrived also. They would come in buggies, an automobile or two, and possibly a spring wagon.

The food which all of us would take out in big baskets was all homemade, for there was really very little food then which was not. And anyway by the ladies of our church canned goods were suspected as being impure and considered a sign of a bad housekeeper into the bargain. Most people brought home fried chicken, homemade potato salad, jars of homemade pickles, homemade cakes, pies, rolls, jars of relish. And usually there would be ice cream which was actually frozen by hand out there during the morning. There would also be soapy-tasting lemonade made in a washtub.

The games for the children during the morning would consist of three-legged races, potato races, running races, broad jumps, and jump ball. In jump ball a ball was fastened to the end of a long rope so that it could be swung in a wide circle at about knee height by the Sunday School superintendent. We children stood at the perimeter of the circle and jumped in the air and over the ball as it came swinging in at us, and you were "out" if the ball hit you. We also played Going to Jerusalem, which is simply Musical Chairs in essence. Then there would be informal games of Kick the Can or Red Light.

The games after lunch for the adults consisted of a spelling bee between the members of the William J. Benddict Bible Class and the Henrietta Carr Sloan Class or any other class desiring to compete, a baseball game between the married and unmarried men, and in much later years a Slipper Kicking Contest for the ladies.

Naturally there was no drinking at the picnic and very little smoking either. And the young people didn't get into trouble either as the books I read nowadays like to suggest about such occasions, or if they did it was very much of an exception. The truth is, as I look back on it, we young people were almost as strait-laced as our elders, kissing games really being almost the only deviation from this. And somehow it seems to me that, strait-laced as we were, we were about as well off as the young people today, my own included, who have been pretty much allowed to run wild.

2

Although this second story which I wish to correct here has more basis in fact than the first one, essentially, and as far as I am concerned, it is an untrue one. It has to do with the fire which occurred in one of the houses which Selleck and Company owned in South Gateway. It happened the summer of 1914. The implication of the story is that I virtually set that fire, and naturally I wish to deny this.

With the exception of the war years of the First World War and the winters when I was in school I worked in one way or another for Selleck and Company from the age of sixteen to the age of thirty-eight at which time I went into business for myself, about which I shall speak later. The summer of 1914 I was twenty years old and working as usual in the business. It was Father's idea that his sons should be usefully employed at all times, and it was his intention that we should all learn the real estate business from the ground up, which was what I was doing.

We owned a number of houses, shanties really, in South Gateway in the packing house area just north of the stockyards, and one of my jobs that summer was collecting the rents there. Another was to check on the repairs which our tenants were always demanding and which we made only in a very skimpy way since the houses were actually of very little physical value. And the repairs which were done, frequently as not, I did myself although I disliked very much to do them. It was the humiliation of being down there one day in my business suit collecting rents and then on the next appearing in white overalls and carrying a hod of plaster which was disturbing. But it was learning "from the ground up" if I do say so.

The story concerns one particular house which was in very bad condition and which did burn very shortly after I had talked with the tenants about it.

The story goes that, after looking over the whole ramshackle building, the tenant had asked me whether or not the place was adequately insured, to which I answered affirmatively. The story then says that that tenant said to me, "Well, then shall we?" and that I said, "Why not?" in answer. The story concludes that two days later when the wind was right the house burned down and that we collected the full insurance on it.

This story is a very good example of the second kind of lie which I mentioned in the introduction to this chapter, the lie told simply because someone likes to think that it might have happened.

Fortunately, I remember the circumstances of the fire very clearly. I had gone down there to collect the rent, and I always did hate to go down into that section of Gateway because the whole district in which our houses were situated was so dirty, so dilapidated, and so full of foreigners, in short the worst kind of slum which you can imagine. It verged into "Little Poland," "Little Croatia," "Little Lithuania," "Little Czech-town," "Little almost any country you can think of." And in those days the foreigners were really foreign, fresh from farms all over Europe, and would have kept the pig in the parlor if they had had a pig to keep there.

I don't want to suggest that I have ever had anything against any man simply because he was foreign or of foreign extraction. Actually I could not afford to if I so desired for, as a member of the County Central Committee of the Republican Party, I know as well as anyone that one man's vote is just as valuable as the next one's. And furthermore some of my best friends are foreign or of foreign extraction. Sam Zadina, the City Park Commissioner for instance, is one of my closest friends and he was born and raised very close to the district about which I am talking.

But still that district in which Selleck and Company owned those houses was foreign and undesirably foreign also, and it

was out of that very district that some of the most un-American
features of the city today sprang during the 1930's. The C.I.O.,
for instance, had its first strength in Gateway in the packing
house districts of South Gateway.

I disliked going down there for another reason too, which was
that it was a long streetcar ride which I had to take to get there,
long and hot on a summer's day, and it was summertime on this
day of which I am speaking. It was hot in a way which only the
Middle West knows hotness.

The streetcar went out on Thirteenth Street and then west to
the stockyards on Forty-ninth Avenue, a journey which took at
least an hour. The stop where the streetcar lines crossed the
railroad track of the old belt line was the stop I had to get out at.
From there I had to walk up a long hill to the area which we
had control of. The houses were little more than wooden boxes
without running water, and there were sheds, outhouses, and
lean-tos behind them. There was a drab saloon at one of the
corners and it was one of our best paying properties down there.
But even it was in pretty bad condition. You hear workingmen
complain today. They should see what workingmen put up with
in those days. If they did they would stop complaining and
thankful.

The roofs of those houses always leaked. The windows were
mended with brown butcher's paper. And small as these dwellings were they contained unbelievable numbers of people. They
were always bug infested. I hated those trips down there, hated
them especially because I knew beforehand that most of the
repairs requested would have to be ignored completely for, as
Father pointed out to me, those houses just weren't worth re-
pairing although they did bring in a nice return considering the
investment. And at first that shocked me. However Father explained that it was all a part of our American incentive system,
that if you gave a workingman a fine house to live in he would
have very little incentive to better his situation. At first, I remember, that struck me as rather brutal, but the more I have
thought about it, especially since the advent of "our friend

Franklin," the more I have felt that Father spoke more wisely than was at first apparent.

As I have said it was very hot on the day about which I am speaking. It was what we call "corn weather," which is very good for the crops but really hell upon the people. At such times tempers become difficult and almost anyone is capable of committing some desperate action. The air is muggy like the air in the bottom of corn rows, and it usually takes a thunderstorm finally to clear it.

It was afternoon when I got down there. The street up which I walked was smelly and dusty. There were no paved streets down there in those days, and the garbage collection was rather poor or, as far as I know, nonexistent. There were cur dogs behind most of the houses trying to knock the garbage can lids off. It was really a very bad area and the same area, it is interesting to note, which came to be called "Bloody Corners" during the Packing House Strikes of the 1930's.

I made the rounds of all dwellings and finally the building which is the subject of this story. It was a fairly large brick structure two stories high which once upon a time had been a livery stable. The partitions between the stalls downstairs had been carried up to the ceiling although wire-covered gratings had been left between the rooms, so created, to improve the ventilation. The upstairs had been divided into cubicals also, but as a matter of fact this was a better place for a workingman to live in than a great many others for the roof was tight and at the end of each hallway there were a toilet and a sink with running water, and although one toilet froze up every winter the other one was almost always in working order.

The man who ran the place for us was an Italian whose name was Gino. He was one of those short burly Italians, a black hairy man built like Caruso. On that day he was wearing only a pink silk undershirt, a pair of pants, and battered Oxfords with no laces in them and no socks either. He was carrying, I remember, one of those plungers which are called "plumber's helpers" and he was chewing a cold cigar.

He paid over the rent money and then took me around the building and pointed out items for repair. I wrote down his suggestions in a little black book which I carried for the purpose. The drains were out of order, which was the reason for the plumber's helper. Two or three treads on the stairway were broken. There were some glassless windows.

"The best thing that could happen to this building," Gino said, "would be for it to catch on fire."

"It could catch pretty easily too," I said, "with all of those oil stoves the men have in their rooms to do their cooking."

That was actually all I ever said about it. There wasn't any "Shall we?" and "Why not?" If the fire was set, and no one knows that it was, I had nothing to do with it. I merely said to him, "It would certainly be a relief to me if I never had to look at this house again or any of the other houses down here either."

That was everything that happened although one peculiar circumstance did occur after the fire had finally happened and the insurance on it been collected. Gino came into the Selleck and Company offices one day wearing a brand-new suit. He asked for Father and he was closeted in Father's office with him for perhaps an hour. And strangely enough when Gino came out he had been given one of our good uptown apartments to manage. But Father never said a word to me one way or another about their conversation. And that is the truth, the whole truth, and nothing but the truth about it.

3

The last story which I want to correct here happened, or was supposed to have happened, in 1918 when I was twenty-four years old and in France in the Army. And actually the story did happen although not in the form in which it was reported.

Before telling this story, though, I would like to pause for a moment and say a word or two about the Army, which, as with a number of institutions, has been overpraised and overmaligned in the course of my lifetime, its status being more or less directly proportional to the state of national emergency, to my mind. The soldier who was a hero in 1919 became a bum in 1920. He became a hero in the early 1940's again and then again a man of no particular importance in 1945 when the war was over. His status at this moment [1] is somewhat indeterminate for currently the status of national emergency has become indeterminate also.

As for my own experience in the Army I hesitate to say so, but actually I enjoyed it, or at least in looking backward on it I would say that I enjoyed it and what I feel about war itself I feel also about the Army. It may not be a good place to be, but it is a good place for a man to have been at one time or another.

For me it was a going away from home, and, as it seems to have been for Tom, a chance for a self-realization which I had not had before. The Army, as has been said frequently enough, makes a man or breaks him, but to my mind this is not very much different from life itself. Fortunately for me it made me.

This is not to say that I was remarkably successful in the Army for I wasn't. I was a private from the time I enlisted until it was over, an infantry private, and the young men who were in this last war will understand the meaning of that position for I doubt if the infantry has changed very much since the days of Julius Caesar. When I say that the Army made me I only mean that I came out of it with a knowledge that there were few men whom I could not compete with.

These things I have said in general. Specifically, however, I am indebted to the Army for two things — my long and close friendship with Sam Zadina,[2] whom I might not otherwise have known at all, and Gertrude whom I might not otherwise have met and married.

[1] The moment of this dictation would be the spring of 1950, probably March or April, certainly several months before the Communist aggression in South Korea.

[2] Sam Zadina was of Polish extraction. He was born and brought up in the packing house district of South Gateway, and it is very unlikely that Mr. Zadina's and Mr. Selleck's paths would have crossed except for the Army. As with all foreign groups in Gateway the Polish were apart from the older American stock to which Mr. Selleck belonged. The two enlisted on the same day in 1917 and served together until the end of the war.

I would not have met Sam, for we came from different parts
of Gateway City, and I would not have met Gertrude in all
probability because her group socially was a different one from
my group. The Sellecks, while always solid and respected people,[3]
were rather humble people also. We did not belong to the Sleepy
Hollow Club for instance, in those days, and as a young man I
did not know the people who did belong to it either, as Gertrude
McCullough [4] and all the McCulloughs most definitely did. The
people I knew I had come to know in grade school and high
school. And the people Gertrude knew she had come to know in
finishing school in the East.

It was directly due to the war that I met Gertrude. It happened during the war that I, along with Sam, was awarded a
medal.[5] I was wounded which he was not, which was how I happened to get home before he did. Because of the medal and the
wound and the times, I found myself unexpectedly hailed at
home as a hero. This is unimportant except that as a hero I was
entertained in Gateway in homes in which I had never been
before and by people by whom heretofore I had been unnoticed,
one of the homes being the McCulloughs' and one of the people
being Gertrude.[6]

And now I can go on to the untrue story which I wish to
correct here.

[3] Mr. Luke Selleck, Mr. Selleck's father, left an estate of something just
under two hundred thousand dollars, which is an indication of just how
solid the Selleck family was. But as Mr. Selleck says, his way of life was
humble and unspectacular as would be expected from a Baptist deacon.

[4] The fact that the McCullough family, Mrs. Selleck's family, were bank-
ers and one of them a U. S. Senator of the old school indicates as clearly
as anything else the upper social group to which they belonged. And the
fact of Eastern education also would seem to be a caste mark in Gateway.

[5] The Distinguished Service Cross, as has been mentioned.

[6] Unfortunately the citation for Mr. Selleck's medal has been lost, and
he makes no other mention of the incident than that in this chapter. But
what he did in addition to what he describes here apparently was to lead
the small group he mentions back to safety after nightfall and, on the way,
take several prisoners. It is perhaps hard to see Mr. Selleck in this role, but
it is hard to see any middle-aged man as he was in his youth or especially
as he was in battle.

The story happened, or it was supposed to have happened, during the Meuse-Argonne drive of 1918. And, as no one probably now remembers, the Meuse-Argonne was a fortified wilderness with miles and miles of barbed-wire entanglement, shell holes, ridges, machine gun nests and so forth. The French had even gone so far as to say that it could not be taken. It *was* taken, however, and it may be of interest to note, in this day of big figures, that it was taken at a cost of one hundred and seventeen thousand dead or wounded, a figure which will still stand up with all the others. But to return to the story, you may have heard of a Lost Battalion. Well, Sam and I were in a lost platoon, a thing which more frequently happens.

There was a spot which we were supposed to take and then hold in order to protect the flank of someone else who was supposed to be advancing. We took this position, dug in, and set up our machine guns. We never did see the fellows whose flank we were supposed to be protecting, and what the over-all plan of things was we had no idea. We just went to the place and stayed there for we never received any further orders. Perhaps we should have pulled out while we were able to, but we didn't. At first we stayed because we had been told to. Then later we stayed there because there was no place for us to go. We were right in the middle of the whole German Army it seemed to us after a while. We lost our lieutenant and then we lost our sergeant, and then one by one most of the others. We didn't hold out, I might add, because we were brave, but because we were unable to surrender. In the stories I have read, and in the motion pictures I have seen, there is always a trim German officer who comes forward under a flag of truce to offer the chance to surrender, but actually surrendering is not as easy as one might think it. At any rate along toward the end there were just Sam and I, a boy from South Dakota, a man from Colorado, and two brothers from Kansas City, Kansas. And up to this point the story told about us pretty well corresponds with what actually happened. But the thing which caused the wrong story to get out was that we met a newspaper correspondent shortly after we were rescued.

He talked to all of us, and then went back and wrote up the story the way it pleased him.

He wrote that during that time we had been stuck there Sam had said to me, "I'm glad that I believe in God and the justice of our cause because it doesn't make me mind so much if I'm dying."

And he wrote that I answered, "I'm glad that I believe in God too and that we're here fighting for right and justice."

Now all of that, although it appeared in the Gateway papers and was widely quoted, was pure fabrication, and what it stemmed from was simply this.

There was a moment when Sam turned to me while we were stuck there and said in kind of a funny voice, "Do you believe in God, Jeff?"

"Kee-rist yes," was my answer.

And the boy from South Dakota said, "Then for Christ's sake you had better get to working them over with that there God-damn machine gun."

It gives me a definite sense of relief now to have gotten that story, at long last, corrected.

4

I have now dealt with three untrue stories about myself, and now would like to tell a true one. I don't suppose that this is really as good a story as the untrue ones, but it is a story of my manhood, and I like to tell it and remember it because the whole thing describes a moment when I was happy. Not that unhappiness has been common with me either, for I would say that my life has had more than its share of pleasant moments.

The Chowder and Marching Society is a little club, hardly even that for we have no charter, constitution or bylaws, to which I have belonged for many years now — I suppose really it's little more than a luncheon group for we usually meet at luncheon although we actually have done many other things together.

It started many years ago in the days of Prohibition. We would meet then before luncheon in a speak-easy called the Hound and Hare which was in the Gateway Hotel in those days. We would have a drink and then go downstairs for luncheon. Since then we have moved our eating place several times and now have a special table in the dining room of the Commercial. We enjoy these luncheons very much and there is always something amusing happening at the table, a funny story, an interesting conversation, or someone hiding spoons in someone else's pockets and then accusing him of stealing silver. But enjoyable as these luncheons are they do not really compare with the various outings we members of the Chowder and Marching Society have had together. And now it is about the duck shooting expedition of 1939 that I would like to tell you.

One cold afternoon in late December Doc Crocker called me on the phone at the office and proposed the expedition for the following Sunday morning. He was going, he said, to the Waubaunsee River, some twenty miles west of Gateway, where a duck blind owned by Herb Johnson, who is owner and publisher of the *Times Examiner,* was situated, a blind which Herb had loaned him. The proposition was especially attractive, for the land was all private property and it seemed unlikely that he would be disturbed by other hunters as was usually the case that close to Gateway. Doc said that Charley Mason, a good friend of ours who writes more insurance than almost any other insurance man in the city, was going, also Jack Morgan who writes a very witty column for the *Times Examiner* called "Just Us People," also George Jerome, the undertaker, and Ben Paine who is head of the local branch of Merrill Lynch, Pierce, Fenner & Beane, good fellows all of them and good sportsmen. Naturally I was delighted to go with them.

It was a dark, cold, and clear morning when we set out, pitch dark except for starlight. We met at Sam Zadina's new house in Greenwood.[7] Sam and Peggy, his wife, had breakfast ready when

---

[7] Greenwood is the newest suburb of Gateway, northeast of Fleetwood, begun in the late 1930's, but it only came into its own in 1946 when the war was over. Mr. Zadina, in a sense, pioneered it.

we arrived, hot coffee with whisky in it, fried chicken, hot biscuits with gravy and so forth. By five o'clock we were on our way on the long cold drive out to the Waubaunsee. It was almost six o'clock, almost daylight by the time we were settled in the blind with our decoys set out in one of the shallow backwashes of the river. And when daylight did come, and the sun finally rose, it was one of the most magnificent mornings of my lifetime.

There are a great many people who are under the impression that the Middle West is a dull and ugly country, but I think that they, for the most part, are those who have never taken the trouble to see it. I am certain, at any rate, that they have never looked at a sunrise over the Waubaunsee. They, I am sure, have never seen a narrow "V" of birds flying in over the sand-bar willows.

Of course the land all around is flat or only gently rolling and there are immense fields on all sides filled mostly with broken corn stalks. But in that huge flatness I, for one, find a sense of space and bigness unparalleled by either the mountains or the ocean. And those broken corn stalks, if the light is right, have the color of gold upon them.

The river itself is broad and black and shallow and channeled tortuously between the sand bars. You can wade all the way across it in the winter in hip waders if you care to. On the banks of either side are dense fringes of willow trees which are gray and dead looking in the winter, jungle lush however in June, July, or August. The tops of these willows made a definite plateau in the landscape with a higher plateau formed by the cottonwoods behind them. Although they are all dead looking in the winter you can see, if you look closely, tinges of green and pink about them.

I have seen a great many of the beauty spots of our country, the Yellowstone, Colorado, Niagara Falls, and so forth, and I honestly believe that in its own special and subtle way the Waubaunsee ranks among them.

Herb Johnson's blind was a good one. It was set on a sand bar in the middle of the river so that it was possible to shoot in all directions. It had a wooden floor and wooden sides with rushes piled up around them. Inside it were a small coal-oil heater, a bench to sit on, and a shelf for shells, gloves, or, on occasion, a bottle.

When the sun came up the channels of open water in the Waubaunsee were gun-metal colored and gray where they were frozen. The willows and cottonwoods on the shores were buff-colored. The sky was absolutely clear and clean-washed looking. And over everything was the loneliest feeling you can imagine. Doc, Sam, Charley, George, Ben, and I all sat there and just waited. It was a fine feeling, the feeling that birds would come and that when they did come there would be no one else there to scare them away from us.

And a little after sunrise a small flight of birds did come skimming in. There were three as I remember, but we could hear more of them "quacking" somewhere on the water. We took our mittens off our shooting hands and then saw that our guns were ready. The ducks came steadily right for us and when they were almost within range we stood up to shoot them. And then, just as they did come into range, suddenly from all around us we heard other hunters shooting. It was one of the keenest disappointments of my life. There must have been at least fifty trespassers out there on the Waubaunsee. The birds simply flew up into the sky and away into the distance.

I was just plain mad. Sam was mad too. And poor Doc looked embarrassed. Charley fired his gun at the closest blind and shook his fist at the others. Ben sat down on the bench and looked as though he might start crying. But then I suppose that all the hunters out there at that moment were just as disappointed as we were.

But finally our anger wore off, and all of us decided that there was no sense in letting this mishap spoil a good time for us. We sat down in the blind and opened the bottle which George Jerome had brought with him, and we started drinking. We just kept on drinking too, for there was no use in even trying to do any shooting. We drank and the combination of the rye and the warmth of the sun as it rose and warmed us restored our humor. And then, as men will when they drink, we started telling stories. Sam told his story about the Three Canadian Sportsmen, and Charley told one about a "French girl and zee blue ointment," and George Jerome did a little pantomime which he called the "Plight of the Constipated Hunter," and all of us got to laughing and having a good time. And then a very strange thing happened.

Jack Morgan had to leave the blind for a moment, but as he started to he stopped suddenly and crouched down again inside. He didn't say anything, but he motioned for silence. Then he pointed toward something on the sand bar. All of us stood up and looked, and what we saw was a duck, a duck just walking on foot round and round our duck blind. It couldn't have been more than twenty feet from us.

All of us silently got our guns and all of us took aim. And then all of us fired on a signal from Charley Mason. And the most extraordinary thing happened. The duck simply flew up into the air and rapidly away for, unbelievably, all of us had missed him.

We all sat down again in silence for it was an extremely sobering thing to have had happen.

It was Jack who finally broke the silence, and the remark he made has, since then, become a Chowder and Marching Society byword.

"It all goes to show," he said, "that you just can't tell how far to lead a sitting duck."

We all began to laugh, for that one remark had suddenly made a day which might have been a keen disappointment into a very good one.

Perhaps this is a foolish story, but I have always liked it.

In the first half of the following Jeff describes falling in love in 1915, and the fact that Helen Flanagan came back into his life again fifteen or more years later gives this incident more significance than it would otherwise have, for it is quite the usual for men to fall in love with girls who do not become their wives. But with Helen we have something different, and the publishers have suggested that I attempt to clarify Jeff's and Helen's relationship more than he does within this book.

Of course I knew Helen and knew her well for many years, and I have sometimes doubted whether Jeff could have functioned without her. In some ways she was the most important person in his business, but I believe him implicitly when he says that she was nothing more, in the hackneyed use of the words, than his very very competent secretary during the years of their business association. And beyond this it is difficult to make a clear statement. His own kind of loyalty would forbid him to recognize a deeper affection if there was one. And Helen's taciturnity would forbid any statement on her part.

There certainly was never anything even in the nature of an affair between them in any physical sense, but the secrets within their hearts, unadmitted even to themselves no doubt, will have to remain matters for speculation only. There is nothing clinical here, at any rate, to judge from.

1915 and 1920

IN THE just preceding material I have allowed a certain levity to come into my memoirs which is permissible if it goes no farther, for it is time to return to serious matters. Twice in my life have I been in love, once at the age of twenty-one and once at the age of twenty-six, at which time I got married.

Perhaps a proper reticence should restrain me from mentioning my first adventure, but it was all an innocent enough business. Strangely enough however the young lady I fell in love with . . . young then for she is my age . . . and I later found our lives woven together in a most peculiar manner. She is my secretary today, but I do not mean to infer that she is anything more than my secretary as the careless phrase might suggest here. Helen Flanagan and I forgot all about that early foolish business once it was over. Or I imagine we forgot about it, for neither of us has ever mentioned it since we have been associated in the business. But it is curious that our lives should have come back together.

This first love affair was not only an innocent enough business, but it tells something about what life was like in the second decade of the century, which is another reason why I here include it.

The strangest thing about that prewar world to me is that it was just exactly the way it always is remembered. I mean the movies in which it is shown always look just right, and the books about it always say the right thing, which is that it was an extraordinarily nice time to live in. No one ever seems to have

the wrong idea about 1910 to '15. It was a young time, an innocent time, and a very forward looking time also. Great things
were happening every day, and boys were rising from poverty
to riches as James A. Garfield, not too long before, had risen
from the towpath to the White House. The world, although it
was going that way, was not yet so tightly knit together as it is
today and there was still room for quiet, for friendship, in short
for people. Perhaps it was because we were still an agricultural
nation and even townspeople like all of us who lived in Gateway
kept horses, chickens, even cows, and were still almost half
farmer.

We were more independent too, or at least we believed so.
The Atlantic and Pacific Oceans gave us a sense of safety. Ex-
porting and importing were not yet quite so vital. We were
reaching out, of course, but by and large we were nationally
self-sufficient. And what was true on a national scale was
largely true locally as well. I mean that a town the size of Gateway, then about ninety thousand, could have been cut off from
the world without causing it any really fatal hardship. We had
our agricultural surroundings to feed on, we manufactured
locally a good many of our essentials. Shoes even were made
locally still to some extent. Clothing was also, and a good deal
of that was made in one's own home. Every house contained a
sewing room, and the sewing room was always busy. We had
our local slaughterhouses, our local flour mills, our local brewery.
We even had our local foundry for the coal stove in my father's
house at Thirty-seventh and Taft was cast at the Gateway Iron
Works, although the furnace in the basement had been built in
St. Louis. We were more independent then, I think, and I also
think that it was because we were more independent that we
were more tranquil. The vast machinery of the world today,
although I would be the last person to give it up, was not yet so
frightening.

However, this is all somewhat far afield from falling in love
in the summer of 1915.

I have already said that those times were just the way they
always are in the movies. And even more strangely, it seems to

me anyway, the people also acted very much the way they seem
to in the movies. And I suppose that this was because if you
were brought up right in those days, for given circumstances
there were limited ways of acting. I suppose that that is merely a
complicated way of saying that then, by and large, we knew
what right and wrong were. I doubt if this is true today. In the
case of Tom, it has often seemed to me, a number of his troubles
have arisen, not through his fault either, simply because right
and wrong today are not clearly stated. For instance when I was
twenty-one it was quite easy to tell at a glance a good girl from
a bad one. But this is no longer an easy thing to do. Anyway, at
least, I can't.

This again may seem far afield from 1915, but what I think
that I am saying is that my first serious love affair, although
broken up in somewhat the same way Tom's first one was, was
a much happier sort of business than his was.

It is curious how Helen and I became acquainted, and very
much like the movies I have mentioned also. It was a summer
evening, and everything, as it turned out, was quite perfect.

The summer of 1915, as every summer, I worked at Selleck
and Company, for my father. To make all of this clear I must
describe the neighborhood around the Selleck Block where we
were situated in those days. Today with all the warehouses in
that part of town everything is different.

The Selleck Block when it was built in 1900 was a very fine
one, five stories high which was quite high for then, red brick
with Vermont marble in the lobby. It occupied, as it still does, the
southwest Corner of Thirteenth and Kingman. On the southeast
corner was the old Commercial House which was already second-
rate. It was a brownstone building with a mansard roof. On the
northwest corner was Burnside's Business College, another red
brick building which was torn down not too long ago to make
room for a parking garage. And on the northeast corner was a
saloon called Quigley's. The car line, as it still does, ran along
Thirteenth and then west up Niles.

Beyond Burnside's was the old *Examiner* office before it com-

bined with the *Times* and moved uptown to Fifteenth and Kingman, and in the front of the *Examiner* building was a large plate-
glass window through which you could look down into the
pressroom at the presses. On my way home from work I always
loved to stop and do so. There is no sight more impressive than
that of a big press running off the evening paper.

Now the moment which I am coming to came on one of those
soft summer evenings which we used to have in those days. I
had had to stay late at the office, lock it up in fact, and the time
was about nine or nine-thirty. The street lamps were gas lamps
and they shed a kind of greenish whitish light against Burnside's
Business College, our building, and Quigley's. And the business
college itself had a strange look too, for through the windows one
could see young men and women, some of them wearing green
eyeshades, sitting at long tables busily typewriting exercises
with the light around them like light seen through an aquarium
filled with water. The only other matter of note which I can
remember was that from Quigley's one could hear the shrill
playing of an old time nickel piano.

I said that it was about nine o'clock or nine-thirty when I left
the office. I was headed for the streetcar stop in the next block,
but I loitered along my way for one car had just gone by, and
they came infrequently that late in the evening. I stopped and
looked down into the pressroom at the *Examiner* building. The
presses were silent and no one was there with them except a
night watchman sitting on an iron stair eating a sandwich and
feeding milk to the pressroom kitten. As I stood there, for some
reason, I looked back at Burnside's, and I saw a girl come out of
the wide front doorway and timidly down the steps to the sidewalk. There was something frightened about her walk which ar-
rested my attention. She was wearing a dark skirt, a white shirtwaist, and a straw sailor. She was holding a notebook of some
kind or other tightly to her bosom. She headed down in my
direction, for she too was on her way to the car stop.

At about this moment I heard the sound of voices inside of
Quigley's in a violent altercation of some sort. The swinging

doors were suddenly thrown open and a man was flung bodily out onto the sidewalk. He was coatless. His shirt was torn, and he had skinned one hand to the point of bleeding. He was obviously quite intoxicated.

He picked himself up and staggered across the street toward the young lady I had been watching. She quickened her step in my direction as soon as she saw him. The drunken man, upon seeing her quicken her step away from him, started to run and ran around in front of her and this was where I came into the picture. I have already said that in those days people acted just like they do in the movies, and that was just the way I acted. Like Jack Dalton or Captain Jinks of the Horse Marines or something I ran back and hit him. He hit me too, but I managed to hit him again and he reeled off to the side and hit his head against the *Examiner* building, and it was fortunate that he didn't hit the plate-glass window and go through it. Then he just slumped down against the wall and sat upon the sidewalk and started swearing while I escorted the young lady to the car stop. Actually there was nothing of courage or gallantry in my action. It was just the way you acted in those days if you had been brought up the way you should.

I think that I was in love with her then even before we reached the next corner and the next street light. You see in those days also, if you had just saved a girl from what was loosely known as a "fate worse than death," by and large you fell in love with her also. I suspected this before we reached the street light, but when we were at the light and I could actually see her face I knew it.

Now, although one might find it hard to believe today, Helen Flanagan was a very beautiful girl in those days. She had the blue eyes, the dark hair and fine color of the black Irish. She was tall and slender and well proportioned.

"You shouldn't be walking around the streets alone this time of night," I told her as we stood there waiting for the streetcar.

"I have to," she said, "because I go to business college."

I said, "Then you should go in the daytime."

"In the daytime," she said, "I have to make my living."

Although it was out of my way I rode the streetcar with her that evening all the way out to her house, and on the way I learned all about her. In the daytime she worked behind a counter at Beckerman and Chandler.[1] At night she went to Burnside's to learn typing and shorthand. She lived with her mother who ran a boardinghouse at Twentieth and Van Buren, which was way north in those days. Her father, a railroad engineer, had been killed in an accident, and had left a small pension which was not enough to quite keep them going. I had never met any girl remotely like Helen, for all the girls I knew, although they lived simply, would have been frightened of making their own living. As I talked to her on that first evening on the streetcar I resolved that there would be a good many nights after that on which I would be working late and available as an escort for her through those dark blocks of the city.

And the result is that even today I have a singular affection for those old Gateway streetcars, especially the old summer cars which were different from the ones they used in the winter. They were almost completely open and you got on from the side rather than the rear end, and there was something gay and adventurous about them, much more fun, I think, than anything we have now. I don't know how many evenings Helen and I rode the old north side line out to her house. We would get off and walk half a block to her porch where we would sit for the rest of the evening. There would be lemonade and we called each other "Miss" and "Mister," and it seems now as though there were lilacs in bloom all of that time I knew her, not the kind of lilacs we have today but old-fashioned really big ones, bushes with branches so heavy that they had to be propped to keep them from breaking.

We used to talk and talk, but what we talked about I cannot now remember. But I do remember this, that the feeling of that first being in love was as though there was nothing in the world which ever could be denied me.

[1] Beckerman and Chandler was and still is Gateway City's largest department store.

Well, what brought this to an end now? The ending came quite simply. Father found out about it, and Father fixed it. Right in the middle of the summer he packed me off to my uncle's farm in Illinois where Father's family had come from. Why did I obey Father? I don't know except that in those days by and large sons obeyed their fathers.

And last of all why did Father object so strongly to Helen, who, after all, was as nice a girl as you could find and which he admitted frankly?

Well it wasn't that Father thought that she was socially beneath me for he had no prejudices of that nature. In fact except for prejudices against Negroes, Jews, and Catholics, Father had almost no prejudices whatsoever.

It was the fact that Helen was Catholic and that she was Irish which so disturbed my father. Perhaps that is another thing which is hard to understand today, the fact that the Irish, even when I was young, were considered a more or less unclean people. In fact I myself have seen want ads in the old *Times* with "Irish need not apply" below a request for help. And in Father's case this was a matter beyond the current feeling. For him it was a religious issue, Catholicism, Romanism, Popery, for him, strict Baptist that he was, these were terms of ultimate condemnation.

I have often wondered what might have happened had Helen and I been uninterrupted, and I have never arrived at any answer except that few men ever marry the girls they first fall in love with. However it is curious though, it seems to me, that Helen's life and my life should have crossed again as much later as 1932 when Yaw-Et-Ag came into being, curious that after all, as my secretary, she should have become the woman I most depend on. But probably, after all, Father was right, for had he not interfered perhaps I never would have met, fallen in love with, and married Gertrude.

2

I have described falling in love at twenty-one. Falling in love at twenty-six was something completely different, for I was a man by that time. And the difference between a man and a boy is that a man knows what he wants, whereas a boy doesn't. It was 1920. I had been in the Army. I had been in France, and I had been in battle. I had come back decorated and also wounded. For a short time I had been made a good deal of, and there had even been a parade in which I had ridden on the top of the back seat of a Cadillac touring car beside Honest Bob Brady who at that time was our mayor. I was suddenly a welcome guest in homes in Gateway which heretofore I had never even been in.

And in passing I would like to say that I owed a good deal of all that to Henry Burton, young Henry, that is, who had been my captain.[2] Henry seemed to like me, and Henry's family had always been prominent in the city.

As I was saying, I was a man now and knew what I wanted and it was something different from what in 1915 I had thought I wanted. Helen Flanagan, as I look backwards to her now, had never been an actuality, but a dream rather, a dream that probably every boy has at one time or another. Did I ever know Helen as she really was I sometimes wonder, or did I only know her as some idea or fancy which I threw around her? Be that as it may, by 1920 it was actuality which concerned me, and I wanted things which, I realized, my home had never given.

I wanted things like the Sleepy Hollow Country Club which we had never belonged to, like cocktail parties which had not yet really been invented, like having gone to school at Yale or Harvard rather than our State University which I had attended. And when I met Gertrude McCullough I realized that in her all of these things were represented.

Strangely enough, however, I do not remember the first time that I met Gertrude. It was a bewildering time when I first got back with only one stable peg in it, which was that I was again

---

[2] Henry Burton, Jr., a childhood sweetheart of Mrs. Selleck's, left Gateway the autumn of 1919 for New York, married Emily Ritter of New York the spring of 1920, is today a member of the law firm of Ritter, Rand and Burton of that city.

working for Father, which, when I had gotten out of the Army,
I had not intended. It was a bewildering time, and Gertrude, I
remember, when I did become aware of her, had also looked
bewildered. Of course it was only the way she looked for she
never was really bewildered. And it was a charming look of
bewilderment also which made a man want to put his arm around
her. And it still seems strange that it should have been I who
married Gertrude instead of Henry, for she was definitely his girl
when I met her.

It was on the rebound, of course it was on the rebound, that
she acquiesced to my proposal, for Henry in the spring of 1920
unexpectedly and to everyone's surprise married the daughter of
the senior partner of the law firm he went to work for in New
York City. But rebound or no rebound I remember that I thought
myself inordinately lucky, and I was inordinately lucky if you
care to face it.

Here was Gertrude who had everything that I wanted. She was
lovely looking. She had the background and breeding which I
lacked. She had been educated at Miss Darling's which was our
only private girl's school in the city outside of the Convent.
Her family was one of the most prominent families in the city.
She had even spent a winter in Washington, D. C., with her aunt
and her uncle, Senator William McCullough. She knew about
things like art and literature and music.

And in addition I was as much in love as I ever had been or
ever would be. I had proposed to her at least twice a week ever
since I had come to know her, and even while Henry was still in
the running.

That she took me on the rebound is quite clear from what I
have to say later and also from the fact that it was on the evening of the day on which Henry got married that she finally accepted my proposal.

I had come to call that evening, and I had found her alone in
the little old-fashioned sun porch of the McCulloughs' house,[3]

---

[3] The McCullough mansion still stands at Twenty-eighth and Pike, a
monument among the boardinghouses to that once most fashionable resi-

sitting on a love seat in the dark and, I soon realized, crying.

"Jeffrey," she said, "you've said you want to marry me. Do you still want to do it?"

I don't remember what I answered, but I remember what she then said.

She said, "Jeffrey, I'm getting so old and lonely." [4]

To make a long story short I then went upstairs to speak my intentions to Mr. McCullough, and our engagement was announced shortly and in due time we were married. [5]

We said our vows in the Third Presbyterian Church which still stands at Twenty-eighth and Niles, which was then one of the most fashionable churches in one of the most fashionable residential districts of the city — Mrs. McCullough's church which she supports generously even up to this moment.

I should like to interrupt this for a moment to say what a charming neighborhood it was down there on Twenty-eighth Street in those days. There was the McCulloughs' big old yellow frame mansion with all the towers and bay windows on it, the Burtons next door which was the same kind of house only made of red sandstone with an iron picket fence around it, then the Tourtelottes' who don't live in Gateway any more, and then Judge Sammons, and the William McCulloughs' on the opposite side of the street, all of these fine old mansions with spacious grounds around them. And today, except for Mrs. McCullough's which is still kept up, inasmuch as she still lives there, all these houses are either gone or turned into rooming houses of the most tawdry description.

But to get back to the business which was Gertrude's and my wedding . . .

That Third Presbyterian Church was a sweet little church and, for that matter, still is although, with the exception of Mrs.

---

dential district of the city. The Gateway National Bank was and is the McCullough Bank.

[4] Gertrude McCullough, Mrs. Selleck, would have been twenty-six years old in 1920, for she and Mr. Selleck were the same age almost exactly.

[5] July 14, Bastille Day, 1920.

McCullough, I doubt if there is still a member of its congregation who lives closer to it than two miles. I like those little old-fashioned gray rough limestone churches with stained glass [6] and a bell tower over the doorways. My brother Will was my best man, and Marion Sammons was Gertrude's maid of honor.[7] However I remember very little about the wedding service except that it was an evening wedding.

And I remember very little about the reception held afterwards at the McCullough house either, but I suppose no bride or groom ever does remember too much about her or his own wedding. I just know that there were several hundred people at the house and that dazed and with a fixed smile on my face I stood along with Gertrude, Mr. and Mrs. McCullough, and my father and mother in front of some potted palms shaking hands with people for what seemed like several hours. I remember that my main thought was that I wished I had a drink, but there was nothing to drink except a fruit punch, this being the first year of Prohibition, which made very little difference really because neither my family nor Gertrude's believed in drinking. I was hoping, I remember, that someone would spike that fruit punch, but who would have had the courage to spike anything at the McCulloughs' I cannot imagine.

Finally the reception was over and Gertrude and I found ourselves being propelled out the front door with rice flying around us and into the old Hudson town car . . . "brougham," they called it . . . which belonged to the William McCulloughs, where we found ourselves staring at the back of the neck of Lyle, the William McCulloughs' driver. We were alone, or almost alone, at last, and suddenly it seemed awful.

We were spending the night at the old Gateway Hotel, then the New Gateway, and that suddenly seemed awful too.

[6] The McCullough window on the west side is probably the most handsome. It was ordered from Tiffany in 1913 as a memorial to the McCullough child which died in infancy in 1912.

[7] Marion Sammons became Marion Ecles and has already been mentioned and will be mentioned again. Mrs. Selleck and Mrs. Ecles grew up together and later became next-door neighbors and close friends.

We had difficulties from the very outset. In the first place the desk clerk stopped us and made us register which was unnecessary really, for I had already made all the arrangements. Then when I did sign I forgot to sign Gertrude's name, and when the clerk called me back had to put "and wife" after my own name. Then when we finally arrived at our room we found that some of my friends from the Army had been there before us, for in the center of the room on a stand was a horseshoe of flowers similar to the ones presented to Derby winners with a ribbon across it which said, "Good Luck from the Old Rainbow Division." In addition to that someone had somehow wired one of those old-fashioned Klaxon automobile horns to the bed in such a way that when I touched the bed it went *ah-ooo-ga*. Gertrude was in tears even before we found out about the Klaxon. In fact as soon as I closed the door she sat down on a little gilt chair in the corner of the room and burst out crying.

"Look, dear," I said, after I had moved the horseshoe of flowers out of sight into the bathroom, "it's only a joke the boys have been playing." I sat down on the bed as I said it, and that was when I discovered the Klaxon.

Then she said, "O God, O God," and kept on crying.

"What's the matter, honey?" I said.

She said, "I want to go back to Mother."

I said, "Gosh, dear, don't you love me?"

"Yes," she said, sobbing again, "but I know Mother better."

I shall never forget what that bedroom looked like because after that we just sat saying nothing at all to each other and staring at the wallpaper and the pictures, Gertrude on the little gilt chair in the corner, and I on the edge of the bed, for I had disconnected the Klaxon by this time. The wallpaper was striped vertically with gold and purple. Over the bed, which was a brass-bound monstrosity, was a picture of a sleeping cupid with a girl holding a lamp staring down upon him. In the wall near the door was a steel engraving of the "Last Days of Pompeii."

It was up to me, I felt, to do something, but what to do I could not imagine. I thought again of the drink which I had been wanting all evening and then decided to go out and get it.

"What are you doing?" Gertrude said in alarm as I stood up and put my hand on the doorknob.

I said, "I'm going out and get a bottle of whisky."

"Oh no," Gertrude said in sudden terror, "no, not whisky."

"It's not for me," I said, "it's for you because you've got to have something to make you relax a little."

"Something is terribly wrong," she said in answer.

"Yes," I said, "but a little whisky, I think, will fix it."

"No," she said again, "no, not whisky."

I ignored her and walked out of the room, which was on the second floor, down the hallway and stairs down into the lobby. I was quite sure of one thing even though we were under Prohibition — that if there was anyone around from the old Army outfit, as there seemed to have been, there should be a bottle of whisky around somewhere. That was what I thought, and I was not mistaken.

When I got back to the room with the bottle of whisky I found that Gertrude had undressed and put on her nightgown and gotten into bed. But she had the sheets and blankets so tightly wrapped around her that she looked like an Egyptian mummy. She had unpacked my pajamas, dressing gown, and slippers and put them on that gilt chair for me. "You can undress," she said from the bed, "in the bathroom."

In the bathroom I hung my pants and shirt over that horseshoe which had been sent by the old Forty-second Division. I put on my pajamas and robe, and then I made two highballs in tumblers, two highballs of whisky and plain water. When I took them back to the bedroom I found that she had made up sort of a bed for me on a love seat which stood under the windows. I took her highball to her and said sternly, "Drink this. It's medicine. It will make you feel a good deal better."

She took it after a little urging, reaching her hand out timidly for the glass from the tightly enveloping bedclothes.

"Will it make me drunk?" she said after she had tasted it.

"If you drink enough it will," I said.

Then she said almost eagerly, "Will it make me unconscious?"

I said, "If you drink enough it will make you unconscious."

She started to cry again and then said, "I know it's wrong, but I want to be unconscious."

"If you feel that way," I said, trying to be gentle about it, "why did you want to get married?"

"I didn't want to get married," she said, "I didn't want to marry you. I wanted to marry Henry Burton. I wanted to marry Henry, but it's too late now. It's too late to do anything about it."

I have taken a great many blows during my lifetime, but I doubt if I have ever taken another one like that one. I don't know what I did or said, but probably I did nothing and said nothing. I think that I just sat down on that gilt chair in the corner.

"Oh Jeffrey," she started wailing then in contrition, "oh, I've hurt you. Oh, Jeffrey, what's the matter?"

"The matter," I said, "is that I love you."

"Oh Jeffrey," she kept on wailing.

And I just kept on sitting.

"What are we going to do now?" she then said to me.

"As for me," I said, "I'm going to get drunk now. You can do anything you want to. Nothing's going to happen."

"May I," she said after a while, "get drunk also?"

I went over and poured some whisky into the glass that she was holding.

Then she said, "Jeffrey, you've got to be good to me because I feel so alone and frightened."

I filled my own tumbler with whisky and went back to my chair in the corner and just sat there.

Then after a while she climbed out of the bed and came over and put her arm around me and said, "Oh, I'm so sorry."

"I'm sorry, too," I said. "Just drink another drink and maybe we'll be able to talk it over."

We ended up with Gertrude in the bed and me sitting on the end of it sadly passing the bottle back and forth between us. We sat there and got drunk and drunker. Finally Gertrude got sick because she was completely unused to liquor. I didn't get sick. I just passed out where I was sitting. And that was the first night of our marriage.

That was thirty years ago, and perhaps if this story of mine has no other value it has a value in saying that we were able to go on, build a house, raise children, and take our places in the world after such a bad beginning.

The Chowder and Marching Society, as Jeff has said, was a great pleasure to all of us for many years and especially to him. He was the center of it really although we did not realize it completely until he was no longer with us. It was not Jeff who had the ideas, but it was Jeff who could be counted upon for the support of the ideas once they were suggested. Once upon a time to satisfy the wives, who were rarely included in Chowder and Marching Society activities, we gave a masquerade ball, and Jeff, who went representing White Horse Whisky, was bitterly disappointed when the Gateway Hotel where we gave the function would not allow him to take the horse, a big draft animal, into the elevator and upstairs to the ballroom. I mention the incident as a demonstration of the energy he brought to our association.

The hunting trip which he here describes shows this also and, in addition, shows him in a moment when he is completely happy.

The Big Elk Hunt
in the Gunnison River Country

❦

ALREADY too frequently perhaps I have mentioned the Chowder
and Marching Society. Inasmuch as this group of men, this unusual collection of good fellows, has meant a great deal to me
throughout the last fifteen or twenty years I want to mention it
again and then forget about it completely, as far as these memoirs
are concerned. I want to describe the elk hunting trip on which a
few of us went in 1941 because it shows us all when we were
having fun and because, historically, it seems like the last vacation of an era. I mean that Pearl Harbor happened not long after
we had returned to Gateway.

Also it was a very successful trip. What I wanted out of it
was a nice set of antlers to put over our fireplace in the house
in Fleetwood, and I did get my antlers although Gertrude,
for some reason which I have never been able to understand,
would not let me put them up over the mantel. They, head and
all, are now in my office down at the plant and they have been
very much admired by various salesmen and customers who
have seen them.

2

There were four of us on this trip: Sam Zadina, Jack Morgan,
who later wrote it up in his column, Bill Boardman, a sort of un-

official member of our group, from Denver, vice president of the
Denver Earth Mover and Road Builder Corporation, and myself.
Bill unfortunately has passed on since the moment about which
I am writing.

Sam, Jack, and I went by plane as far as Denver. Sam arranged the whole trip for he has a cousin who is in our local
office of United Air Lines. But as far as that goes it was always
Sam who arranged the details of any of our outings. Sam always
enjoyed arranging details, and was good at arranging them also.

I was very glad that we had planned to fly out, for I have
always enjoyed flying. I took my first flight in France in 1918.
I was one of the first in Gateway to agitate for a municipal air-
port, and it was through my influence that the slogan "Gateway
Must Have Wings" was for a long time on the letterhead of the
Chamber of Commerce. It was partially through my efforts that
Gateway finally possessed Ransome Field, our fine new airport on
the western edge of the city.

As I was saying we flew as far as Denver. It was a good flight
although Jack Morgan did get air sick. But then Jack would
have gotten air sick on any flight, for his stomach, as any constant reader of his column "Just Us People" knows, is an extremely delicate kind of machine. In fact I would say that in the
last ten years he, very much to the amusement of his readers,
has written several hundred thousand words about it.

Jack was air sick, but that was pretty funny. "Doesn't anyone
realize that I'm suffering?" he said and the way he said it got
both Sam and me to laughing. And Sam, too, was pretty funny
about everything during the flight, and embarrassed me quite a
bit by trying to fix up a date for me with the air line stewardess
who was a very nice girl and a Delta Gamma, she said, from the
University of Wisconsin. There wasn't anything serious about
any of this, I hasten to add, for I have never been a man to play
fast and loose in any way at all with my marriage. It was just
good fun, and to my mind there is never anything which is more
fun than for a few good fellows to get away for a while from
the old grindstone and the wife and children.

It was a fine clear day and, in spite of what Jack said, fine calm flying weather. Flying anywhere in fine weather is a fine thing, but to be flying over our great western states on such a day is just about the finest thing I know of. I like to look at the tan and green color of those wide Nebraska and Colorado prairies. I like seeing that great big bend of the Platte River which once was the highway west. Especially I am excited by the abrupt transition of the land, just beyond Denver, from prairie into mountains. It seems to happen in less than half a dozen miles. It is absolutely beautiful, and it makes a man recall the trials and tribulations of all the old old-timers who at one time made their way across it.

Then I always like the setting down in Denver, the sudden "mile high" feeling of Colorado, and the arrival, finally, at the Brown Palace. I always stay at the Brown when I am in Denver. I like the high feeling of that lobby. And at the Brown, too, it seems as though there is always something happening. For instance that afternoon when we arrived the lobby was filled with Indians dressed in buckskins, beads, and feathers. Why they were there I have no idea, but the *Denver Post* somehow was behind it, for the *Denver Post* is a live-wire outfit. Our rooms were ready when we got there. We had one double room and one single and they connected so that really we had one large apartment. We all bathed and cleaned up, and while we were bathing and cleaning up we were able to shout back and forth to each other and drink while in the bathtub. We called up Bill Boardman who asked us to come out to his house, but we did not, for we knew by experience that Mrs. Boardman was rather narrow-minded about these expeditions of ours although in other ways she is a very perfect lady. We asked Bill to come down and join us, but unfortunately he was unable to do that either.

When we were all cleaned up we sat down in the double room to do a little quiet drinking.

Now there are all kinds of ways of drinking, but to my mind this kind is the best kind: just a few good fellows who know each other sitting down with their shoes off and talking about one thing or another. And while I am at it I might as well say what I think is the worst kind. The worst kind is at a cocktail party for several obvious reasons. The first is that there is never any place to sit down. The second is that there are always too many women there and women, as far as I can see, were never planned to be drinkers. And in the last place at a cocktail party one never knows when or where one is going to get one's dinner.

But this was the best kind of drinking that we were doing that evening at the room in the Brown Palace. We had several slow drinks and then somehow we lost Jack Morgan while Sam and I were looking out of the window at the sunset. But we weren't very worried about that because on trips of this kind Jack had a habit of being periodically missing. He came back finally, as we had known he would, and he was wearing a regular western-style ten-gallon cowboy Stetson. He was walking bowlegged, and he looked so much like a real old westerner that we nearly died with laughter and what he said was very funny also.

"Either I've found a hat," he said, "or else I've lost a cowboy."

That was a very funny remark, and there is one thing about a funny remark, which is that it gets funnier the more it is repeated.

When no one was looking I slipped out into the hall and brought back a potted palm and said, "Either I've found a palm tree or lost a tropical island." And that was very funny too. Then, when Jack and I were talking, Sam slipped out and was gone quite a while. But when he came back he had a very pretty blond girl with him who was wearing a white manicurist's uniform. And he said, "Either I've lost a barbershop or found the prettiest manicurist in the business." And then Jack slipped out again and came back this time with one of those *Denver Post* Indians, a very nice young fellow whose name was Eagle Feather. The girl was a very nice girl too, the kind of girl who knows how to get along with men on a vacation without getting herself, or them, into any kind of trouble.

We all had several drinks there in the room, and then Sam, Jack, myself, the girl, and Eagle Feather, all of us decided to go on somewhere for dinner. We caught a cab outside of the Brown and went to a night club called "Café Society Out-of-Town," but just where it was I have no recollection. We had drinks and steaks there, and everyone had a good time although we did have a little trouble in getting drinks for Eagle Feather. Jack was especially funny, for he still wore the Stetson and he kept telling people around us that he was a big bull shipper from West Texas. Then Sam tried to get into the floor show, and I, they tell me, got up behind the microphone and made pertinent announcements. And it shows what good fellows we were that we were able to do all of this without in any way becoming obnoxious. It was all good fun, and there is certainly nothing in the world better for a man than going off on a hunting trip like this one.

Except for Jack, who really can't drink and shouldn't, we all felt fine the next morning. Jack's stomach was acting up again, and I had to buy him a bottle of milk of magnesia at the drugstore across the street before he felt much better. By the time he felt better Sam and I felt like one million dollars. We had breakfast in our room and then put on our old hunting clothes, and that gave us a fine feeling also.

Bill arrived at about nine o'clock, and all of us had a drink to get the day started rightly. Then we had our things taken down to his station wagon which was parked at the Seventeenth Street entrance. Finally we set off in the highest kind of spirits.

But it was not the drinks which we had had or did have along the way which intoxicated us so completely. It was the mountains and the mountain air which was all around us. It was a wonderful late autumn day, a little bleak, but still with a few spots of color. When one is away on a trip like this one, one cannot help but feel that the out-of-doors life is the life that man was planned for. You breathe deeply, laugh heartily, and all of you feel the greatest affection for each other.

The drive to the Gunnison that day was as comical as everything else which happened. We sang songs and told stories. We probably would have yodeled if we had known how to do so. And then we discovered a quite fascinating phenomenon connected with the whisky bottle.

As our altitude increased naturally an air pressure would be set up inside the bottle. Then it would stop audibly when we uncorked it. The air pressure inside and outside of the bottle, you see, would have become unequal. The result was that when any one of us wanted a drink he would say quite formally, "Gentlemen, let's equalize the pressure," and the phrase always sounded awfully awfully funny. We "equalized the pressure" all the way up Turkey Creek and through South Park and so on, and the result is that that phrase has now been included among the Chowder and Marching Society bywords. At our regular Saturday afternoon Heart games any one of us is likely to lean forward and say, "Well, gentlemen, let's equalize the pressure."

But, as I was saying, we had a fine drive that day down to the town of Tailing, where Bill Boardman's ranch was in the Gunnison River country.

The town of Tailing was not much, a grocery store, a saloon, and a few falling-down houses, but there were magnificent mountains all around it and magnificent stands of timber. The peaks were all covered with snow and, as we arrived in late afternoon, they glistened in the sunlight.

To get to Bill's ranch you drove through the town and across a bridge and then up a mining road which seemed to go straight up the mountain.

You went up through a dense grove of blue spruce and then around a barren-looking switchback up to a ridge behind which the mountain opened abruptly into a wide flat meadow. The main house was on the edge of the ridge and looked down at the valley, and it was the kind of mountain hide-out any man would long for. There was the main house which was a large log cabin where Mrs. Boardman took Bill's children in the summer. Behind it were one or two guest cabins, some sheds, a

corral, and so forth. And behind the meadow the mountain kept
on rising.

The inside of the main cabin was beautifully furnished. The
peeled rough logs made the inside walls and there were some
Navajo rugs hanging on them. A huge stone fireplace almost
filled one wall and in the center of it was mounted a twelve-
point elk's head just like the kind I wanted. In one corner of
the room was a small rustic bar with a regular old slot machine
mounted on it.

There was heat in the house, hot and cold running water,
every luxury, in fact, which you could have wanted.

There was a cowboy there who met us at the door. He looked
after the house for the Boardmans during the winter and it was
he who was in charge of the hunting trip which was to start on
the next morning. He was a fine-looking young fellow, hard as
leather, slim, good-natured, a really typical cowboy. His name
was January, and when I asked him how he got it he said, "Because it was a cold day in the morning when my momma and
daddy got me."

That was typical of him, typical of the good hearty humor
of the Gunnison country also.

I have always envied men like January. I have always felt an
irony in the fact that men like myself work hard all year to be
able to do for two weeks what he does all the time for nothing.
I don't suppose I mean that a cowboy doesn't work hard in the
life he lives, but somehow it seems to me that the kind of hard
work he does is more fitting to a man than the kind of work
which I do.

And the proof of this, it seems to me, lies in the fact that men
like January always seem to be happy. They laugh. They walk
with freedom. They seem to be in good health always. The
only disease January ever had, he told me, was of a venereal
nature and it was cured for him easily and quickly when he was
in the Army. And the price of the cure, he said, was more than
paid for by the pleasure he had while he got it.

How frequently since then have I thought of the free-and-easy life he leads out there in Colorado. He comes and goes as he pleases. He works only when he wants to or needs the money. He is drunk or sober according to his inclination. He lives in the out-of-doors, knows the ways of the weather and of the fish and deer and elk. He cares for horses. He has a wife somewhere, but inasmuch as she is a good strong working girl who also can make a living, neither she nor his children are much cause for worry. It's enough to make a businessman almost disbelieve in the system which he lives in.

January made a little toast that evening when we started drinking which went as follows:

"*May you live as long as you want to, and may you want to as long as you live.*

"*If I'm asleep and don't want to, wake me. And if I'm awake and don't want to, make me. Cheers.*"

I collect little items of this nature, and I have found this a very good one for bachelor dinners, weddings, and such occasions.

We were all cold when we arrived at the ranch, and Sam went behind the little bar which I have mentioned and made us a drink as soon as we were settled. Then Jack Morgan and I went out to the meadow behind the house to sight in the new telescope which I had had put on my rifle. We did that and then target-shot a little until it was too dark to see, then went back to the house where the dinner was already cooking. January was broiling steaks over the fire in the fireplace. Sam, who cannot keep himself out of any cooking, was busy making a salad. Bill was dry shooting his rifle at the elk's head over the fireplace. Everything, in fact, was quite domestic.

We all had good honest shots of straight whisky the way they do in the mountains, and then we had our dinner. We had big juicy steaks, honest country-fried potatoes, salad and homemade bread. I hadn't had homemade bread in years, but the difference in taste between it and the store kind is certainly worth the additional effort.

After dinner Sam and Jack got out the deck of cards, and I

would have played with them had not I found something to do more important. Normally I love card games of any kind, but on this occasion January had to go down to the village to make some arrangements for the morning, and he asked me if I would like to go down with him. I jumped at the chance for always when I go to a new place I like to see it.

We drove down in a pickup truck which belonged to Bill's ranch, and it was a very fine night on which to be driving down a mountain. The valley was deep and wide below us with hardly a light anywhere to mark the town. You could smell the cold blue spruces and horses somewhere in the darkness where we couldn't see them, and the night air was like it always is in the mountains, cold, and sharp and bracing.

It was a rough old road and we bumped down it and into the town where only the saloon seemed to be lighted. And it was a regular old-fashioned western saloon too, with a hitching rail in front although there were no horses hitched there. On the inside the saloon was just a big square room with calcimined beaver board walls and ceiling. There were some calendars with pictures of girls not wearing very much tacked up here and there, some booths around the walls, and a beaten-up looking bar in the end opposite from the doorway. There weren't very many people there when we got there, only a party of cowboys who were the ones for whom we were looking in one booth and a party of hunters in another. The hunters, though, were only that kind of hunters who come from the city and spend most of their time drinking, and shoot each other before they are done most likely. I really spotted them, as it turned out, the first moment that I saw them. We sat down with the cowboys, and January introduced them.

One of them was a lean young fellow named Wesley who went hunting with us the next morning. The other two were named Bert and Jim, and all of them were good fellows. I bought a round of straight shots with beer chasers for them and we got along famously with each other right away. They were real people, and I have always been able to get along with real people. After a while two girls named Frankie and Lucile came in and joined us too, and they also were really real people. Some people might have said that they were a little rough, but there was one thing about them — they did know how to have a good time when they found one.

I put some nickels into the jukebox, and the jukebox played some regular old western songs like "An Old Cow Hand from the Rio Grande," "Bury Me Not on the Lone Prairie," and "You Are My Sunshine."

I bought another round of drinks and put some more nickels into the machine, and then we got to dancing. And it is a curious thing about my dancing — Gertrude always says that I am the world's worst dancer, but on occasions like this one the girls always say that I have a real sense of rhythm. We danced and had a lot of fun dancing, and then I bought everyone a round, and then we started doing tricks with coins and match sticks and so forth. And then we had another round of drinks which I was delighted to buy because I really enjoy buying drinks for really real people. Then we got to telling some little stories, nothing off color actually, but still rather cute ones.

By this time we were having great fun and were all feeling very silly, and we began pinching the girls, nothing out of line you understand and everything just good fun really, and the girls were squealing and giggling. But one of those city hunters that I have mentioned then came over and tried to join us, and I had certainly pegged his type right from the beginning. He sat down and tried to pinch the girls too but in a way which just was not nice. The girls didn't like it, and they said so too. Frankie told him that he certainly was no gentleman which he wasn't, and then Lucile found it necessary to slap him, and after that . . . although I don't quite know how it happened . . . I found it necessary to hit him, and when I did that suddenly everyone started fighting. Now I am not one normally to approve of barroom fighting, but in this case it seemed to be one of the customs of the country; so I enthusiastically joined in and started slugging. And the next thing I remember was that I was out in the street in front of that saloon with January standing beside me laughing.

As I think back on it I believe that I must have been a little bit carried away by the excitement of the moment, for I said to January out there in the darkness, "Let's go back in and stop their clocks, Jan."

But he said, "No, you're paying me to take you hunting tomorrow morning and, by God, I'm going to take you hunting."

I suppose that it was a good thing that he looked at it in that way, for I was feeling so fine that I might have had my head knocked off if he had let me. We got back into the pickup and started back up the mountain, and as we drove up the steep grade January paid me one of the finest compliments of my lifetime. "Jeff," he said, "I don't really cotton to a lot of the people I have to take hunting, but I think you and me are going to have a real good time tomorrow and the next day." A compliment like that from a real real person certainly does mean something.

3

The next day was the day before the opening of the season, and on that day we packed up to the spot from which we would base our hunting, and that trip itself up Sawmill Gulch was worth all of the effort we had made regardless of the success or failure of the hunting. Of course the mountains themselves were magnificent and every foot of the way it seemed to me was fraught with interest. January drove the pickup. Sam, Bill, Jack, and I rode with him. Wesley followed behind us with the horses, and we made quite a little cavalcade on the trail up into the high mountains.

It was an old stagecoach and mining road which we followed, and that in itself was a cause for wonder, for how men, wagons, and horses had ever been able to crawl up it was hard to imagine, for the grades were extravagant and the road bed in places almost nonexistent. It was such a steep climb that I was amazed that our pickup could make it in some of the stretches. But what

was even more impressive was that this road represented something in the history of our country and in the history of ourselves which by and large is forgotten. Where the road ended I
have no idea, but the fact of the road was that it was a road
into wilderness, which, at one time in America, all roads had
been. And it was an exciting thought to be traveling into "wilderness," for it was labeled as such on the map, and then even
more exciting to see the signs of the men who had been there
before us.

We zigzagged up the gulch through stands of spruce and
lodgepole pine and aspen. On rotting corduroy bridges we
crossed and recrossed the little stream, in the springtime probably a torrent, which tumbled down that canyon. In some places
it ran smoothly in long flat pools of water, and in other places it
dove down through cuts which it had made in the course of
thousands and thousands of years in the flat ledges of rock which
at one time had probably dammed it. There were boulders as
big as houses with ferns and lichens growing in the cracks and
crannies and around which the pickup had to snake its way
sometimes with much backing and filling. It was after an hour
and at the head of this first gulch where we saw the first major
sign of the old-timers who had come that way before us, and
this was an abandoned sawmill, or rather the dam of a sawmill
and the lake, for nothing remained of the mill itself except a
rotting bunkhouse and a huge weathered pile made up of the
slabs of saw logs. It was an impressive sight though, that dam
which was made of log riprapping and dry stone wall every bit
of which must have been snaked or heaved into position with no
greater mechanical aids than a crowbar or a peavey and no source
of power other than a man's back or a team of horses.

Beyond the dam, beyond the little lake made by it, the mountain opened again into wide grassy mountain meadows where,
we were told, sheep and cattle grazed in the summer. It was perhaps a mile wide, this upper valley, with sharply cut rock walls
on either side, walls which very slowly narrowed as we made our
way up onward some five miles to another steep point of climbing.

And all along this trail up the valley we saw signs of all those people who had once been there, rotting cabins, the openings of mine tunnels worked into the side walls, rusting iron rails coming out from the rusting iron ore cars lying on their sides in the long grasses and the tailing piles of these old abandoned workings. The amount of material which had at one time been lugged up there was impressive and the silent abandonment of everything was awesome.

> The boast of heraldry, the pomp of pow'r,
> And all that beauty, all that wealth e'er gave,
> Await alike the inevitable hour.
> The paths of glory lead but to the grave.

We followed that trail up through that grassy valley, always in the direction of the snow summits above us, to a point where it pinched in again and formed another narrow gulch up which the road went, and here all of us had to get out of the pickup and walk, push sometimes too, so that it could make it. And it was then that we discovered how high up we were and how thin and inadequate the air was around us. All of us were puffing when we got over that part. The altitude must have been about ten thousand or ten thousand five hundred feet right there.

At the head of this gulch we found another mountain meadow similar to the first one except for the fact that it was more narrow and that here and there were snowdrifts in which were tracks of deer and elk and snowshoe rabbits, although not particularly fresh ones. We also found, way up there, an old sheep corral and more old cabins, quite a large mine with a lot of quite heavy machinery rusting around it.

We traversed that valley into another gulch which took us up almost to timberline, eleven thousand five hundred in that country, and to another abandoned sawmill, lake, and rotting pile of slabs, and this became our camp site. January and Wesley wanted to go up even higher, but the pickup would go no farther and Sam, Bill, Jack, and I were ready to stop for even here we were puffing over even the slightest kind of exertion.

It was midafternoon by this time. We pitched our tent, pumped up the air mattresses, and picked out our spots in the tent for sleeping. We unrolled our sleeping bags and laid them on the mattresses, set up the gasoline stove which we had brought along, dragged in firewood from the pile of slabs left by the sawmill. Then, since it was still early, from the same slabs we made a table and bench for eating, some shelves between two trees to hold the food and dishes where it would be safe from most small animals if not from the camp robbers who live way up there in that high country. When we were finished it was as comfortable a camp as you could have wished for.

We had now finished all our preparations and it suddenly seemed a pity that there was still some eight hours left before the season would technically be open.

January and Wesley suddenly stood up and pulled their rifles from the truck where they were lying.

"What's up?" Sam asked them.

"I don't believe in shooting nothing before the season starts," January said, "but I do want to go out and tiptoe around a little." He pulled a piece of rope out of the truck and stuffed it into his pocket.

"I don't believe in shooting nothing neither," Wesley said too, "but I would admire to tiptoe around a little also," and he stuffed another short piece of rope into the pocket of his jacket and checked the safety on his rifle.

"I'm quite a tiptoer too," Sam said, getting his rifle and going over and joining Wesley.

Well if everyone else was going out tiptoeing, I thought, I might as well go tiptoeing with them. I got my rifle and January and I went off together.

Jack was the only one who stayed in camp, but he was again having trouble with his stomach — altitude sickness was the way he described it.

To the north of our camp was a wooded ridge. Wesley and Sam went off up the west side of it. January and I started up the east side.

We climbed for quite a while and then stopped a minute for I was puffing like a locomotive.

While we stood there January said, "You know, Jeff, every autumn I get this here same sickness."

"What sickness?" I said, alarmed for the moment.

"Why, buck fever," he said grinning, "this goddamn buck fever, and I just ain't no good for nothing until I get out and cure it."

I said, "Well, here's hoping that both of us cure it in a hurry."

Then once more we started climbing and not talking. He had talked about tiptoeing, but he didn't tiptoe at all. He just seemed to have a sort of careless way of going along. He didn't even carry his rifle at the ready. He carried it upended over his shoulder with his fist around the barrel. He didn't seem to be looking around at all, but still it was he who first spotted the game there. He just stopped suddenly and motioned for me to stop too. And then he pointed, and I still don't know whether he had seen the game or smelled it.

At first I couldn't see anything at all, but finally after following the direction of his finger I saw what he saw. There were three deer, a buck, a doe, and a fawn, standing right on the top of the ridge at a range of about three hundred yards looking curiously down at us.

"They seen us already," January whispered. "They seen us and they already know that we seen them. We won't be able to stalk to 'em so you better shoot from here, Jeff."

It seemed to me to be an incredibly long shot, but I was game to try it.

January whispered as I took aim, "Shoot the one with horns on."

A peculiar thing then happened. I have always been a good shot, but now as I tried to hold my rifle steady I was unable to do so. I started to shake and shake all over. Talk about buck fever — I was the one who seemed to have buck fever. The crosshairs on the scope seemed to wander all over the sky and mountain. Finally I fired when the crosshairs seemed to be wandering

in the right direction, and naturally I missed him. But in spite
of the shot that buck just stood there and kept on looking down
at us although the doe and fawn dropped back behind the ridge
crest.

"You shoot him, January," I said still shaking, "I just don't seem
to be doing much good here."

January didn't answer. He just lay down on the ground behind
a stump on which he steadied his rifle. He took a long time
aiming, and I didn't see how he could even hope to hit the deer
at that range with a "Thirty-two Special." He did hit him though.
On the first shot he hit him. The buck went straight up into the
air and spun in a half circle and then made another half circle
after he hit the ground and then died there. We didn't have to
trail him ten yards from the spot where he was standing when
we shot him.

And then I had another peculiar thing happen to me. I just
felt sort of sickish, and wished that it hadn't happened. And
when we climbed up there to get him I still felt sickish and his
eyes, I remember, were as blue as emeralds. You would have
thought that I had never seen anything die before that moment.[1]

January dressed the buck out, and tied the rope around its
horns so that we could drag it.

Then he said, "I hope you got yourself a buckskin license
when you got the elk one, because that little buck is going to
make someone some very nice steaks and roasts and stew meat."

And strangely enough this was the first moment either one
of us realized that the hunting season was not yet open.

"Good God," I said, "we've broken the law."

"Well," he said, "it wouldn't be a law if it couldn't be broken.
It would be a fact of nature. And if you haven't got a deer
license I can go down tomorrow in the pickup and get one."

We left the buck there where we had dressed it, and then
went on tiptoeing to see if we could see anything else to take a

[1] Probably Mr. Selleck had never seen any big game die before, for
nowhere in his record can I find evidence of his having gone big game
hunting before this although for many years he had owned a big game rifle.

shot at, but we didn't. At dark we dragged my buck into camp and January cut the liver out to cook for dinner. Sam and Wesley hadn't seen any deer or elk, just some tracks leading higher up, but they did have two grouse with them and although it was against the law to shoot grouse at any time I doubt if they could have done much damage. And while we had been gone Jack had seen a beaver in the lake above the sawmill, and while I guess that was against the law too, he had shot it also, but then, as January had said, a law wouldn't be a law unless you could break it.

We drank only sparingly that evening, just a couple of good stiff ones before we had our dinner and another one for a night-cap before we turned in for the night. There was a cold wind coming up the mountain so we chopped down a couple of spruce trees and put the branches around the outside of the tent walls to keep the wind from blowing in on us.

I didn't go to sleep at once, but just lay there listening to that wind and smelling the smell of spruce boughs and letting myself become filled with the great sense of peace of the mountains. It has been said that there are "no atheists in fox holes." Well, I would add to that that there are no atheists in the mountains.

It was perhaps midnight when I finally dozed off to sleep, and it was about four o'clock when I woke up with a sense of something having happened. At first I could not imagine what it was except that I was surrounded by the deepest kind of silence, a silence so deep that it was almost oppressive. Finally I lifted up the tent wall near my head and looked out at the valley, and saw one of the most beautiful sights which could ever be imagined and one of the strangest of sights also. Outside it was snowing, and behind the snow the moon was shining. Moon-light and snow light had combined to make everything white and soft and lovely. And anyway there is something about just the motion of falling snow which in itself is entrancing.

I reached over and shook Wesley, who was sleeping next to me, and told him what was going on.

"Yes," he said, "and when it's finished the elk will be down all around us and we'll have a field day. By God, we'll have a slaughter."

He went to sleep again and after a while I did too, and I dreamed happily for the rest of the night of the hunt we would have in the morning.

However as it turned out we didn't go hunting in the morning, for by five o'clock, which was when we had planned to get up, it was snowing so hard that a man could have been lost in it had he gone far away from camp. January said that it would be dangerous for us to go out so all of us slept until well into the morning, and even then it was still snowing so hard that from camp, we could not even see the mill dam.

It snowed heavily all that day. It just dropped and dropped those big wet flakes, and all of us were confined to the thirty-foot circle of the camp site. I had never really believed before that a man could be lost in a snowstorm, but I made one trip down to the pile of slabs in order to drag back more wood for the fire and almost lost my sense of direction. I have read stories of the old days of how men became lost in blizzards during the short trip from house to barn, and that day I learned to believe them.

We stayed inside all morning and afternoon and spent a large part of the time in cooking. For breakfast we made flapjacks, cooked sausages, eggs, bacon, and so forth, anything we wanted, for there was all kinds of time in which to cook in. And breakfast was hardly finished before we started in on luncheon, and for luncheon we had what was left of my deer's liver. After luncheon we put the coffeepot on and kept it there, drinking the coffee with shots of whisky in it. We played cards all afternoon and into the evening. And the silence and heaviness of that snow were amazing. It was like being packed in the center of a bale of cold cold feathers. We amused ourselves by figuring out ways to alarm Jack Morgan.

"How long do these storms keep going?" Jack at one point had asked Wesley.

"Days and days sometimes," Wesley said, looking solemn.

"What do people do about them then?" Jack asked.

Wes said, "Did you ever hear of the Donner party? They all et each other."

"Usually they eat the women," January said. "Usually they start with the women on such occasions."

"But," Jack said, really becoming alarmed, "there aren't any women in our party."

"In that case," Wes said, "they usually eat the weakest member of the party to give the strong ones a chance to make it."

You should have seen Jack's face when Wesley said that. It turned the color of putty and it was all Sam and Bill and I could do to keep from laughing.

"Hunger makes wild beasts out of men," January said gravely.

Jack said, "It's lucky we've got the deer because if we were snowed in, really snowed in, it ought to last quite a while."

"If a bear didn't get it," January said.

"A bear?" Jack really started.

"Lots of bear up in here," Wesley added. "You just look at your elk license. There's a bear mentioned on it too."

We kept worrying Jack that way all afternoon and it was funny to see him get more and more nervous, and about the middle of the afternoon he put his gun where he could reach it if he had to. And along about five o'clock he went outside the tent for a while and took his gun with him. He was out for quite a while, and then suddenly we heard him shooting. All of us jumped up from the card game and ran outside the tent to see what had happened. He was standing just in front of the tent and peering out into the snow, his rifle in his hand still smoking.

"By God, boys," he shouted as we came out, "by God, boys, I got it." He started dancing up and down. "I just shot the biggest old elk in all of this old country."

And sure enough out in the snow just close enough for us to see it was a big dark spot which was the animal or whatever it was that he had shot at. We all ran out to look, and it was a poor old Hereford steer which had gotten lost in the snowstorm.

"Well I'll be damned," Jack said, "I thought it was a cow elk because it didn't have any horns on it."

The joke was on him, and he has never quite lived it down up to this very moment. Sam and I had that steer's head mounted at Jonas's in Denver, and we presented it to Jack for Christmas. We presented it at the *Times Examiner* Christmas party so that all the reporters could be in on it. They put it up in the city room where it still is with a brass plaque underneath saying, "I thought it was a cow elk. It didn't have any horns on it."

But what he said after that was even better. He said, "Anyway, if we're snowed in, we'll have something to eat this winter even though it's a straight protein diet."

On the strength of that we decided that it was time to knock off the card game and start the dinner. We put on some potatoes to fry and butchered out a steak of deer meat. Then we had a drink or two, ate, played cards again, had another drink, and then we discovered that it had stopped snowing.

Sam said, "By God, it ought to be good hunting in the morning."

But January said, "Morning? By God, I'm going to be out there waiting by moonrise. And I'm going right now to get in the horses. Them there elk are down below us now, but if we wait till morning they'll have walked right through our camp while we was sleeping."

When he had said that everything turned at once into a hustle and a bustle.

He and Wes went out and got the horses and got them saddled and bridled. The rest of us got ourselves ready, put on our warmest clothing, drank more hot coffee and more whisky, looked to our rifles to see that they were clean, loaded and ready. It was almost midnight when we started out, January and I together on horseback, Sam, Jack, and Bill with Wes and mounted also.

We split up and went in different directions.

"By God," January said to me, "this is where you're going to cure your goddamn buck fever."

That young fellow certainly liked his hunting, and at that moment I was right behind him.

On the horses we floundered up the ridge of the mountain to some spot on which January had already determined. Then we dismounted and tied the horses to a tree. Then on foot we floundered on through the snow and darkness, for the moon had not yet arisen. By the time it did rise we were sitting on a log right at the edge of a clearing or a long glade rather, a natural highway really for game moving up or down the mountain. It must have been two o'clock or later when the moon came up, and the view was absolutely lovely, the glade without a footprint on it and clean and white as silver. It was full moon and more than enough light to shoot by, light enough actually to read by.

I don't know how long we had been there but January suddenly tapped me on the shoulder, and looking down the glade I saw a great big snow-covered elk as big as a horse and with horns spreading out like the branches of a tree. It was working its way up toward us, and when I started to sight in on him January stopped me and motioned for me to wait a while. I waited and I waited because he was coming up awfully slowly, and the reason was because he was old, so old that he might even have been rheumatic. I waited until he was less than a hundred yards from me. Then I aimed, and this time I wasn't the least bit nervous. I aimed as carefully as one would on a target range at a fixed target. And I squeezed off the shot just as carefully and slowly. And just before I shot that old bull elk raised his head proudly and almost as though he knew exactly what was going to happen. I shot and at first I thought that I had missed him, for he just stood without making a motion. But then, like a ship sinking slowly at first and then faster and faster, he started dropping where he stood and in the course of almost a full minute collapsed completely. He still wasn't quite dead when we reached him, but he looked as though he knew quite well that in a moment he would be. He shook his antlers at us, and I put another bullet in him and then he died.

We dressed him out and went back to the horses and rode on looking for another.

We heard shots from the others frequently after that, and January got an elk, a cow, for himself sometime just before the moon set. We went back to camp and the others had all gotten either deer or elk meat. It had been a glorious hunt, and we turned in after a short drink of celebration, leaving the work of bringing the meat in for the morning.

And now in conclusion I should like to state briefly the values which come to a man while hunting. First of all there is the fellowship of good sportsmen with each other, secondly the thrill of pitting your own skill, craft, and marksmanship against the prey which you are seeking. But thirdly and lastly the whole out-of-doors is our American birthright, a heritage from the frontiersmen who were our fathers or their fathers. Straight shooting, fair play, good humor, taking the rough with the smooth, the hard with the easy, these are the things which all of us believe in.

Over and over again in Jeff's book he keeps returning to his illness, which is not unusual with cardiacs. For some reason which I do not know the man who has had a heart attack seems to have had a preview of what death is as Jeff describes in the following section, and this may account for his preoccupation with his illness.

For Jeff it became more than a preoccupation. It became a symbol of his own success or failure in generalizing on life in toto. The result was that he gave more importance to my remarks than they warranted, but I am not sorry now that I made them.

Coronary — Heart in English

Is rr the old pump, Doc?" I said to Doc Crocker.

"Yes, it's the old pump," he said back at me. "It's the old pump, and the old arteries, and the whole old contraption."

"The one-hoss chaise?" I said.

"Yep," he said, but not unkindly. "All to pieces, all at once. Ah but stay . . ."

"The wonderful one-hoss chaise."

That was the beginning of the conversation when I landed up at Saint Luke's Hospital, in a way the beginning of this book which I am writing, and it has only recently occurred to me that this actually was the beginning and not the ending.

"A heart attack," Doc Crocker said, "just doesn't happen unexpectedly and without reason simply to end a story. If you really look at the matter you'll probably find that it's there right from the beginning."

I will try to get back to that later. It is enough right here simply to tell how it came upon me and what it felt like. It happened at Tinker's [1] wedding — or rather at the reception which was held at the Park Lane Hotel [2] in the Town and Country Room right after the wedding itself was over.

[1] Tinker was Elizabeth Selleck, Mr. Selleck's daughter, twenty-four years old at this moment of her wedding, four years junior to Tom, who has been mentioned frequently so far. The wedding occurred on November 12, 1949.

[2] The Park Lane was Gateway City's fashionable residential hotel. It was situated uptown at Forty-first and Niles Avenue rather than downtown as

I was standing in the reception line just at the entrance to the room. Gertrude was standing next to me, George next to her,[3] Tinker and George's parents after that and then the bridesmaids. There were potted palms and greens behind us, and the actual spot was the sort of hallway leading from the elevators to the French doors of the Town and Country Room itself where the cake, the champagne, everything else, was. You could hear the babble inside, the roaring which a few hundred wedding guests can make during the last long mile of the business of getting one's daughter married.

The line of people which all of us there in the reception line had to shake hands with seemed to go on forever. We had had to invite almost a thousand people, of which we expected and got about three hundred. Three hundred people is an awful lot of people, but with a wedding you either have to make it big or limit it to almost no one, there being no middle ground in these matters. Anyway there I was, and I was wearing a cutaway and striped trousers, a wing collar, and a carnation. And as I stood there that cutaway coat got to feeling heavier and heavier, as heavy after a while as a horse blanket. In fact I felt something like a horse which has run a race and now, in blankets, is almost back to the stable. And I could feel the sweat inside of my armpits. I was holding a glass of champagne which someone had brought out to me in my left hand and sipping it now and then, but it didn't taste right, and the whole hallway seemed stuffy and full of cigarette smoke which drifted out from inside where all the people were smoking as they chatted and drank champagne. Shaking hands for me at about that time stopped having any meaning and became simply a sort of automatic gesture. That line of guests just seemed to extend forever and forever.

---

were the Gateway Hotel and the Commercial Hotel, the other important hotels in Gateway. The Town and Country Room was created in 1946 just after the war.

[3] George Manelle, Tinker Selleck's husband, born in Montclair, N. J., educated at St. Paul's, Yale, Harvard Business School, USNR, employed in New York by Oatly & Otis. After the wedding he and Tinker removed to New Rochelle, New York, where George had bought a house.

How I managed to do it I now have no idea, but I did stick it out until the last guest had been greeted. The line then broke up and the other members of the wedding party all went on into the Town and Country Room and I could hear the corks pop and toasts being proposed, the kind of thing which usually I enjoy but which on this occasion I suddenly felt I wanted no part of. I just felt tired, terribly tired, and I wanted to lie down. If I could only lie down for a moment, I thought, I would be able to revive and then go in and enjoy it.

I hunted around behind the greenery and palms which had been behind us and found a little parlor there which they had been using as a place in which to store the champagne and so forth. There was a sofa in there in a corner so that no one, if anyone should think of looking through all of that greenery, could see me if I lay on it. As I lay down I suddenly had the feeling of indigestion and the feeling that if I could only belch loudly it would help me. I undid my tie and collar for they became intolerable at that moment. I wasn't really alarmed yet, but I was after a little while. But why I was alarmed is hard for me to tell you.

I have been told since then that it is quite common for men suffering from coronary occlusions to be alarmed long before they have any idea of what is happening, and this was certainly true in my case. I just couldn't seem to get my breath, but I suppose that at any time that is alarming.

I have no idea of how long I lay there before Tom came into that little parlor, and just why he came in I also cannot remember. I just remember opening my eyes and seeing him standing there in a cutaway, striped pants, carnation and so forth also, and hearing him say in alarm, "Dad, what's the matter?"

"I just can't seem to get my breath," I said.

Tom said, "Can I get you a glass of champagne? A glass of champagne might help you."

"No," I said and although I like champagne at that moment the thought of it just brought a fruity, unpleasant taste into my mouth. "I'll be all right," I said, "if I can just lie here for a minute. But if you could find a pillow to put under the small of my back I think that it would help me."

And then there was another indeterminate time which I can't remember in which he went out and found me a pillow.

"Does that feel better?" he said.

"Yes," I said, "I feel fine," but the truth is that by that time I had never felt more awful. I felt as though someone had put a weight, a big rock, centered right upon my breastbone. And then slowly the weight seemed to turn into an iron band all the way around my chest and back, an iron band which was slowly contracting and squeezing. And then I began to suspect what the thing was that was happening although I couldn't quite believe it either. I had always made a point of keeping myself physically fit. I had never been a hypertensive. And although I had not been able to get back into the Army, much as I had tried during World War II, it had not been because of any coronary failure. But strangely enough I suddenly knew that I was dying.

"Dad," Tom said to me, "Doc Crocker is inside drinking champagne with the others. Would you mind if I called him in here?"

Then I began to feel pain in my left chest which went through the shoulder and way down even into my left little finger and I began to get scared completely.

"Yes," I said, "you can get him, but try to get him in here without anyone knowing what you're doing. And don't tell your mother or your sister."

And by that time, although about this too I have no idea why, I knew what was going on inside me. And I suppose that the reason I knew was that today a businessman reads about so many other businessmen who have had heart attacks and knows so many who have had them too that in the back of his mind there comes always to be a wonder about the possibility of its happening to him also. As I lay there I thought of Gertrude's father, old John McCullough, who had gone that way in the middle of a board of directors' meeting. And it was as I thought about him that suddenly the fear of death came on me.

And I knew that it was the fear of death too because I had had the fear of death once before during my lifetime, the real real fear of death which there is no mistaking and which, if you have ever had it, you can never forget completely. The other time for me had been in 1918 in the St.-Mihiel salient when we were surrounded, and that time to illuminate this time is worth describing.

First of all it was a sick feeling, a listless kind of sick feeling so foolish that resistance against it seemed even silly. I remember that I just felt all green and rotting down inside me, and everything around me felt completely pointless. Everything everywhere seemed completely wasted. All the time and effort which had gone into producing me then seemed to have been spent to no purpose, and with the end of me the world also was ended. It wasn't fear perhaps so much as the feeling that every serious thing had turned out to be just silly. That is the beginning of the fear of death, but there are two or three stages after that one.

The next part in a horrible way was almost attractive. And to me it came in the form of a picture which I could see as clearly as I could see the battlefield around me. It seemed to me as though I were in a theater of some kind, the old Orpheum . . . not the new one which is a movie house, but the old one we used to have in Gateway which was vaudeville only. It seemed to me, as I've just said, that I was in that theater, as I had been frequently enough when I was a child, and that on the stage was a magic act with a magician . . . Houdini, perhaps, or Thurston . . . in tail coat, white gloves, and so forth asking for some boy in the audience to come up and assist him. Well the attractive part of it was that I wanted to go up onto that stage with all my heart, and the horrible part was that I didn't want to go up there because death was on the other side of those footlights and I full well knew it. That was the second part of the feeling of the fear of death, that first time, a feeling of desperate and unstable balance.

And right on top of that came the third part, the real fear

part, and at the same time the part that saved me. The balance was suddenly destroyed and destroyed so that I fell on the wanting-to-live side, for if I had fallen on the other side I don't think that I would have gone on being frightened. The wanting to stay alive was the most frightening thing, for it seemed to come bursting up from somewhere which I didn't know about, like the water in an artesian well under terrific pressure. Well, although that was the thing which saved me that time, it was also the thing with the really absolute terror in it.

Well, this fear of death, as I had known it that time in France, now began to repeat its stages as I lay there on that sofa in the little parlor in the Park Lane Hotel just off of the Town and Country Room where all the others were drinking champagne and proposing toasts to the bride and groom and sundry.

I don't remember how long I lay there faced with this but the next thing I remember is Doc Crocker, his face almost foolishly serious, looking down at me. He was alone because he had sent Tom down to get his bag from his car which was in the parking lot outside.

"What is it, Doc?" I said.

"It's your ticker," he said after he had taken one glance at me.

"Am I going to die?" I said.

"No," he said, "I don't think so."

I don't quite know why but that made me angry. "For God's sake," I said, "don't you know so?"

He said, "As soon as I get you down to Saint Luke's I'll tell you all about it."

Then Tom came in carrying Doc Crocker's bag.

Doc said to Tom, "You had better go and call your mother."

"No," I said, "I'll be all right just as soon as I've rested."

Both Tom and Doc ignored me. Doc got out his blood pressure apparatus and his stethoscope and a hypodermic needle.

"I'm going to shoot you with something," he said, "that will make you feel better."

Tom came back and Gertrude came back with him. Gertrude looked even more frightened than Tom did. Her face was very white and looked more white than it was because of the lavender dress which she was wearing and the lavender orchid pinned on it. "What is it, Dr. Crocker," she said, "is Jeffrey dying?"

I tried to grin and bluff it out, and I said, "Take it easy, I'm still in there punching."

"Tell me, Dr. Crocker," she said, "you've got to tell me." She suddenly put both hands to the sides of her head in a queer grotesque way as though she had a headache. "Is he dying?" she said again. "Is he dying?" And then she started sobbing.

"Everything's going to be all right, Gertrude," Doc said and then to me, "You're feeling better already, aren't you?"

The fact was that I was, and I said so.

Then Doc said to Tom, "Look after Jeff and Gertrude while I phone Saint Luke's and have them send an ambulance up here."

He left the room and Gertrude kept on crying. I suppose that it was dope that he had shot into me because after that again I stopped remembering clearly until I was at Saint Luke's and asking Doc Crocker what the score was.

"Remember," he said, "you didn't get this way all at once. And you aren't going to get well all at once either."

And I suppose that it was at that moment, not long, long ago, that this book was started, but this is enough of this for the present.

The subject of death and sickness brings in its wake a certain gravity which a man cannot ignore at this point. What is the meaning of death and sickness, one begins to wonder, and what . . . for that matter . . . is the meaning of life and wellness also? At the age of fifty-five, one would think, a man would have considered and answered all of these questions. But a man hasn't. A man hasn't answered anything, it seems, and suddenly he feels ashamed of himself for these shortcomings.

What does it all mean? Who am I? And where do I get off at? Why am I here, and where am I going?

Justice and injustice? Birth? Love? Wife? Children? Myself? Other people? Honor? Courage? Success or failure?

Should I know the answers, or have I somehow missed all these matters?

All of this suddenly comes upon one.

When I was a young man attending our State University a professor there said to us, "Boys, life for me has been lived for the most part alone, and one of the purposes of this education which you are getting is to teach you how to be friends with yourself when you are lonely."

Abruptly one finds oneself alone, and one is unused to aloneness. One finds oneself alone and one cannot help but wonder just what one has learned of importance about oneself or about the world in the span of a lifetime.

As for me, I am sorry to say, about the only thing that I have learned is that there is truth behind almost all of the clichés.

Is it strange for a man to sometimes wonder where he is or feel that somehow he never has grown up and that none of it, nothing, has ever happened?

To a man of Jeff's and my generation I think that the most disconcerting and alarming aspect of the world has been change, not that change is not one of the essentials of life itself but that the rate of change today seems to be all out of proportion to man's ability to meet it. And I think that this idea was in Jeff's mind while he dictated the three following sections, for he talked about it frequently that spring of 1950. "Honestly, Doc," he said to me one afternoon, "do you realize that my house here was the first house built in Fleetwood?"

We were sitting in the sun porch where we could look out at all the close residential building which now extends eastward into the city without a break.

The fact of it seemed to dumfound him. Then he said, "Where's it all going to end, Doc?"

And I think that this was what was in his mind while he talked off the incidents which follow: 1920 when change was only barely apparent; 1924 when it seemed already to have begun to gallop; and 1932 which was in the time of the depression.

This is metabolism with a vengeance.

Yes, We Have No Bananas

Oɴ our honeymoon Gertrude and I went to Yellowstone Park, and we drove both ways in the old Oldsmobile which I had given her as a wedding present. In those days touring anywhere was an adventure, for neither cars nor roads were what they are in these days. It was a fine trip, the two of us gypsying our way across our great western states, and we saw many interesting sights before we had finished — like Old Faithful, the Mammoth Hot Springs, and the Grand Canyon of the Yellowstone River.

We were gone for about three weeks. We returned to the little house, our first house, at Fortieth and Madison Streets which, incidentally, still stands there. As houses go it was not a very good one, for just as after this last war there was a shortage of houses after the first one. It was a one-story frame house with gingerbread and a bay window, in some ways a very sweet little house for a honeymoon house, but in other ways terribly inconvenient. It had, as Gertrude used to say, all the conveniences of the nineteenth century, or was it the eighteenth? But we were only in it for a year.[1] In the spring of 1921 we started building

[1] Mr. Selleck does not, as heretofore, give his reasons for dealing with the material he has selected. Perhaps he did not know his reasons yet and planned to revise and include them later. Perhaps he did not yet understand his major theme. To the editor the theme is obvious and it is Change. The three episodes here described are three moments showing change, the first in 1920, the second in 1924, the last 1932.

because Tom was on the way,[2] and Gertrude refused to bring a child up in that first house.

How we ever managed to build then I have no idea, but what with the co-operation of the McCulloughs' bank, my father, and the much maligned system of installment buying we managed somehow to do it. And in passing I should like to say that debt is not such a bad thing for young people to contract. It makes them more serious. It makes a man stay in there pitching.

But what I want to describe here isn't either the old house or the new one. I want to describe a moment during the autumn of 1920 shortly after Gertrude and I returned from our honeymoon, a moment of that year which was still the time before everything in the world started changing. It is the moment of a picnic which Sam Zadina got up for all the local members of the old Forty-second Division. Perhaps all of this may seem pointless to the younger people, but in some ways I think that a man is entitled to a little respect for just having lived as long as I have.

Strangely enough, although I keenly anticipated the occasion, Gertrude from the first mention of it was dead against it. And, to give her her due, I do not suppose that it is unnatural for a wife to resent the war associations of her husband. War in itself is not unlike marriage and a woman looks at it as she might at her husband's previous marriage if he should have had one. There is so much which she cannot understand, so much which she cannot share in, a whole part of her husband which existed then and which exists no longer by the time she has met him. This may be farfetched, and it may not hold true in other families, but I think that it is the explanation of what maintained in our case. I cannot deny that the First War, although comparatively short in duration, was as important an event in my life as the whole time of my marriage. For a little while, anyway, I was a different person from what I had been and from what I came to

---

[2] The primary purpose in all of this is the idea of change, but the secondary aim is to tell, as delicately as possible, how Tom came into the world, for research discloses that he was born almost exactly nine months after the moment about to be described here.

be when it was over, and a woman cannot help but resent this. Women, Gertrude that is, seem to hate the idea of secrets, especially the kind of secrets which still seem to be secrets after you have told them.

"Jeffrey," she has said, "I sometimes actually think that you enjoyed that war."

This, of course, is true in one way although in another way the falsest statement which can be imagined, but how can a man explain this?

At any rate when Sam got up the picnic for the old outfit and I wanted to go Gertrude bitterly opposed it.

"You can go if you want to," she said, "but as for me, leave me out. I'll go over to Mother's house for dinner, and you can continue your love affair with the grand and glorious old Forty-second Division."

Perhaps there is another explanation of all of this which is that during the first years of marriage couples are fighting all the time to win advantage. I would not have said that at the time, but as I look back now it seems to me that it was something like that in our case. Perhaps, though, this was a special thing for us and cannot be taken as a general statement, for sometimes in later years Gertrude and I admitted to each other that in some ways we were mismated. But strangely enough love doesn't seem to pay much attention to whether a couple are properly or improperly mated, and I want to say this, that always, whatever happened, Gertrude and I always loved each other deeply.

At any rate Gertrude said that *she* would not go to the picnic.

I said, "But dear, the boys may think that you're stuck up if you don't come to the picnic with me."

"I am stuck up," she said, "and you might as well understand this, that I'm not going to go to Forty-second Division functions any more than I'm going to go to real estate conventions."

I said, "Well, Henry Burton" . . . Henry was back in town at the moment ". . . Henry Burton isn't too stuck up to have fun with the old outfit."

"Well, he isn't taking his wife to the picnic, I notice," she said.

That was unfair because Henry's wife was back in New York, but it was also typical of the way we argued when we quarreled.

"Gertrude," I said, "you don't like me very much, do you?"

And she said, "Yes, I like you, but sometimes I can't stand you."

I don't know why husbands and wives have to nag each other in this manner. Recently I read in the *Reader's Digest* somewhere that it is healthy for husbands and wives to fight with each other and get their meannesses out of their systems, but this makes no more sense to me than saying that it is healthy for nations to get into wars because it lets them get rid of inhibitions.

But to cut this shorter, we did quarrel about this on several occasions. And both of us were ashamed of ourselves, I think, although even now I cannot see, and I wish I could, how those quarrels could have been avoided, for although all of us seem to be grown up in some directions hardly anyone seems to be grown up altogether. We quarreled, and even on the day of the picnic when I went off to the office in the morning I had no idea whether or not Gertrude would accompany me to the picnic. And I wanted very much for her to go too, for I wanted all the boys to see the girl whom I had married.

So it was a wonderful surprise then when I did come home that evening to find the old Olds out in front of the house and Gertrude all dressed and ready.

What she was wearing may seem odd today as a costume for a picnic, but it was right out of the fashion plates of the moment. It was a short pleated skirt . . . short I mean for those days, for it came midway between knee and ankle . . . a shirtwaist, and over that a jacket just like my Norfolk jacket except that it was longer and that the belt tied in front instead of buttoned. Her hair was done in a Psyche knot the way the women wore their hair then, and her hat was what was called a "toque" and looked something like a cake pulled on firmly.

"You hurry up and get your clothes changed," she said as I came in through the front door. "I'm all ready, and I told Henry that we would pick him up at the Burtons' house at five-thirty."

Now I would be lying if I did not admit that that was a somewhat disturbing statement. On the one hand it gave me pleasure that she was going, but on the other hand it was depressing to realize that a word from Henry had made the picnic tenable where a word from me had been completely insufficient. However, I had sense enough to keep my mouth shut. I went into our bedroom [3] and changed my clothes quickly.

And what I wore may be of interest too, for this was a day in which men did not yet have special clothes to play in. I wore a suit, a tweed suit not very different from the suits I wear today except that the trousers were a good deal shorter and slimmer. I wore a stiff starched collar and a tie. The coat to my suit would come off once I got there, but the collar and tie wouldn't because, although the collar was detachable, to detach it was not the custom. I wore a tweed cap which was enough to proclaim that we were off on an outing.

It was a wonderful September evening when we set off, and once I was driving my spirits began to soar. There was something entirely different about driving in those days. It took more skill in the first place, and in the second place motorcars were still something of an adventure. They were things which you could spend a lot of thought on in those days and about which you could argue, and most of all your car, then, seemed almost like a person. It had temperament and sicknesses and wellnesses which responded to your own nature. And on this particular evening the old Olds was running like clockwork.

Gertrude and Henry chattered gaily with each other, and the car and I were talking to each other. It was late September and still a little warm although we knew that it would be cold after sundown. The leaves in the country had all turned red or yellow, and there was a smoky smell in the air from weed burning by the farmers. The picnic was being held on a farm north of the city down next to the river, and to get there there were several steep hills we had to go down. I just pushed the clutch down, for I was feeling reckless, and let the Olds coast as fast as it

[3] Perhaps it is significant that in the first house they shared a bedroom, but built separate ones in the second. *O tempora! O mores.*

would. Gertrude shrieked, and Henry shouted, and the wind was all around us. We coasted faster and faster, and I loved it.

When we got there some twenty or thirty people had arrived already. They were all laughing and running here and there the way city people do when they are in the country. Some of the men, like schoolboys, were down at the riverbank throwing stones and dirt clods out at the water and some of their wives, or girls, with their skirts held up, were in the shallows wading, which was a little daring and a little naughty. Two or three men were out in a punt, their trousers rolled up to the knee, poling it around, and a few people were fishing from the bank with throw lines.

Sam was there and standing beside a great roaring fire and he, like most of the men, was wearing dark trousers, a white shirt and a tie and stiff collar. He had an apron on though, and his sleeves were rolled up to the elbow. Sam, in those days, was one of those quick dapper men with dark romantic eyes, and the girls always liked him. Even Gertrude liked Sam although she always disliked to say so. He had a way. He had a way with women, and always had them laughing or giggling or blushing.

"Hello, Mrs. Selleck," he said to Gertrude, and to Henry, "Hello, Captain." He didn't like Henry and, as far as that goes, none of us had really liked Henry at the time that he had been our captain. "There's beer over in the washtubs," he said, "and I can arrange something stronger if you want it."

And that was typical of Sam who was always right in tune with times, for he was already making homebrew and dealing with the bootleggers whom all of us came to know a few years later.

"Jeff," he said, "if I can borrow you from the missus I need some help here with the fire. The captain can take her around and introduce her."

And again I felt that little twinge of jealousy, for I had wanted to take her around and introduce her, but again I had sense enough to keep my mouth shut.

Henry and Gertrude went off to join the others, and I took

my coat off and helped Sam. I was worried at first about how Gertrude would make out, but I did not have to worry about her on that score. There was always a lot of Mother Eve in Gertrude and it only took men, whether she liked them or not, to make her want to exercise it. I looked over at the group which she had joined and I could see that she had them all spellbound. Then Sam and I went to work on the fire.

It was already burning as high as it could burn, and our job was to break it down with rakes so that it would make coals for cooking. When we had it burning down nicely, we turned our attention to the steaks and they made a mountain of meat on a table set up close at hand. We trimmed the fat off the cuts, salted them, and we would have put garlic on except that in those days garlic was considered a little common. Then we sliced and buttered buns, and Sam put together the coleslaw which was the salad. Then we loaded up a three-gallon pot which Sam had provided for the coffee.

And from time to time while I was working one or another of the boys would come up to me and say, "Jeff, how did an ugly old so-and-so like you ever get hitched up with a girl like that one?" which made me feel almost as proud as I would have had I been taking her around in person. I doubt if wives ever fully know how proud they sometimes can make their husbands.

There must have been about fifty of us there when everyone had arrived. A good many came in cars, for this was 1920, and a good many came by streetcar, which came within a mile of the spot, and then walked over. Everyone seemed carefree and happy and well behaved for, although there was plenty to drink, it was still good manners not to get drunk in those days. But there was a good deal of honest horseplay, a lot of running around and joking, and the unmarried men showing off in feats of strength, Indian wrestling, and so forth, in front of the young ladies they had brought with them.

By the time the sun went down Sam had the fire down to coals which were burning so slowly that you could hardly see them but so hot that you could hardly get near them either. He had some wire grills to put over them and a whisk broom and a pan of water with which to slow them down when they were cooking faster than they should cook. And when we put these steaks on the smell was so delicious that it gathered quite a crowd around us. And then presently everyone was eating around the fire. This is always the best and biggest moment of a picnic.

After the steaks were cooked Sam and I built the fire up again until it was roaring and throwing flames up twenty feet or higher. Then everyone sat around it and all of us got to singing.

> You're the only g-g-g-girl that I adore,
> When the m-m-m-moon shines, over the cow shed . . .

We sang all the war songs, "Madelon, you're the only one," but we didn't sing "Mademoiselle from Armentières" as we might have a few years later, for the world was still pretty much the way it had always been and you didn't say or sing off-color things in those days.

We sang those war songs and then we sang a lot of old old favorites, "We were sailing along on moonlight bay-hay," "Velia," "Drink to me only," "Tipperary," and "Good morning, Mr. Zip Zip Zip . . . you're surely looking fine."

I don't know when I've had such a good time, that is, I don't up till the moment when I suddenly missed Gertrude. I had been putting a log on the fire and when I came back to where we had been sitting she was gone, and Henry Burton was gone too, and again that awful deep feeling of despair really more than jealousy came across me. But what does a man do about that? What is there for him to do about it except sit there and wait there?

I do not know whether these moments come to other men, but they have come frequently to me during my lifetime and still can occur even up to this moment. To hear your wife talking over the telephone and laugh in a way in which she never laughs with you, to miss your wife at a moment when you had hoped for her presence, her sympathy and comfort, these are matters which a man can never mention except in a work of this nature, but they are moments which give him a pause, and in my experience it is the pauses in life which are the hard parts.

How long I sat there I have no idea, but for the time all the pleasure had gone out of the evening, for I would not be telling the truth if I did not say that there have been times in my life, too many times, in which I have been jealous. And one wonders whether a man has any right to any of these petty jealousies at all, for of all the vices I think that jealousy is the basest and the most destructive.

I sat there and stared at the fire and I no longer heard the singing or had any part of the good time going on around me. And I would have been either a fool or else incredibly innocent if I had not remembered what Gertrude said to me about Henry on our wedding night which I have already mentioned.

And, although they returned to the fire after a time at different moments and from different directions, I would have been equally a fool or equally naïve not to have known that during this interval they had been together. But I still kept my mouth shut.

When Gertrude came back to the fire she came directly to me and sat down and leaned against me so that I could put my arm around her. She was never one to make spontaneous gestures of affection in public, or even in private for that matter, so this became something special. We sat there, her head on my shoulder, for quite a while, and Henry, after he came back, sat on the opposite side of the fire and stared moodily and bitterly across at us, and although I had no idea what had gone on between the two of them and do not up to this moment, I would be lying also if I did not say that then I felt a sudden small glow, a thing that I am not really proud of, of victory and triumph.

How long we sat there with my arm around Gertrude, her hand in mine and her head upon my shoulder, I have no clear idea, but finally she looked up at me and said, "Jeffrey, let's sneak away from the others."

"What about Henry?" I asked her.

She said, "Let's just forget all about Henry."

We stole away from the fire and as we stopped beside the old Olds, again with that unusual spontaneousness of affection she put her arms around my neck and kissed me and said, "Take me home,[4] Jeffrey."

And that was in 1920 before the world had really started getting different.

2

Labor Day, 1924, and the Kangaroo Golf Match which all of our crowd held at the Sleepy Hollow Club stands out, and always will stand out for me as a moment typical of something the world had changed into. Not that the world did not keep on changing after that either. I simply think of this as a convenient pausing place from which to stop and look at the peculiar scenery which had grown up so unexpectedly all around us.

Although I was still working for Selleck and Company and my father, a thing which I had never expected to do when I came back from France and the Army, my life after my marriage had become a very different thing from what it had been before. I was emancipated by this time from a great many things which heretofore had stood in the way of my progress. For one thing I had almost entirely stepped out of the world which is so well represented by my father, symbolically anyway from the world of the Baptist Church, the Sunday School Picnic, lemonade on summer evenings and so forth. And mostly I have Gertrude to thank for this widening of my horizons. While I have never lost my old friends I had new friends too by this time, and these new ones, the members of the crowd we went with, were Gertrude's friends mostly and they represented something different in life and in business from the old crowd.

We belonged to the Sleepy Hollow Club [5] by this time, the

---

[4] Apparently this is Mr. Selleck's delicate way of saying that this was when Tom was started, for the next section obviously is the moment which produced Tinker, Tom's sister.

[5] The Sleepy Hollow Country Club was secondary in the social hierarchy to the Gateway Country Club which the Sellecks joined later. The Gateway Club, the downtown club, however, was first-rate socially in Gateway City.

Gateway Club, and numerous other organizations.[6] And Gertrude was beginning to be very active in the Junior League, of which she had been a member since before our marriage. We had begun to entertain frequently and to be entertained frequently also. Businesswise I was doing as well as I have ever done, that is as well as up to the period of this last World War when the Yaw-Et-Ag Manufacturing Company began to make hand grenade fuses for the Navy. Culturally I was very much liberalized also, for we had joined a book club and I was reading *The Man Nobody Knows*[7] by Bruce Barton in which I found a number of entirely new and illuminating ideas. We had turned in the old Olds on a Packard "Twin Six" touring car, the one that had one of the first "V" engines, and still, to my mind, the best car we ever had. I had started playing golf, and Gertrude had had her hair bobbed.

I suppose that in view of all this it is odd for me to think of the Kangaroo Golf Match on Labor Day, 1924, as a representative occasion, for in a great many ways it was not and was actually, on my part anyway, a rather disgraceful thing to have had happen. And yet the whole thing stands in my mind as a thing which I find myself compelled to mention for contrast value if for nothing else. I mean that the thing could not have happened say in 1920.

The idea of a Kangaroo Golf Match, for those who have never been in one, is actually extremely simple. Each player uses one club and one club only. He can choose what club he prefers, brassie, midiron, spoon or whatnot, but he must use that single club for every shot he makes. Accordingly the golf bags are emptied and then are filled with drinks, in this case shakers of Martinis. Now this would suggest a random kind of drinking going on, but this is not the case. The winners of each hole

[6] Mr. Selleck by this time belonged to the Masons, the Elks, Rotary, Lions, American Legion, Veterans of Foreign Wars, the Athletic Club, and the Carpe Diem Club which was a businessman's lunch club.
[7] Mr. Selleck is mistaken, for *The Man Nobody Knows* was not written until one year later, but he probably did read it in 1925 when it was a best seller. Also, book clubs did not come into being until 1926.

drink, and the losers have to go on empty. But this does not mean that winners get drunk and losers stay sober. Not at all, for there is something extremely equalizing about a few Martinis. The winners of one hole seldom are the winners of the next one, and everyone has his fill before the match is ended.

The match is generally played in foursomes, each foursome composed of two couples. And if there are some forty people in the entire match it pretty well obstructs the golf course.

It is hard now to reconstruct that afternoon in 1924, for it was a long long time ago now, but to some extent I can reconstruct it. There were about ten foursomes and all of us met at about two o'clock that afternoon at the first tee, and a number of us had drunken freely at that time. The men were all dressed in plus-fours, which was what we wore for golf in those days. We also wore heavy woolen socks in very wild patterns and sweaters in wild patterns also. The girls wore short straight skirts and sweaters which made them look shapeless, potlike hats or sunshades of the kind made popular by Mrs. Helen Wills Moody. It was such a hot day that Labor Day that all the sweaters came off almost at once. And perhaps the heat, almost as much as the Martinis, accounts for our behavior. We had had hot weather for almost a week and the kind of hot weather we have in early September can be extremely oppressive. I remember that I said something to Gertrude about "keeping cool with Coolidge," and she almost snapped my head off.

For the purpose of the match I was teamed with Marion Ecles and the other members of our foursome were a man from Chicago named Proctor, of Proctor Moving Parts and Pulleys, and Jane Mason, Charley Mason's wife in those days. And this was a strange thing too as I look back upon it. In all the things we did in those days husbands and wives were never teamed up with each other. At dinner parties this was true of course, but it was true in all sorts of functions. After cocktail parties when we would all drive out to the club for dinner, husbands and wives even split up for the journey out there. At dances, except for the first dance, you rarely danced with your own wife even if she was a good dancer. Occasionally, although I myself never went in for anything like that, you saw couples outside in cars and husbands and wives seemed to be split for these occasions also.

But as I was saying I was teamed up with Marion Ecles against Jane Mason and this man named Proctor. Marion was slim then, that is not exactly slim but certainly not the heavy woman she grew into. And it is strange that Marion and I should have been teamed together, stranger still that what happened should have happened, for we never really liked each other and only spoke usually because Marion was a very old friend of Gertrude's and had been maid of honor at our wedding. Marion, Jane, John Proctor, and I were one of the first foursomes to get started. On the first hole Marion took a four and I took a six. John took a four, and Jane took a four also, which gave John and Jane the drinks and made Marion quite angry. John and Jane took number two as well, but on number three the Martinis had begun to work on them nicely. John had a seven and Jane went into the rough and came out with a twelve. Marion had a five and I had a five too. We had our drinks and Marion began to feel a good deal better. Then all four of us sat down and had a drink which we didn't count because the two foursomes ahead of us were piled up on the tee and there was nothing else to do while we waited for the fairway to be open again. We sat under some nice elm trees and it was really very pleasant sitting there and drinking.

So by the time we teed off on number four all of us were beginning to feel our liquor, and so were the people in all the foursomes behind us. Charley Mason, who was using a driver, had been reversing it for his putting, using it like a billiard cue, and one of the girls in his foursome was complaining loudly. A man named Bert Bandollar who lived in Gateway in those days had found a garter snake, and he was running around with it scaring the girls so that they were shrieking. And one group of people were throwing golf balls at the limb of a tree in which there was a birds' nest.

I took a six on number four and Marion, who played better and better with each additional Martini, had a four and once again she and I were winners, but we let John and Jane drink too because they were beginning to look unhappy.

Well, it takes a long time for some forty people to play nine holes under these conditions, nine holes being all that we were supposed to be playing. It takes a long time and a lot of Martinis can be consumed in the process, so many Martinis in fact that a good many of the people never got much farther than number six or number seven. And as a matter of fact the greens keeper had to go around that evening with his truck to collect all the people who failed to make it back to the clubhouse, a matter which caused a good deal of very unfortunate gossip. And actually it must have looked very bad to all the older people who had come out to the club that afternoon to sit on the porch and look out at the landscape.

And I suppose that as far as that goes our crowd came in for criticism pretty generally from a good many different quarters. But in extenuation of this I would like to say that it was our crowd also which did a good many things when things had to be done in Gateway. When the Community Chest came along it was us, both wives and husbands, who pitched in and asked for money. I always canvassed the real estate men and Gertrude had several blocks which she canvassed in Fleetwood. When the prize was gotten up for the best out-of-door home display at Christmas time it was all of us fellows who put it across and got the Gateway Power and Light Company to put up the prizes. It was our crowd which every year chartered the special train to take people down to the big homecoming football game at the State University, and we were some of the people too who had to underwrite the Princeton Triangle Club when it came every winter.

But that is that, and on that afternoon in 1924 we had no thoughts about these matters.

Strangely enough the more that Marion and I drank the better golf we seemed to play. I have always been able to drink, and

I have noticed that all of those big women like Marion seem to be able to hold their liquor.

Marion got to where she was really winding up and really socking them out there. And I seemed to be able to sock them out there too. But John and Jane, on the other hand, just kept slowly folding, and on number eight they gave it up completely. And that was too bad, for if they had not dropped out I doubt very much if what happened ever would have happened.

Number nine, in those days, was a dog's leg, and Marion, who was trying to hook around it, sliced, and her ball sailed off into the jungle of weeds and swamp which still is on the north side of that fairway. And I did almost exactly the same thing. Both of us lay somewhere down in that hot steamy jungle. Marion and I and both of our caddies went down there and began thrashing around in that tangle, and that tangle was so thick that one person could be thrashing ten feet from another and neither one see the other. And it was swampy and muggy in there too.

It was when we were all thrashing around that the strange thing I'm about to describe happened, although why it happened I still have no idea. In both word and deed I have always been a completely faithful husband and I have always had a contempt for husbands and wives who do not play fairly with each other. And then add to that the fact that I have never liked Marion or, for that matter, big women of her type either. Of course I must admit that I am not as finely made as Gertrude is and that to me things like this have always been more important, and hence more frustrating, than to people more finely put together. And I have frequently heartily wished that I were more finely made because had I been both Gertrude and I would have been saved a number of extremely difficult moments.

But to cut a long story short, as I thrashed around down there, half drunk, in the muggy jungle Marion and I suddenly came face to face with each other. We stared at each other and then, without quite knowing why, I suddenly stepped forward and put my arms around her and kissed her, and strangely enough, considering the antipathy we had for each other, she acted just as oddly as I did. We didn't say a word, but we kissed for several moments, and then just sat down on the ground with our arms around each other, and just how long that went on or where the caddies were at the time I have no clear idea. However nothing progressed any farther than what I have described here and it probably would not have even if it had been allowed to. But what did happen was that suddenly we looked up and there was Gertrude standing there in the tangle, her golf club in her hand, staring right at us. Then for a moment all three of us were silent staring back and forth at each other. Then Gertrude uttered a little shriek and went running back to the golf course, and I immediately went running after.

She paid no attention to me when I shouted at her. She went on a dead run toward the clubhouse, and I pounded up the hill behind her. She ran, and I after her, through the groups of older people who were sitting on the club veranda, through the clubhouse to the parking lot where we had left the Packard. She jumped into the car, slammed the door of it, and drove away before I could say one word to her.

And then there happened one of the most peculiar things of my lifetime, for the things which ran through my mind as I stood there were none of the things which I had expected.

"This is it," I found myself saying, and by "it" I meant the end of Gertrude's and my marriage, and that was strange, for while we had quarreled on occasion as all husbands and wives do we loved each other deeply, had built the house together, had had Tom, who was three by this time, and although differing in some of our tastes had never had any reason whatsoever for estrangement.

"This is it," I found myself saying, and the strangest part of that was that rather than being sad, frightened, or desperate about it I suddenly felt quite elated. And although I describe this emotion I am in no way proud of having possessed it.

I have sometimes wondered whether or not these psychiatrists whom we read about today and who seem to claim to be able to explain so many things can explain any of what I felt at that moment. I doubt it very much for I am the most normal kind of person and this emotion, from every way that I can see it, is most definitely abnormal unless it might be that there is something of the original Adam in every man which on occasion wants freedom from even the best of wives and families.

The emotion I felt was perhaps not exactly elation, but at least it was relief, almost as though there had been something I hadn't cared for very much and which now was ended. But of course this was ridiculous because the wife, the life, and the status I had were those which I had always wanted. But now suddenly it was as though all of this were dust and ashes.

I was sick, I suddenly felt, not only of marriage but the whole idea of it. And I was sick, too, of the whole crowd we went with, sick of the Sleepy Hollow Club, sick of our house in Fleetwood, sick of cocktail parties and Saturday night club dances, sick of drinking, even sick of business.

I have heard of this sort of thing being described as a regression, a going backward, that is, to something childish which should by this time have been abandoned. And that must have been what it was, for standing there still holding my midiron in my hand I found myself thinking of childish things which I had once upon a time wanted, things like a porch somewhere to sit on and the smell of lilacs, or the old-time streetcars we used to have in Gateway, and the gas street lights they used to have and the man who had to go up on a little ladder to light them and, my God, of Helen Flanagan even.

The feeling which came over me was almost overpowering. I had an impulse to run away and go somewhere else and begin everything again under another name and in another business. And . . . the reader must constantly remember that nothing I thought then represents me and that I am ashamed of it completely . . . a new elation came over me as I said again, "This is it and everything is finished," for then it seemed to me that with everything finished I didn't even need to run away to do the things I wanted, I was free, free as anything you could imagine. I could go to the Klondike to look for gold and drive a dog team. I could visit the South Seas or the ports of China as a deck hand on a tramp steamer. I could play professional baseball.

I have sometimes wondered whether or not other men have had feelings comparable to the feelings I had at that moment, but I have always been ashamed to ask them.

I walked slowly back to the locker room where I found Charley Mason taking an ice-cold shower. I asked him if, as soon as he was dressed, he would drive me in to our house, for whatever it was which had happened on the golf course and in the parking lot now had to be concluded without delaying for even a moment.

And strangely, as we drove into town I knew already everything that was going to happen.

She would be in her bedroom, and the door would be locked and through the door I would hear her crying. "You must know," she would say through the locked door, "that everything is all ended."

I would have to rattle the knob and pound for quite a while before she would open it so that I could come in and we could talk over all that would have to be talked over.

"You realize that everything is finished," she would say when she had finally let me in there.

And to that I would say nothing, because it would be a self-evident statement.

Then she would say, not only because she would be angry but also because she would be hurt, "I don't know why I married you in the first place. I don't know why I ever thought that I could turn a hippopotamus into a human being." I knew that she would say that because she had said that before but only in the course of quite normal domestic disagreement.

I still would say nothing and content myself with keeping a dignified silence.

"Look at you," she would shout then, "just look at you with your shirt tail out and mud on your trousers."

"Gertrude," I would then say calmly, "let's leave all that out of this and just realize that it was a mistake in the first place and that now it's all over. You can have whatever settlement is fair and you can keep Tom. And I'll go pack a bag and go down to the club now."

I knew just as surely as I knew my name that that was exactly what would happen.

I was so sure of this that when I walked in the front door I didn't even look into the living room which was where she really was. I just went up the stairs to the bedroom where I found the door standing wide open. My first thought was that she had gone over to her mother's which would have been natural enough, especially since Mrs. McCullough was looking after Tom for us for that afternoon and evening. Having come to this conclusion I ran down the front stairs again to the telephone in the front hallway. But in doing so I looked into the living room, and there I saw her sitting in the middle of the sofa. She was wearing a Japanese kimono which she used to use for a dressing gown in those days. And of all things to be doing she was working on her fingernails with a fingernail file and a buffer, and each motion of the file or the buffer was definite and vicious.

"Jeffrey," she said before I had a chance to say anything at all, "I've thought it all over. You were disgusting this afternoon, and I will never be able to forget it. And with my best friend also." She cleared her throat then. "However, Jeffrey, I have realized that it is my duty to forgive it."

I suddenly felt so bewildered that I did not know what to answer.

"Yes," she continued, "I've realized that it is my Christian duty to forgive you. My first impulse was to pack up and go directly over to Mother's, but then I realized that for the sake of Tommy we have to stay together. And I also realized that I am not the kind of a person to make a bargain and then back out. I suppose that I should have been able to foresee this from the first, but it is too late now for recriminations. I must say, though, that while I can forgive this I will never be able to forget it."

Well of course what she was saying was only good common sense as I realized later when I had come back to normal, and in passing I might say that by and large women seem to be able to keep to good sense in these emotional situations better than men can, but all the same at that moment when she spoke it stunned me. But I suppose that being stunned was exactly what I needed to jolt me out of that extremely peculiar way in which I had been thinking. In fact if I had continued in that temporary insanity I might have done something which would have made my whole life entirely different.

As I stood there in this momentary speechlessness she stood up then said, "I'm going up to my room now and lie down because I'm terribly tired and have a headache. There is some cold meat loaf in the icebox and some milk which you can fix for yourself if you are hungry."

She went out of the room and up the stairs and I stood there not knowing quite what had hit me, for nothing seemed to be quite in focus. I went to the kitchen then and made myself a drink, but the drink didn't taste right. I tried smoking a cigarette and it didn't taste right either. Then I got out the cold meat loaf and the milk, but somehow I just couldn't face milk or meat loaf either. I finally decided that what I needed was an ice-cold shower, and I went upstairs to my room and undressed and put on my robe and went to the bathroom and started the shower going. As I went to the bathroom Gertrude's door was closed, locked I imagined.

But curiously enough when I came out of the bathroom after my shower her door was wide open and I could see her lying in her bed in the darkness for the shades had been pulled in her bedroom.

"Jeffrey," she called to me from the darkness, "will you bring me a glass of water?"

That bewildered me again because that was usually the way she set about it when she wanted me to come in and talk about one thing or another. I went back to the bathroom and filled her glass and took it to her.

"Jeffrey," she said then, "will you rub my back? It's sore and aching, and I'm so tired."

I pulled her covers back and sat down on the edge of her bed and began rubbing her back slowly as I had on so many evenings. After a while I paused for a moment, and when I did she turned over and looked up at me. Her eyes were trying to say something, but what it was I could not imagine.

"I've forgiven you," she said then in a very small voice. "Will you forgive me too, dear?"

"Of course I'll forgive you," I said, but I did not then and have not now any idea of what I was forgiving.

"Put your arms around me," she said in the same small voice, "and say so."

It seems strange to me now to recall this and to realize that at this moment when we came so perilously close to separation we also came closer to each other than ever we had been before.

"Whatever I do, whatever I say," she said to me then in the darkness, "however I treat you, always remember that I love you."

3

A third contrasting moment occurs to me at this point which again corresponds to the passing of time and the changing not only of the world around me but of myself also. This moment occurred in 1932 which was a time when, for us in the Middle West, the Depression was at its depth. Looking backward at it now, it seems that we could not have picked out a more inauspicious time in which to start a new business, but this was the moment in which the Yaw-Et-Ag Manufacturing Company, of which I am the president, was conceived and founded. Perhaps there are many reasons why this should have been the moment for me to make a new beginning. As I have said before in these passages I had always disliked working for Father, disliked the real estate business, and wanted to have something of my own to work for. And perhaps it is easier for a man to break from the old and welcome the new during hard times than it is in good times. Or perhaps every new business requires some certain set of factors present. Perhaps when those factors appear and combine is the only time for a beginning regardless of good times or of bad times. Or maybe when a man is up against it he is forced to do something, and to some extent in 1932 Gertrude and I were up against it. I had not been in the stock market to any extent so I had not lost my shirt as a number of my friends did, but I did hold two farm mortgages which at the time had become almost worthless. The real estate business along with every other business, and perhaps more than most businesses, had suffered severely from the great deflation. Our losses, on paper anyway, were tremendous, and what we made we made chiefly from rents on various properties which I have already mentioned. Gertrude and I had resigned from both the Sleepy Hollow and the Gateway Club and this was the only time we were forced to do so.

I was ready for a change, and I shall now describe how that change came upon me, how incidentally Helen Flanagan came back into my life, and more important still how enterprises start as frequently as not in this our American System, for I like to think of Yaw-Et-Ag as conforming to the tradition which all of us inherit.

First I want to ask and answer one question: How do businesses in America get started? The chemistry is roughly what follows. On the one hand is creative mechanical genius which in our case was Jake Brawn, whom I shall mention again in a moment. And on the other hand there is capital or money. A third element is organizational ability, Bert Bernstein in Yaw-Et-Ag, and the fourth element is steady plugging. When these forces are assembled around a product or an idea you suddenly have a business. This is no myth for I have seen it happen.

It was a cold and snowy afternoon in late December when Bert called me at the office and asked if he could come right over and see me. And perhaps I should say a little bit more about Bert here, for he, also, is typical of our American System. His father was a German Jew, a regular bearded pushcart sheeny, who established himself in the junk business in Gateway. Out of this background came Bert, an intelligent and ambitious boy, who went through our public school system and then our State University. Then, while working in the daytime as an automobile salesman, he went to night law school. He was admitted to the bar finally and employed by one of our better law firms. People today forget those hard beginnings and think of him only as a successful corporation lawyer. He has been successful, has sent a son to Harvard and married a daughter into a prominent Jewish family, is one of the most influential members of the Athletic Club although, I am sorry to say, he has not been admitted into the Gateway Club though both he and I still have hopes that he may someday make it. But at any rate this is a typical American story and, while the young people in my family have frequently treated Bert with condescension, I am happy to say that he could buy or sell them three times over.

But as I was saying it was a cold and snowy afternoon in late November when Bert called me at the office. It was toward the end of the day and I was doing nothing and I told him to come right over.

"Jeff," he said when he came in, "put your hat and coat and overshoes on because I want to take you someplace and show you something."

He would not say what was on his mind and my curiosity made me go with him to wherever it was he wished to take me.

It was snowing, as I have said, and almost dark. The streets were sloppy and the traffic more than heavy. Wet snow was slopping and caking on the overhead street lights. We walked down a block to Bert's car and then started north across the city. We went out Twentieth Street all the way to Zenith where the street names stop and simply begin over again according to alphabetical letters. We went out as far as C Street, and Twentieth and C in 1932 was an extremely depressing district, almost as depressing as the Hooverville by the city dumps just below it. There were run-down garages and automobile body shops out in here interspersed with old frame houses, not too far really from where Helen Flanagan had lived when I had first known her, although the area had been fairly nice in those days.

We stopped at a house midway between C and D Streets, a one-story frame cottage which might once have been a farmhouse, for it was old enough, this having been farm land when I was a child and the old circus grounds a little later. I could look into the house through the front window, and inside I could see a rather pretty young woman wearing a shawl working over a coal stove. We did not go into the house at first. We walked in the snow around it to a large shed in which an electric light was burning. It was Jake Brawn's shop although at that moment I had no idea who Jake Brawn was.

I have no idea what I expected to see there, but what I did see certainly was not what I had expected. It was a machine and automobile repair shop, one of the most complete private shops of my experience and a word on such shops may be in order. I have never known how men like Jake assemble around themselves the tools they need, the machines which frequently are expensive. I have no idea how they do this, but I do know that somehow they do it, and at this very moment in this country there must be hundreds of thousands of such shops which poor men of mechanical passion have somehow assembled. He had a lathe there, drill presses, grinders, a machine for milling metal, a small forge in the corner, on the walls racks and racks of wrenches, files, calipers, gauges, hammers and so forth. There was a chain hoist suspended from the ceiling beams and hanging on it the front end of an automobile under which the man, as we entered, was working. In the center of the shop was a large stove ingeniously made from an old oil drum and which burned old crank-case oil so that the room was gratefully hot when we came in from the cold.

"What do you think of it?" Bert said as we stopped there in the doorway.

"What's it all about?" I said for I still had no idea what was coming.

At that point the young man crawled out from under the automobile, and wiping his hands with cotton waste came over and joined us. Jake was a stocky young man in those days with a broad engaging smile, a round head and black, close-cropped hair. He was wearing dirty overalls, a dirty shirt, and a black machinist's cap which was quite greasy.

"Jeff," Bert said, "I want you to meet Jake Brawn. Jake, this is Jeff Selleck." Then Bert said to me, "Jake and I have a proposition and we hope that you're going to like it."

Jake just stood there wiping his hands with the waste and grinning.

"Jake's invented something," Bert said and led us all over toward the workbench. Then to Jake Bert said, "Okay, Jake, let's see it."

Whatever it was it was standing there on the workbench covered up with an oilcloth cover so that I could see its outlines only very vaguely. On the bench beside it was a small bakelite panel with two push buttons mounted on it.

"Push the right-hand button, Mr. Selleck," Jake said, and I pushed it.

I couldn't have been more startled for what the invention was was an automobile air horn, and not an ordinary automobile air horn either, for it played a tune. When I pushed that button there sounded out from under that oilcloth the first few bars of a song popular at the time, a song which also was credited as being one of the songs which took the country out of the Depression, a song going "Just around the corner there's a rainbow in the sky," * and the part of the song the horn played was the part which goes "Let's have another cup o' coffee," and the part which it played when I pushed the other button was the part which goes, "And let's have another piece o' pie."

I was startled when I heard it and delighted completely.

Then Jake pulled away the oilcloth cover and I saw mounted there on the bench the prettiest pair of chrome-plated air horns I had ever seen, the pilot models, in fact, of the whole line of them

* Copyright 1932 Irving Berlin.

which Yaw-Et-Ag manufactured so successfully after it was founded.

"How do you like them?" Bert said after I had stared and pushed the two buttons several times and listened to that air horn music.

"Where do you get them?" I said, for as soon as I saw them I wanted a pair just like them to put on my own car.

"You don't get them," Bert said, "unless you go into business with us and help us make them."

"I'd love to go into business and make them," I said, "but I haven't got a dime to put into a business even if it were General Motors."

"Let's go into the house," Bert said, "and talk this over."

So from the shed we went into that little frame cottage which I mentioned earlier and sat down at the kitchen table in front of the coal stove. It was a pitifully bare little house for whatever money there had been had gone into the shop, I imagine. But at the same time it was as clean a little house as you could ask for since Mrs. Brawn, the girl I had seen through the window, was a scrupulously tidy housewife. She had hot coffee ready when we came in and a bottle of schnapps to drink with the coffee. After we were comfortably seated Bert told us, or me, the whole story of the enterprise up to that point.

He, Bert, he said, had been engaged in some special work for the Gateway National Bank which held a mortgage on Jake's shop, his house, his tools, and everything else he had ever had to offer. The bank had sent Bert down to investigate the situation with an eye to foreclosing on the mortgage. And, Bert admitted, before he had really talked to Jake he had been completely in favor of a foreclosure. But once he had seen the horns and studied the situation he had come to the conclusion that the venture should be set up on a profitable business basis. He had recommended to the bank not foreclosure but the advancing of money to put the items into production. And this brought the story up to the moment at which I entered. Of course some kind of management organization had to be set up but in addition to that I found, which I certainly had not suspected, that there was one very tangible thing which I could contribute.

It was a building and the building which Bert and Jake had determined on was a Selleck and Company building vacant at that moment. In fact the building had been vacant so long that we had stopped thinking of it as having any value at all except the negative one of the taxes which it cost us. In payment for the use of the building, Bert said, he would issue to me stock in the company which he was forming, and he wanted me as an active part of the firm also.

"Why me?" I said.

Bert said, "Because I think you can add the thing which Jake and I will need to work together."

I was flattered at the moment, but the years have shown Bert's astuteness, for while I have rarely been the man of ideas in the company I have had the ability to stand between these two other men who were men of ideas and, on occasion, keep them from tearing each other's eyes out. The wheels of a business frequently need oil and providing that oil, and also a good deal of the steady plugging, I believe, has been my function.

I thought about what Bert was saying. I thought of the building which was situated down near the gasworks at Seventh Street and Nineteenth Avenue. I tried to decide whether or not I could sell my father, who was still active in Selleck and Company, on the idea, and then a peculiar thought came to me.

"Other than because of the building," I said, "how did you decide on me? Who brought my name up?"

"Oddly enough," Bert said, "it was Miss Flanagan, who is my secretary and who now and then injects an idea into my business."

Helen Flanagan. . . . It suddenly seemed not strange but almost predestined that Helen Flanagan should enter my life again at this most crucial moment. It had been almost seventeen years since I had seen her, and now amazingly the mention of her name . . . I knew that it was Helen as soon as he had said it . . . dumfounded me for the moment.

But as I sat there in silence at that kitchen table Bert went right on with facts, figures, details, potential markets, schedules of production, costs of getting started, Jake giving answers to questions which I had not asked.

It was strange to be thinking about Helen Flanagan, and more strange still to think that she had thought of me. And I suppose it is always strange to learn that anyone whom one has forgotten should still remember. I suppose that in every man's life there are a number of lost people, people lost to him that is, whom he regards almost as being dead and buried, regards them so much in that way that it is almost a shock to learn that all the while they have been quietly going on living.

What would Helen, who had been eighteen when I had last seen her, look like at thirty-five, I wondered.

And by this I do not wish to imply that there was any old sentimental thing between Helen and myself still lingering on or that this re-emergence into my life ever revived anything of a romantic nature between us, as the reader might easily conclude from the fact that she became my secretary after Yaw-Et-Ag was founded.

We simply met and I said, "Hello, Helen," and she said, "Hello, Mr. Selleck," and that describes the relationship which existed from then on between us.

However, there is one incident concerning Helen which I would like to relate before I get back to Bert quoting facts and figures at Jake Brawn's house.

It happened in the spring of 1933 when we were struggling desperately to keep Yaw-Et-Ag going through its initial trying stages. And if there ever was a difficult time in which to keep an infant business going it was the spring of 1933 when all the banks were closing.

The simple fact of the situation was that we were broke, and there seemed to be no place anywhere to turn for money. I had been to John McCullough at the Gateway National, and I had gone down on my knees before him asking him for credit. But, although I was angry over his refusal, I suppose that there was nothing he could have done, for the banks were as frightened as everyone else was at that moment.

It was a Friday afternoon, I remember, and the situation was so desperate that if we could not get some money . . . just a very little was all we needed . . . we would simply have to go out of business over that week end. I had come back to the office and I was sitting there after everyone else had gone home, wondering just how I was going to tell Gertrude about it, for she had no idea of the desperateness of our condition. I had been sitting in my private office for a long time when Helen knocked on the door and then came in.

"Mr. Selleck," she said, "I don't know whether or not you're going to like what I have to say."

I said, "If you're saying that you've been offered another job, you had better take it, Helen, because we can't go on any longer."

"That's not what I have to say," she said frowning. "I wanted to say to you that I know exactly how things are, and I want to tell you how much faith I have in you and in the business."

"Faith won't pay the bills," I said.

"Mr. Selleck," she said, "I believe in you, and I want to help. We don't need much to get over this hump and what I have here might do it."

From behind her back, where she had been holding her hands, she brought out ten one-thousand-dollar Government Bonds and laid them on the desk before me. I doubt if any queen has ever made such a gesture, for those ten bonds must have represented her whole life savings.

It would have been hard to refuse her, but it was equally hard to take her money. But it was that money and her faith which pulled us through at that moment; so I would like to pay a tribute here to Helen if I can find the right words with which to do so. I would like to pay a tribute, not only to Helen, but to all of the Helen Flanagans in business, for I suspect that without the Helens a great many businesses would shuffle along very poorly.

But none of these things had happened yet when I was sitting in the Brawns' kitchen with Jake, Mrs. Brawn, and Bert Bernstein.

"Well, how about it, Jeff?" Bert said after he had finished.

And then on impulse more than from my reasoning mind, I said, "You can count me in, Bert."

After I had said that, a wonderful feeling of elation came over all of us in that bare little kitchen. We poured more schnapps into our little glasses and drank a toast to the occasion. Then all of us and Mrs. Brawn too went back out to the shed and took the bottle of schnapps with us and drank from it as we pushed and repushed the buttons controlling those air horns. Then we joined hands to form a ring and sang the music of those machines there.

> Just around the corner there's a rainbow in the sky;
> Let's have another cup o' coffee
> And let's have another piece o' pie.°

° Copyright 1932 Irving Berlin.

"I'm an Indian Too" *

THE READER, if he is unfamiliar with Gateway City, may be curious concerning the origin of the name Yaw-Et-Ag which we gave to our little manufacturing business, and it is to satisfy that curiosity that I am including the little section which follows. The matter is of some importance for Yaw-Et-Ag is definitely something more than Gateway spelled backward. I have another reason for describing Yaw-Et-Ag, not my company but the organization for which it is named, and this is that frequently a Middle Western businessman whose children have gone East to school finds himself somewhat on the defensive before a viewpoint which these children bring home with them from Eastern schools. Yaw-Et-Ag, to my mind, is the best answer to the people who say that the Middle West is a place without life or color.

What is Yaw-Et-Ag? The Powwow held every autumn by Yaw-Et-Ag has been called by some a mammoth promotion stunt for Gateway City, but, while it certainly does bring in business, this description is completely inadequate unless you call Mardi Gras in New Orleans nothing but a promotion stunt also. The picking of the Princess of Yaw-Et-Ag has sometimes been likened to the beauty contest at Atlantic City, but this description is also extremely misleading, for the Princess is never chosen with regard to beauty but because of the wealth, position, and service to Gateway City of her parents, and the fact that our Princesses have generally been very pretty girls only indicates that we raise a good many very pretty girls out here in Gateway.

But what then is Yaw-Et-Ag? Yaw-Et-Ag is a mythical tribe of Indians. We are all Yaw-Et-Ags in Gateway, all members of the Ancient and Celestial Yaw-Et-Ag Nation, or at least all of us who care to be, for it only costs fifteen dollars a year to be a member. But perhaps a little history can clear up the matter better than anything else that I can say here.

The idea was conceived in the 1890's by the merchants and professional men of the city, and it was conceived in terms of the Service Club, and conceived also in the finest terms of that tradition. The name Yaw-Et-Ag was ingeniously constructed from Gateway spelled backward, and this name along with the historical background of the state and region suggested the mythical Indian Nation, and the paid-up members were called "braves," their wives "squaws," of the tribe. Then the Powwow was thought of, and the Powwow was and is the real fun of the whole institution, and I shall describe the Powwow after I have said a word concerning the serious accomplishments of the organization.

Yaw-Et-Ag to date, to name a few of its projects, was responsible for the bond issue which built the new sewage disposal plant for the city. Yaw-Et-Ag is responsible for the annual stock show and horse show. Yaw-Et-Ag owns and constructed the fine race track just west of the city, and the magnificent coliseum also in Yaw-Et-Ag Park which is known generally as the Teepee. Yaw-Et-Ag supports more charities than there is space to name here.

And now I can return to a description of the Powwow which is held annually in October after the harvest. In the old days, when I was a boy, a torchlight parade with magnificent electrified floats was always held on that night, but while this is no longer the case, the Powwow is still a very gala occasion.

On the night of the Powwow, the inside of the Teepee, that is of the coliseum, is magnificently redecorated for the occasion. At one end of the arena, the west end that is, is set up a huge Indian wigwam known as the Sachem's Wigwam, and at the east end are several large, but smaller wigwams known as the "lodges of the Indian Maidens." The Sachem's Wigwam is white, and

sprinkled with diamond dust which makes it glitter in the spotlights. The other wigwams are sky blue, and glittering also.

In the center of the arena is a huge kettledrum known as the
Ghost Drum, and the wigwams and the Ghost Drum are all that
you see when you take your seat that evening in the boxes or
general admission sections of the auditorium. The lights are on
full when you arrive, but after a few moments they dim down
and a spotlight picks out the north portal leading into the arena.
Standing there in the portal is a figure in the pageant of the
evening who acts somewhat as a master of ceremonies. He is
dressed in the costume of an Indian Chief, and he is known as the
Sitting Bull. I might say, also, that for a number of years I had
the honor of performing this function.

The Sitting Bull walks slowly and majestically from the north
portal to the Ghost Drum and begins to beat it slowly, at which
time the spotlights turn toward the Sachem's Wigwam, out of
which, with measured tread, come the Medicine Men and Ghost
Dancers, who are actually the board of prominent citizens who
make up the board of directors of the organization. They too
are dressed in magnificent headdresses and buckskins. They form
a large circle around the drum and then the Sachem from the
year before enters and gives the invocation to the Great White
Father, for the implications of Yaw-Et-Ag have always been
highly patriotic. The band then strikes up with The Star-Spangled
Banner and when that is over the Powwow has been started.

The Sachem, the ruler of Yaw-Et-Ag for the year, and a very
great honor it is to be made one, along with the Medicine Men
and Ghost Dancers, seats himself on a blanket in front of the
Sachem's Wigwam and the stage is set for the first spectacle of
the evening. The Sitting Bull announces this by beating again on
the Ghost Drum.

The first spectacle is generally some kind of a drill on horseback. We have had the United States Horse Artillery maneuver-
ing in the ring with caissons at a full gallop. We have also had the
Culver Military Academy Black Horse Troop, and they make a
fine show also. And this is sometimes followed by an intricate

drill put on by a crack platoon of the high school R.O.T.C. drill corps. When this has been concluded, the Sitting Bull again beats on the drum to announce the Great Spectacle of the evening, which is always the same and is called "The Fight Between the Indians and the Settlers."

The lights are dimmed very low at this moment and the spotlight picks out the south portal through which you will then see enter a covered wagon drawn by horses, and the wagon is filled with settlers, wives, and children. The covered wagon is drawn into the arena and circles counterclockwise slowly around it. At about the moment when it is passing the north portal, a group of some twenty or thirty Indians, actually members of the Gateway Equestrian Society, gallop in from the south portal and begin riding recklessly around the arena, brandishing spears, bows and arrows, and rifles, shrieking wildly as they do so.

The settlers pull their wagon into the center of the arena and begin defending themselves stoutly. The Indians shoot a flaming arrow at the covered wagon, which sets it on fire. And then at last a troop of United States Cavalry enters and disperses the Indians, which is a very wild moment, horses galloping about the arena in all directions. And when this has been completed, it is time for the biggest event of the evening, the announcement of the New Sachem and the New Sachem's Princess. This is a moment which all the spectators have waited for for months, for who the New Sachem and New Sachem's Princess will be has been kept a secret up to this very moment.

As soon as the arena is cleared, the Medicine Men and Ghost Dancers rise, and there is an intense silence. From the east portal the New Sachem enters alone dressed in buckskins but without headdress. He walks the entire length of the arena to the Sachem's Wigwam where the Old Sachem is standing, and when they are face to face the Sitting Bull takes the headdress from the head of the Old Sachem and places it on the head of the new one. The spectators then burst into applause and cheering.

The next moment is the Presentation of the Indian Maidens and it is a distinct honor for a girl in Gateway to be selected as an

Indian Maiden, for there are only about twenty of them chosen every year and all of them come from prominent families,[1] and for a girl to be in a Powwow in Gateway amounts to what a debut does on the Eastern Seaboard. The Indian Maidens enter from the various sky-blue wigwams at the east end of the arena, and they are dressed in buckskin dresses of various lovely and distinctive colors. They bow to the New Sachem and then form two lines, one on either side of the center sky-blue wigwam. And then, as the Ghost Drum beats, the New Sachem's drum beats, and the New Sachem's Princess enters and walks the length of the arena to join her consort. The peace pipe is then smoked, and the formalities of the evening are ended, to be followed by square dancing in the arena by all, spectators included, who care to. A little later comes the Sachem's party which is given for all the members of the formal aspects of the Powwow, and this is usually held at one or another of the downtown hotels, the Commercial or the Gateway, and is always a very lavish undertaking.

Now I ask the reader — if this spectacle which I have just described is not an answer to those who accuse the Middle West of drabness, I would like to know what is one.

The East may have its traditions and customs, and I do not deny this, but the West has its traditions and customs also. The East may have its Harvard, Yale, and Princeton, but we have the Big Ten, too. The East may have its theater and stage attractions, but we have Yaw-Et-Ag right in Gateway. New York may have Madison Square Garden but the Middle West has the Indianapolis Speedway.

I recall that, during one Powwow, we had an Italian visitor in Gateway, a man named Salembeni who represented Alfa Romeo automobiles, although why he was in Gateway I cannot imagine. But this I do remember, that in answer to my daughter Tinker who had made derogatory remarks concerning the Powwow, he said: "Perhaps it looks so to you, but to a European it seems not

[1] Tinker Selleck, Mr. Selleck's daughter, was an Indian Maiden in the Powwow of 1942, which was the last Powwow until the end of the war.

unlike the horse races at Siena or the football games held in the piazza in Florence," which I considered an excellent answer.

At first, Jeff did not want to include his political life in his book, for the habit of reticence developed through the years in politics made him hesitate. I urged him, however, and when Sam Zadina urged him also, he consented.

"Jeff," Sam said, "you are the only one of us who can do this because you're the only one who never got anything out of all the effort."

And it was certainly true that if Jeff ever got any reward it was not of a material nature.

I cannot sum up his importance in politics any better than he does when he says: "It is quite true that I and men like me have not always been the best men to carry the civic burden, but one must remember also that it is to us that our so-called betters have given over the whole area."

Integer Vitae, Scelerisque Purus

So FAR in these passages which I have dictated it seems to me that I have at least touched upon most of the subjects which have concerned me or in which I have been concerned: the eras through which I have lived, something of love and something of marriage, something about the town and land which bore me, a little about my children, although I want to talk about them again as I go on, my heart attack, and my business. However, my life in local politics in Gateway I have not yet mentioned. I don't wish to claim undue credit for anything, but a number of my friends who have become interested in this book which I am assembling have urged me to include my political experiences in it.[1]

The area of local and national politics, I need hardly say, has been a much maligned one and here, before I describe my part in it, I would like to say something to those who do the maligning. It is probably true that I, and men like me, have not always been the best men to have carried the civic burdens, but one must remember also that it is to us that our so-called betters have

[1] For many years Mr. Selleck was a power in the Republican County Central Committee of Gateway County, and since Gateway County was the largest in the state, this made his influence in the state organization of importance also. For a time, Mr. Selleck was chairman of this County Central Committee, and in this capacity he met and was catered to on occasion by almost all the nationally important Republican figures. One must remember that to make a nationally important figure a few hundred Mr. Sellecks always have to give approval.

given over this whole area, which is an area which cannot be said to be unimportant.

I would like to begin this whole discussion in the way which I began this book, which is to tell the truth behind two true stories which have been told about me. I would like to tell these stories and then comment upon the matters which they suggest to me. And some of my friends seem to feel that what I have to say here is not unimportant, either.

1

The first of these stories concerns how I happened· to enter politics, and it is as malicious a story as one can imagine. The purpose of the story, as the reader will see quickly, was simply to discredit me in the eyes of those who had put some measure of faith in me. As to my honesty, as the record will show, no one was ever able to attack me, so it was natural that they should attack rather my wisdom and my acuity.

The story goes that, as a young married couple, Gertrude and I possessed two dogs, and this was true. At the time we did have two springers whose names were Rags and Mopsey. And, according to the story, one evening the two dogs ran off and I was forced to hunt for them through the neighborhood shouting for them. Well, that much was true too, or could have been true, for on several occasions I had to do this, for it always worried Gertrude very much for us to go to bed at night without the two dogs safely at home sleeping in her bedroom. Now the lie told rests completely on this slender burden of truth which I have just mentioned.

The lie goes on that on one of these occasions when I was wandering around Fleetwood on a summer's evening shouting for Rags and Mopsey, I went up to the door of a lighted house and rang the doorbell with the intention of asking if the dogs had been seen there. In one version of the story it is said that within this house was a bitch in heat and that my dogs were there with a dozen or so others, but this could not have been true for if it had been only Rags would have been there, for Rags was our only male dog. But at any rate, as the story goes, upon ringing the doorbell I found myself not just talking to a neighbor but in the middle of our precinct's Republican Caucus which, at that moment, was picking its delegates to the State Assembly. I, the story goes, was picked as a delegate before I knew quite what had happened, and in some versions of the story it is said that the Caucus also selected as delegates both Rags and Mopsey. Now the lie, the purpose of which was obviously to discredit both me and the whole Republican organization (although plainly a lie), has stuck by me even until this moment.

Therefore, I now want to say how I did come to enter politics, first at the level of a precinct worker, and then to say that whatever local political position I did attain I honestly came by.

In the first place my whole family . . . Gertrude's rather, for Father took no interest other than to vote . . . was one to push me toward political action.

Gertrude's uncle, William McCullough, had been a Republican Senator to the United States Senate in the days before they were directly elected, and he had been a good one. In fact, it was Senator McCullough who, although it is not generally known, worked very closely with Henry Cabot Lodge as early as 1918 in that highly successful campaign to undercut Woodrow Wilson and the League of Nations which he was endeavoring to drag the United States into. Not only was my uncle-in-law, if there is such a term, a strong party man of the Republican Party, but my father-in-law, old John McCullough, was also and, through the bank, a very generous giver to the party. And Mrs. McCullough, my mother-in-law, was, and still is, as politically active as any of the others. Even today at election time, she rides around in her old electric which, I believe, is the last electric in the city, visiting the poor people of her precinct, her neighborhood now being a bad one, and giving campaign literature to them. In fact, she still wistfully will say: "I wish that somehow we could again get the Republican women out to the polls the way we did for Warren Gamaliel Harding, such a nice man really."

I had that political pressure from one side and, curiously enough, I was pushed equally from a very different direction. The other side, perhaps to me the most important, was represented by Sam Zadina, my long-time friend whom I have already frequently mentioned, and who was concerned with politics even before I met him.

Why Sam was a Republican I am not quite sure, for until he controlled the Eighteenth Ward all of those Polish people down there were mostly Democratic. I have always suspected that it was because his wife, Peggy, had been the daughter of Ben Bronski, who at the time had been the Democratic ward boss down there, and Sam and Ben had never been able to stand each other.

But, be that as it may, by 1920, which was the first election I worked in, Sam was the captain for the Republican Party in his precinct, and he was actively urging me to do some kind of work in the election. However, I want to say that these two influences which I have mentioned were only pushing me in a direction in which I was already moving.

There is a saying which says that the safety of the state depends upon the watchfulness of the citizens within it, and it was the force of this idea more than anything else which pushed me toward political action. That a man had a duty toward his government was, and for a long time had been, my personal conviction. I attended my first caucus in my precinct through no accident, but from intention and conviction. I believe in politics and I might even have run for political office at some time in my career had not Gertrude, for women seem to be peculiarly sensitive to the kind of dirty play one must face in running for office, been dead against it.

And now, in passing, I would like to comment on the subject of the political caucus, for here, and not in the primaries, as so many people think, is the real political grass-roots level, and here in the caucus is the principle which distinguished Democracy from all other political systems. The caucus is open to all comers, which a surprisingly few people seem to know. It is completely democratic. Here the delegates to the conventions and assemblies are picked, and it is these delegates and not the party machine, as so many people think, who determine the policies of the party. But it is the fact that the party caucus is open to all who wish to come that is the important matter. And when the Communist Party, I say, opens its caucus to all comers I will cease to violently oppose it.

But to return to the matter of the first precinct caucus which I attended. It was held, as the untrue story says, in a private home in our neighborhood for there are no adequate buildings in residential Fleetwood, and a party caucus with us, I am ashamed to say, rarely draws more than thirty people and sometimes as few as half a dozen, which was the number present at my first one. And, as the lying story claims, I was sent as a delegate to the State Assembly, but not through any accident but because Sam Zadina was very anxious that I should, and had passed my name along through the proper channels within the machinery of the party so that it came up automatically that evening in my precinct.

2

The second lie which I wish here to deal with is, like the first one, compounded of both truth and falsehood. And, I suppose, all good lies are put together in this manner. The story concerns the time when I was County Central Committee Chairman. The story tells that during one of our pre-election conferences when ways and means were being considered, I stood up and said: "Well, gentlemen, I don't know about my ward, but all we have to do in Sam Zadina's is go down to Skid Row with a jug of wine and line up the votes just the way we want them."

Now I want to say that I never said that, although I was present when it was said, or that is when something was said something like it. I want to say, also, that it was never said at any party meeting or conference to my knowledge but at a Chowder and Marching Society luncheon.

I have always been rankled that this story was fixed on me, for to me there is something disreputable about the term "wine jug." It is true that for quite a while I was referred to in speeches and in print as "Wine Jug Selleck," and there was once a cartoon which was published in the *Examiner* which showed me holding a ballot box in one hand and a wine jug in the other. While I have never said anything about this it hurt me in a way in which few things ever have, so I am glad now to be able to tell the truth behind the story.

At the time, my son Tom was attending downtown high school which, although some distance from our home, was the high school all the children of our group attended inasmuch as it was the high school attended by all of us, their fathers. Tom, in his English class, had been directed to write a short composition entitled, "What I Like about Democracy Is . . ." What he actually did write I do not remember, but I do remember that he came to me for advice about the matter. And then I, in turn, brought up the subject at a Chowder and Marching Society luncheon.

"What I like about Democracy," Sam Zadina answered immediately, "is that you, Jeff, in your ward can ring doorbells all summer and get perhaps half a dozen votes while I, down in my ward, can go down Skid Row with a jug of wine and in half an hour line up a hundred just the way I want them."

This was the story, the whole story, and nothing but the story, and I had nothing at all to do with the remark except that I made the mistake of quoting it because I thought it was funny. But this brings me to a much more important subject which is that of how Democracy works in action, for if I have seen nothing else in my lifetime I have certainly seen this thing which I mention.

Democracy, as I have seen it, is not general collective action as is claimed in so many quarters. It, as I have seen it, is largely individual and special action, but this, to my mind, is entirely right, for the thesis of America is actually the individual and not the society in general. It's every man for himself, to my mind, and that's exactly why I like it, although when I was a young man the idea somewhat shocked me.

What I had thought Democracy was at that time was an orderly system of casting ballots, but what I have found it out to be is a constant battle of interested parties in which every man can, and ought to be, an interested party. Life for me in most of its departments has been a battle of one kind or another so I see no reason why politics should not be also. I am not even shocked at the wine jug any more, although I did not make the remark, as long as every man has an equal right to go down to Skid Row and pass it.

But these remarks are purely introductory to the whole subject of politics as I have seen it. I will not begin with the beginning but with the end, that is 1948 which was probably my most important political moment.

3

In the course of years, my political activities have taken me to many of the conventions both state and national. Of them all, the convention in Philadelphia in 1948 stands out for me as a high point. I was not there in the capacity of a delegate but on a much more special and important mission. And I was glad I was not a delegate, for our delegation went pledged to Dewey, and I have never liked Tom Dewey, nor any man, for that matter, who wore a mustache.

It was in the spring of 1948 when a man who knew a man sent another man who came to me.

"Jeff, old boy," this man said to me, "Bob Taft has a ball he wants you to carry at the convention and I'm here to ask you if you'll do it."

Now, to tell the truth, Robert Taft was not any more my first choice for the nomination than was Thomas E. Dewey, but for entirely different reasons. I have the most profound respect for Robert Taft, and I believe that he would make an excellent President could he be elected, but in practical politics the ques-

tion as to whether a man can or cannot be elected must always
be borne in mind, and Robert Taft is a man who just cannot be
elected. To his personal friends, he has a certain quiet charm
which all of us will always value, but to the electorate at large
he has no more appeal than did Mr. Hoover. In addition to that
there were certain elements in his record which, although I ap-
proved of them myself, the vast voting President-making public can never swallow. My first choice for the top spot on the
ticket was Vandenberg, with Stassen for a partner. A lot of the
younger men like Stassen. And I still believe that a ticket com-
prised of Vandenberg and Stassen would easily have beaten
Truman and Barkley. And, for that matter, I think that any
man we could have put up could have beaten Truman except
Thomas Dewey. I have already said that I don't like a mustache,
and I think that the same feeling is general in this country. And
it is a fact that no candidate in modern times wearing a mustache
has ever been elected the Chief Executive of our country.[2] Even
Lincoln was beardless when he was elected.

But to return to the man who was soliciting aid for Robert
Taft at the convention.

It was in the spring of 1948 when this man said to me: "Jeff,
old boy, Bob Taft has a ball he wants you to carry at the convention and I'm here to ask you if you'll do it."

Now this was distinctly flattering, for, as I have said, I have
admired Bob for years. He has stopped at our house on occasion
and always, when he goes through Gateway, he comes to see
me at the office. Also, I have had the pleasure of arranging
Chamber of Commerce luncheons which he has addressed when
he has been in Gateway campaigning on national matters. I was
flattered, as I have said, that he should have turned to me in
1948 in a most important matter.

"What kind of a ball does he want me to carry?" I asked this
man who had come to see me.

---

[2] Modern times apparently started for Mr. Selleck after William Howard
Taft, but it does seem to be true that most of our Presidents have been
clean-shaven.

He said: "Bob wants you to be in charge of noise for him at the convention."

Now the uninitiated reader may have no conception of the importance of noise at a convention, and may even think that noise just happens without any organized kind of direction, may not even have considered at all the tactical use of noise in bringing about objectives. In fact a great many people don't seem to have given any thought to this matter whatsoever. To emphasize the importance of noise I will give only one example. However, it may serve as it is a very good one.

At the 1940 Democratic Convention in Chicago at which Franklin Roosevelt received his third term nomination issues were very touch-and-go and the weight needed to bring off the third term nomination was provided successfully by the proper use of the noise department. Mr. Thomas D. Garry of Chicago [3] sat in a basement room before a microphone which was wired into the Stadium's loud-speaker system. And into that microphone he chanted at strategic moments: "We want Roosevelt! We want Roosevelt!" which amplified as it was by the loud-speakers sounded like the roaring of thousands of determined followers.

This shows how important noise can be, and the reader may now understand why I felt so flattered that Bob Taft had picked me to supervise such matters.

Perhaps some of the readers of these pages attended that convention of '48 or witnessed it on television which took it to the interested viewers on the Eastern Seaboard. Perhaps those readers who witnessed the convention in one way or another will remember a float which was brought in, a float resembling in some ways a tank. Well, I was inside that float with a "walkie-talkie" directing noise from that strategic position. I am not one to brag, but I did do a good job at that convention and I will quote in part a letter from Bob Taft written to me when it was over. "We had noise," he wrote me, "and we had plenty of it and what was

[3] Thomas D. Garry was Chicago Superintendent of Sewers and has been known as "The Voice from the Sewer" since that convention.

more, we had it when we most wanted it. And I sincerely wish that everything else about the convention had been as satisfactory as your noise was."

In order to carry out my job successfully I had gone to Philadelphia some three months before the date of the convention. At that time, I had managed to buy up practically every scrap of noise in that city, all the brass bands, all the drum and fife corps, some Scotch bagpipers, all the whistles, all the horns, everything from as far north as Trenton to as far south as the Potomac. And no one else had any noise potential compared with my noise potential. Stassen's was pitiful, and Vandenberg's was little better. And Dewey, to get what he did get, had to import it from New York State. And it was because of my throttle-hold on noise that my job became more important than I had ever dreamed of. And that takes me to a certain extent into some of the warring strategies of the convention.

The situation was frankly this: Everyone was scared to death of Dewey for his preconvention work had been done in superlative fashion, and the sooner matters came to a ballot the more sure he was of the nomination. So, to meet this threat, Taft, Vandenberg, Stassen, and Joe Martin immediately joined forces. All four of them felt, as was explained to us in a special meeting held at the Bellevue-Stratford, that any one of these four was perfectly acceptable to the three others whoever they might be. In short, there was complete agreement among the four on the topmost level. The difficulty was that time was needed to bring about the same kind of agreement among all the followers on lower levels. And in this situation, noise became of the utmost value.

"All four of the big boys are together on this, Jeff," the man in charge of the meeting said to me. "But it's going to take time to get the little fellows together. With your noise you're going to have to keep stalling the convention every time you get a chance to."

What I was doing, you see, was fighting a holding action, defending a beachhead, so to speak, while the command brought up re-enforcements. I saw immediately how important my part of it was now.

"Gentlemen," I said, "I have enough noise material here in Philadelphia to keep the convention stalled until Christmas."

"Thank you, Mr. Selleck," the chairman of the meeting said. "The fate of the convention, perhaps of the nation, is now in your hands."

"Gentlemen," I answered, "I'll fight it out along these lines if it takes all summer."

Well, perhaps it is anticlimatic to tell now that our strategy, as everyone knows, failed in its objectives. But I would like to say here that I did not fail. It was not my fault or the fault of my noise that we lost the battle, as any one of those four candidates will quickly tell you. I would like to say also at this point that had certain other individuals, who shall remain nameless, done their parts as well as I did mine, the outcome of the convention, and perhaps the history of this nation, might have been entirely different. For example, there was a man who was instructed to slow down the convention by causing a traffic jam in Philadelphia which would hamper the delegates in arriving at the meetings. That man failed miserably, and you would have thought that causing a traffic jam in the Quaker City would have been like taking candy away from a baby. But that man was not the only one who failed us. There were others, also.

But no one can ever say that I failed in my assignment. I provided all kinds of well-rehearsed spontaneous demonstrations. I had bands, drum corps, pipers ready at all times to interrupt all speeches. I had applause well in hand, too. And I am a good man with noise, if I may say so. I am good with it because I like it, which is the secret of success in almost all matters. Even Mr. Dewey congratulated me in a way when the convention was over, for he said: "Now that it's all over, Jeff, I thank God that you're now on my side."

I hope that the reader will excuse my pardonable pride, for this was a moment which I was proud of.

4

However, the wars of politics for most of us who engage in them are not, for the most part, waged in the big, spotlighted and televised arena which I have just mentioned, nor are the issues, important as they are, of the magnitude of the issues within that big arena, either. For most of us who engage in politics with no desire to hold office for any purpose of direct personal gain, the battles are obscure, and the issues all of such a nature that they can be generalized under one issue, which is the constant struggle for good government in municipal affairs. This is really the issue and the only issue, and my almost thirty years of interest in Gateway politics has been concerned with it almost completely, not only mine but also that of most of the men with whom I have been associated. People still, and very justly, criticize our municipal government in Gateway. So, to demonstrate that there has been some progress, I would like now to describe what Gateway government was like during my boyhood and young manhood.

And this that I am about to describe does not only concern Gateway, but most cities in the first decades of the century, for all municipal government, it seems to me, was corrupt in those days.

Frankly, Gateway City from the time of my childhood almost into the 1930's was as bossed a city as Chicago, Kansas City, or Boston is today. In fact, Mr. Curley of Boston is not unlike old Boss Flynn who ran Gateway for so many years, and the same things which are said about Mr. Curley were said about Boss Flynn in those days. "Curley deserves a hundred thousand dollar graft," it is said, "for the job of running Boston is a hundred thousand dollar job if there ever was one." "Boss Flynn deserved a fifty thousand dollar graft" . . . everything was smaller then . . . "because the job he does is worth fifty thousand dollars." A cynical and realistic logic and sometimes a very difficult logic to answer adequately, for most of the old-time political bosses had indisputable ability in civic administration. And, as is the case with Mr. Curley of Boston whom I once had the pleasure of meeting, they had charm, too, which made fighting them an even more difficult matter. Boss Flynn, for example, was probably the most charming man I have ever known and one of the handsomest, also. He had snow-white hair and wore it in a pompadour. He had a thin, finely chiseled face, direct blue eyes, and a wonderfully gracious, courtly, old-fashioned manner.

And I would like to say this, to give the devil his due — those old-fashioned political bosses in their time did serve valuable functions in the development of their cities and of their nation. They maintained a stable order and, while it may not have been the best order imaginable, it was an order in which a man could and did do business. And corrupt as they were, they were gentlemanly enough to keep the corruption hidden where it generally did not meet the eye of the people who did not wish to see it. Prostitution in Gateway was rigidly restricted to the old red light district just north of where the Union Station now is, and in a crude sort of way it even had a kind of medical inspection. Gambling was similarly controlled. Pickpockets were rarely encountered west of Tenth Street. And while Boss Flynn collected in one way or another on almost everything happening within the city, his collections were modest enough, and nothing comparable to the taxes we now pay our government for the same kind of service. And more than that, in his own way he was honest, for when he was bought he stayed bought, which is what a man wants of any government he is dealing with, I imagine.

Interesting enough, for people with a historical inclination, the building in which all of the Flynn affairs were administered is still standing, and it is well worth while to go down to Twelfth and Van Buren in the old Second Ward to see it. It is an old two-story brick saloon facing on City Square where so many vagrants now hang out, and is still serving beer over the old walnut bar which Boss Flynn was once so proud of. It is historically interesting because so many cities throughout our nation were once upon a time ruled from similar establishments. In my boyhood, this one was called "The City Hall" or "the Vatican" since Flynn was sometimes called "the Pope," inasmuch as he personally never smoked or drank and gave large donations to Catholic charities throughout the city.

Inside, it was typical of the better class saloons in those days, although occasionally you might meet one or two rather rough birds at the bar there. It was a big, square room split in half by a shoulder-high black walnut partition on one side of which was the bar and on the other side of which was a restaurant. The tables were covered with checkered tablecloths and there were ornate brass chandeliers — gas, of course — hanging from the ceiling. And, as you would expect, there was a "back room" which was generally known as "the Customers' Room" although the "customers" did not come primarily to buy drinks or dinner. The customers came from all parts of the city: Honest Bob Brady, the Mayor, "plug-uglies" from below Tenth Street, solicitors for charities of all kinds and descriptions, lawyers who served as liaison between various interests in Gateway, contractors, in short almost everyone who did any kind of business. Flynn himself lived in the upstairs and the very special customers went up there.

Now, as one thinks this over, one begins to arrive at an idea of his power and to wonder on what his power depended.

"A ward heeler," Boss Flynn used to say, "is simply a social worker among the poor people of the right party," and that was the way he ran things. Any Democratic voter in his Second Ward, especially if he was part of a large voting family, could count on a sack of coal in January when he needed it most desperately, or the services of a doctor when his wife was about to have a baby, or a helping hand in his business when it was particularly rough sledding. And almost any charitable organization except the Masons could count on Boss Flynn for a good big donation just before elections. So you can see that what he had there, and the thing which we were attacking, was an almost impregnable system, and one which we never could have broken had it not been for the Depression which created a bigger situation than he could handle, his advancing age which made him tired of the struggle, and the Collectors of Internal Revenue who, I suppose, represented modern times encroaching on him.

Our first real brush with Flynn came in 1928 in the municipal election of that year in which legalization, or illegalization rather, of the horse race bookies became the principal issue. And this in itself is a good example of the paradoxical nature of the issues a man in politics must sometimes deal with. There is a short history which I must mention now before I can deal with the actual issue.

In 1922 Yaw-Et-Ag Park was purchased by Yaw-Et-Ag — I mean the organization and not my business. A fine mile and a quarter track was constructed, and also a fine grandstand. And when this was done it was obvious to the board of Medicine Men and Ghost Dancers that if the venture were to be successful or even self-supporting there would have to be legalized betting at the track. An ordinance was therefore pushed through, with Flynn's blessing, which legalized all horse betting in Gateway, and this made not only the pari mutuels at the track legal but also the bookies who operated all over the city. At first the bookies were pleased, but later they were alarmed in a way which will come out later in my story.

In 1928 we of the Republican Party were attempting to line up a strong ticket and platform for our election, a "good government" ticket and platform for, as I have said, locally this has always been the issue.

And curiously enough at the same time a strong opposition, although we did not know exactly where it came from, was growing up within the city against the bookies. Although the Protestant churches of the city were the loudest protesters, the origins of this protest, as will appear later, came from somewhere else, but we were not sufficiently astute then to see it. To us, it just seemed that an anti-bookie issue was a natural one for us to seize upon. We formed what seemed to us a fairly strong ticket and we expected the bitterest kind of Boss Flynn opposition.

But then, to our surprise, the kind of opposition we expected never really came into being. Boss Flynn did form a sort of opposition but only a token opposition which had no real impact. The result was that we put in a "reform Mayor" and won almost everything except the office of Chief of Police, which continued mysteriously to be occupied by one of Flynn's men. We were very elated and continued to be elated until we learned the story behind the story which I have just told here. It was Sam Zadina, whose cousin was a bookie, who first learned what the truth was.

The bookies and Boss Flynn, who derived a sizable income from them, had found out that if horse race betting was legal they would be subject to federal and state income taxes on the money derived from it. If horse race betting again became illegal, they would no longer be troubled by such matters. And if they controlled the Police Department they would have no worries at all about illegal operation.

It was shortly after we had learned about this that I happened to meet Boss Flynn on the street and spoke to him bitterly about it.

He began to laugh and said: "I look at it this way, Selleck. The bookies are my graft, and I'd just like to keep Uncle Sam honest."

And angry as I was, I could not help but admire the old blackguard.

It was 1930 before we really beat Boss Flynn and at that it was sooner than we expected. It was a very special year for me, too, because both Sam and I, and several other men too, bolted from our party affiliations to form a nonparty, "good government" coalition, an extremely dangerous undertaking, for if a man is not successful in a thing like that he can never again count on the trust of the organized party. It was a particularly courageous action on Sam's part inasmuch as Sam, throughout his life, has depended on political appointment or election for his living.

And here at this moment of describing my break with "party" I would like to inject a word or so in defense of the American Two-Party System, for it has, of late years, come under criticism as have almost all the things which I personally believe in.

To the schoolboy or the uninitiated person who looks at the political scene, it may seem that political parties are intended to represent differences of political opinion. And it may also seem to this person unfortunate that the two major parties in America today are so similar in beliefs and practices. However, I do not see the matter in this light. I do not see political parties as ways of expressing differences, but as ways of expressing agreements rather. I am quite sure that if every point of view were to be expressed by a different political party our political scene would today be as confused as the one in France is. Social Democrat, Democratic Socialist, Christian Democrat, Popular Frontist, Frontal Populist, God knows what: these matters only confuse me. No, our system, and to some extent the British system, certainly are the best ones. The parties with us may not mean very much as far as thought goes, but they represent unanimity of purpose which may be our greatest strength in the trying days with which we may be confronted.

But to return to the more specific issue, in 1930 both Sam and I felt warranted in taking the dangerous step of putting an objective ahead of party affiliation. It seemed to be the right time. Not only had the good government which we had elected in 1928 failed to remain good, but also Boss Flynn was having difficulties which put him in a vulnerable position. The collectors of internal revenue were after him, and it was a time, too, in which all established values, boss rule among them, were being questioned in the most searching manner. It was Sam who saw this. Sam, above all things, has always managed to be in tune with his time and for a man to accomplish anything, regardless of objectives, he must be in tune with the time he lives in.

All of the matters which I have mentioned had been in our minds for some time, but it was not until one afternoon at the Hound and Hare Club that Sam brought them to a focus before me. It was about five in the afternoon and just too early for the majority of businessmen who dropped in for a drink after business hours to have arrived. Except for George, the bartender, we had the room in which we were sitting to ourselves.

We had been talking casually about unimportant things when Sam suddenly looked at me and met my eye and said: "Jeff, how would you like to be Mayor of Gateway City?"

I assumed that he was joking and I said: "I'm a married man and I have troubles enough already."

"I'm serious, Jeff," Sam said, and I could see that he was then. "I think that you could be Mayor of Gateway City if you would be willing to run for office."

I said and said quite sincerely, "But I don't want to run for office."

"The trouble with you, Jeff," he said, "is that you've chosen to be a little shot when there's no reason at all why you can't be a big shot."

Knowing Sam as well as I did, I knew that there was something deeper behind what he was saying.

"All right," I said, "just tell daddy all about it."

Sam said, "Whether you know it or not the time is ripe now for a great big change in Gateway City."

I said, "Like who, for instance?"

Sam, who is really something of a scholar, said: "There is a tide in the affairs of men which, if grasped at the flood, leads on to fame and fortune."

I still had no idea what it was all about and I said, "If you please, Sam, let's get down to cases."

"Republicans!" he said. "Democrats! At the moment everyone is fed up with both. Reform mayors! Everyone is fed up with reform mayors, too. It's time to get out the new broom and sweep everything completely. Boss Flynn, although no one knows it, is dead, and it's time for someone else to get in and boss things."

"Who?" I asked directly.

"You and me," Sam said — "that is, if you want to."

"Why me?" I asked him.

"Because you're a perfect man to run for office. You're honest, or at least you have a reputation for being honest. You have the common touch and at the same time you belong by marriage to one of Gateway's most important families. You are a member of damn near every service club in the city. With your war record and your activity since then, the American Legion would have to be behind you. People like you. And you're a fair although not brilliant public speaker. In short, you're the American flag if you'll let me say so."

Well, this was all very flattering, but I could see several important objections.

I said, "But would the party swallow me when there are so many others who have earned a shot at mayor?"

"Party, hell," he said. "This time we're going to say to hell with party and make up our own party."

And that really did alarm me, for Sam has always been a good strong party man right from the beginning, and one to insist on the strictest kind of discipline within the organization.

"What kind of a party?" I said in astonishment and weakly.

"Good government," he said. "Good, honest, efficient, economical government the way people want it."

"All right," I said. "But what's in it for you, Sam?"

He said promptly, "I want to be County Attorney."

I was relieved that that was all he wanted. "The time is ripe," he repeated. "If it was a national election year I wouldn't suggest it, but this year you and I can get the support of the best elements in both parties. The Republicans, as you ought to know, are all mixed up, and the Democrats are ready to bolt from Flynn, and he's failed so much in the last two years that he can't hold them. He's finished and it's our chance now."

I said, "Our chance for what, Sam?"

He said, "Our chance to be the ones who run things."

It is strange how excited I became when he said that. I think that there must be something in every man which, when tapped, makes him desire influence and power, for if there were not,

I, who am the last man to want those things, would never have felt the agitation which I did feel.

"And you," Sam said to me, "are the perfect person around whom to build our party."

I was so agitated that for a moment I was almost ready to go along with him completely. I actually found myself, in spite of the fact that all my usual inclinations went the other way, wanting to be mayor and wanting to be a good one, wanting to achieve for Gateway all the things which Gateway had always needed. And I do not think that the reader can imagine what it was that saved me. It was Gertrude who has saved me so many times from doing things which would have been foolish, and this would have been foolish too, for, in thinking back on it now, I can see that I would not really have been the good mayor that I imagined I could be. It takes a smart, hard-boiled man to be a good mayor, and I have learned often enough and to my sorrow that I am just not hard-boiled. However, the way this came to me at that moment at the Hound and Hare Club was something different and perhaps even amusing. At the moment there flashed before my mind various times in which Gertrude had upbraided me . . . not really upbraided perhaps, but at least been difficult . . . when in the winter I had forgotten to get the snow shoveled from our front walk, or similar instances. "What then would she say to me," I suddenly thought, "if I were responsible not only for our front walk but all the walks and streets in the city?"

"Let's be sensible, Sam," I said. "I'm not going to run for mayor. But as for the rest of it, I'll go along with you if you'll show me how it's possible to do it."

Then Sam started explaining, and I could see that this was no thing he had thought up on the spur of the moment. Ward by ward, he went over the city, and ward by ward he showed me the situation. And then I began to see, not that we could not help but win, but that there was a fighting chance that we could do it. The only big edge Flynn had over us was in the Roman Catholic wards which his machine was very strong in.

"Perhaps we'll have to get out the old wine jug," Sam said.

"The wine jug isn't enough," I said. "We need an organization, some good, loyal, experienced precinct captains, some fellows who for years have been handling coal and flour and lard in winter. And we haven't got them, and we won't have them in the important parts of the city."

Sam sat in silence for several moments. And then he said slowly to me, "Jeff, do you know what a parish priest is?"

I said, "Sure I know what a parish priest is."

Sam said, "A parish priest is a description of a damn near perfect precinct captain."

"You can't buy the Church," I said quickly.

"Well," said Sam, "not exactly."

Now in order not to be misunderstood I want to interpolate here quickly that I am quite sure the Catholic Church would never for one minute engage in party politics in an election. And I am equally sure that no bishop would ever instruct any parish priest how to vote or to tell his people how to vote either. But all the same I am just as sure that there are occasions on which many a parish priest would appreciate knowing the political sentiments of his bishop, and that, if he did know these sentiments, they would somehow filter down into the consciousness of the members of the parish. And this is why, if a candidate can be one who is unmistakably under the Church's approval, it can be a tremendous advantage to him. And this also was what was behind the remark Sam made to me at that moment.

"Are you thinking what I'm thinking?" I said.

"I'm thinking," Sam said, "that our candidate has to be a damn good Roman Catholic."

And when he said that, our eyes met again in a complete understanding, for both of us had thought of the same man at the same moment.

It so happened that in Gateway City at that time we had a prominent Catholic who was also a very successful businessman, the founder and chairman of the board of directors of the Gateway Iron Works, which he had built from practically a blacksmith shop into the company which it is today. His name was William Lynch. He was a generous donor to Catholic charities, an important figure in the Knights of Columbus, and a Papal Knight. He had five fine sons and three very pretty daughters. He was a man of high integrity and an enemy of the Flynn machine — with which on occasion he had had to do business.

"Yes," I said, "but do you think he would ever be willing to carry the ball for us?"

"He's Irish," Sam said, "and no Irishman can resist politics if he gets a chance to get in it."

And Sam's judgment of the man turned out to be the right one. He was a tough proposition to begin with and one who insisted on seeing all the cards face up on the table. And even after he was in possession of all the facts he had to think over and pray over the situation. And I think that in addition to that he talked it over with his bishop before he consented. But after he did decide to run he became a fighting, hard-hitting candidate, one of the best we ever ran for office. And fortunately also he became an excellent mayor after he was elected, one of the best ones, for that matter, that we have ever had in Gateway. And in 1932 Sam and I were able to return to the Republican Party in a much more powerful position than we had ever enjoyed up to that time.

(Unfortunately, Jeff's political reminiscences are incomplete. He intended, for he told me so, to describe each campaign of his political career, but he was not allowed the time in which to do so. However, incomplete as this section is, one is still able to make some kind of an evaluation.

But a better evaluation than I could make has already been made by one whose opinion in this matter should carry considerable importance. The letter which follows was written to Jeff by Boss Flynn in 1934, which was just shortly before Boss Flynn was sent to Federal prison for evasion of income taxes. Flynn was old, and on evil days, and obviously losing his grip on his political system.)

MY DEAR MR. SELLECK:

I would appreciate it very much if we could get together to-morrow afternoon for the little talk which I suggested in my other letter. I am at your disposal either at my place or any other place which you might suggest, for I wish your advice on several matters. You see we have fought each other for so many years that I have come to respect you very highly.

The truth is that I am an old man now and faced with many problems and am no longer a threat to any man on earth. I find that my affairs have become sadly tangled. I no longer trust my friends to tell me what the truth is. My hope is that in getting together with one of my most respected enemies he may do this service for me. If I may say so, and I think I must, you've come a long way, son, since I first met you. I remain

Your most humble servant . . .

Jeff, myself, all of us, belong to that section of society which is generally considered to be secure, meaning that we will not collapse at a moment's notice. Jeff, as he says, had an income between twenty and twenty-five thousand dollars a year, and when he died he left assets of around one hundred thousand dollars, and yet the insecurity of this security, possibly the insecurity of all of us, occurred to me as I read over the next sections.

Freedom from want for all men may perhaps be a possible goal for politicians to strive for, but freedom from fear is not, for fear is in a man's mind and cannot be legislated one way or another.

Saint Luke's Hospital

THE first morning of my incarceration at Saint Luke's Hospital was probably one of the most difficult moments of my life. It is not a man's intention, if he intends ever to retire at all, to retire at the age of fifty-five unexpectedly and without having put his affairs in order. Fifty-five is ten years short, fifteen years short perhaps, of what he plans on if he plans at all. At fifty-five a man has made a will but not the last will he expects to make or even the next to the last one. He has kept up his insurance premiums, but insurance is made to take care of death, and retirement is a very different matter. He has accumulated a certain amount of capital, but this capital for the most part is in his business, which means that it is not a particularly liquid asset. He hasn't counted on it for income, either. For income, for support for himself and his family, for everything, in fact, he has counted upon his earnings. He is not ready, I mean. He is not ready to give up the battle. He can die comfortably enough at fifty-five, but he cannot comfortably retire.

All of which I do not feel is an argument in favor of carrying an unwarranted amount of insurance, either, for a man can be insurance poor just as he can be land poor or poor in any of the numerous other ways in which a man who owns equities of any kind can be poor. Insurance is a fine thing in its way, but in spite of what Charley Mason tells me, I cannot see how for the life of me I could have afforded the kind of insurance which would have adequately met my needs at the moment. There is no freedom from fear, my experience tells me, in spite of the claims of a national administration which holds a contrary viewpoint. There is no security in this world. There is opportunity only. But the essence of a coronary occlusion is that for the moment anyway all opportunity seems to have vanished.

By the time of the moment of the first morning in Saint Luke's Hospital I had been given my orders already.

The evening before, after they had taken me to Saint Luke's, I had said to Doc Crocker, "Doc, tell me honestly how much time have I got for living?"

He had shrugged his shoulders and said, "A week. A month. Six months. Honestly, I can't tell you."

"I need time," I said. "I need all kinds of time to get things put in order."

Then he had said, "Probably you can have years if you really want them."

"I want them," I said. "But how do I get them?"

He said, "You get them by changing your whole way of living."

"In what way?" I asked him.

"The first part of it," he said, "is the easiest, and consists of following exactly the orders that I give you. And these are the orders. First, you're to lie right where you are on your back in bed for three or maybe four weeks' time. You aren't going to like it, either. For instance, you're going to hate having to use a bedpan."

"God, Doc," I said, "not a bedpan!"

"Yes," he said, "a bedpan, and about tomorrow you'll start telling me that it would be less of a strain on you to walk down the hall to the toilet than to use the bedpan, but I won't believe you and I won't let you."

He was absolutely right about that, for the bedpan was one of the things I hated most about that whole period of my illness, and two days later I tried to tell him exactly what he had just said I would tell him.

"In the second place, you may not have noticed yet that there isn't any telephone in the hospital room. Sometime tomorrow you're going to notice that and demand one so that you can keep track of your business. But I'm not going to let you have a telephone, for, to my mind, the telephone has done more harm in this world than good. It makes people accessible who have no business being accessible at all."

"What next, Doc?" I said.

"Next, you've got to knock off smoking."

"But I've always been a heavy smoker and I've never been able to stop smoking," I said.

"You've got to stop this time," he said. "But you can drink if you want to."

Well, that seemed like something.

"You can drink a little later on to the extent of two drinks a day, and I mean one-ounce drinks when I say that. In addition, you've been carrying too much weight for years, and you have to go on a reducing diet, and you won't like that. Sexual intercourse, yes, but not for quite a while. But you shouldn't be too antsy at your age."

"That's all you know, Doc," I said. "At my age some men get just about as antsy as they ever do get."

"After three or four weeks here at Saint Luke's," Doc went on, "you'll probably go home, but that doesn't mean that you're cured by a long shot. When you go home, you'll have to stay on one floor, probably the second, for quite a while because climbing steps is out for a long, long time for you."

"What else?" I said.

He said, "Isn't that enough for the present?"

I said, "You said that there were two parts to this, and that what you were telling me was the first part and the easiest part."

He sat down on the edge of the bed then and took off his glasses. "The second part, Jeff," he said, "is mostly mental. To change your way of living you've got to change your way of thinking, and changing a man's way of thinking at fifty-five isn't particularly easy."

I said, "What's the matter with my way of thinking?"

"You're a big boy," he said, "and if you want to live and be productive again it's time for you to grow up now."

So when I woke up that morning at Saint Luke's I had my orders, but it didn't seem to help very much for me to have them. If a man hasn't grown up by the time he's fifty-five years old, when is he going to grow up, I ask you? And what was ungrown-up about my life as I have set it down, I also ask you? It is all very well to tell a man to grow up, but sometimes there are things about his life which have not allowed him to grow up the way he would have liked to. I was certainly as grown-up as all the people all around me.

That first morning I couldn't think about growing up. It was money mostly which concerned me.

There were the general expenses of living which I will go into later, but in addition to that at that moment there were all the special expenses of my daughter's wedding, half of which I didn't even know yet and couldn't know until the bills came in for them. But, in spite of not being able to know, I lay there in the early morning and tried to figure out without the aid of pencil and paper just what they would be.

Now in passing I would like to say something to the people who say that a man who makes around twenty thousand dollars a year has no business giving his daughter a five-thousand-dollar wedding. Well, I suppose that in theory I agree, but theory is all very well. In practice things are different. I don't know why it is, and I don't know whether I believe in it or not, but in our system the marriage of a man's daughter is a very special occasion in which a man is expected to stand right up to the line and shoot the works, as the phrase is.

A man can't really beef, for every man he knows seems to have to do the same thing at one time or another in the same way he has to send his sons to college whether they have any business in college or not, belong to the Sleepy Hollow Club, or buy his wife a fur coat when he arrives at a certain station. A family of more established wealth than ours could probably get away with more economy, but our family in our position just couldn't afford to.

And then there may be a justification to it in this, which is that on an investment of around five thousand dollars the children did take in between six and seven thousand dollars' worth of presents, and a thousand to fifteen hundred dollars' profit on a gross of five thousand is good in any business. This may bring the criticism that we were material-minded, but a man cannot help but try to do the best for his daughter that he can do.

But as I lay there in bed that morning I was not thinking about justifications. I was thinking about money strictly, and I think that it may be of interest to tell just how I broke the sum down, or built it up, rather, for that was more like the process. Even if you can't do anything about it, it is always good to reckon up a bill, although I don't really recommend it when you are suffering from a coronary occlusion.

It broke down into expenses for clothes, including the trousseau, which the women seem to have to have for these occasions. Expenses for parties leading up to the wedding. The bridal dinner, the church and minister, flowers for decorations, the reception, and then gifts, which are no minor item.

The trousseau, it seemed to me as I lay there, would come to over twenty-five hundred dollars, possibly three thousand. This seems like an awful amount of money, but there seems to be an awful lot that girls have to have at these moments: street dresses, party dresses, underwear . . . Lord, why can't they just wear shorts and T-shirts . . . shoes . . . Lord, how many pairs of shoes they seem to need . . . nightgowns, nylons, hats, gloves, luggage, handkerchiefs, sachets, plus sheets, towels, flat silver . . . a negligee, a bed jacket . . . I don't know what a girl who expects to start in cooking needs with a bed jacket, but Tinker had one . . . perfume. I set the figure as I lay there at three thousand dollars.

Now certainly there are people who get married every day with few or any of these things, but it is nice for a girl if she can have them.

The next item was the item of expenses for parties leading up to the wedding, not including the announcement of the engagement party which already had been paid for. This was a small department, possibly only about a hundred dollars, for most of the entertaining had been done by friends and relatives of our family.

But after that came the bridal dinner, which had been held the night before the wedding, and that again was a big outlay. We only had thirty people, but we had tried to make it as nice a dinner as we could manage. We had taken over the special dining room at the Sleepy Hollow Club, and the steward at the club had figured dinner at five dollars a plate, which started the bill at one hundred and fifty dollars. We had figured cocktails at an average of three per person, a dollar fifty a head, or forty dollars — fifty dollars in round figures. The champagne plus drinks after dinner came to about one hundred dollars. Decorations would probably come to fifty dollars, and tips probably another fifty, a grand total of something like four hundred dollars.

The item of the church and minister . . . well, George paid the minister . . . I didn't know how to figure, so for the moment I left it out of the accounting.

But then I came to the reception.

We had a choice here of either holding the whole wedding and reception down to very close friends and members of the family, which isn't really fair to the bride and groom, or else shooting the works and inviting everyone we should have. And it was the latter course which we seemed to have to follow although I did tell George and Tinker that if they would elope I would give them a gift of three thousand dollars. I should have made it higher.

We found, on making out the lists for guests, that the smallest number we could cut down to was something like one thousand people, with the list weighted toward the out-of-town ones. And of the thousand people we expected, and got, about three hundred. The bill for a reception for three hundred people becomes high. The champagne was figured at six dollars a bottle, and one bottle for each three people, which means around six hundred dollars. Food, we figured at two dollars a person, which made another six hundred dollars. The Town and Country Room, decorations for it, tips and help, would come to another one hundred and fifty dollars. I added that up in my head and figured out something like fourteen hundred dollars.

And then as I lay there I tried to figure out the grand total: trousseau, three thousand dollars; parties, one hundred; bridal dinner, four hundred; reception, fourteen hundred. It added up to four thousand nine hundred dollars.

That was one side of the ledger. On the other were the Government Bonds which I had purchased during the war to the amount of four thousand dollars which I had planned to sell to pay for this occasion. The rest of it would have to come out of income.

There was one other thing to think about, too, which was that I had promised Tinker as a wedding present a new Ford convertible which hadn't been delivered yet, and that would be another two thousand or twenty-one hundred dollars.

These were the first things which were on my mind that first morning after my coronary occlusion, when the new way of thinking which Doc Crocker had talked about was supposed to be beginning.

2

From a consideration of the expenses of the wedding, as I lay there in the early morning . . . and it was early, too, for hospitals always seem to get the day started for everyone at an unbelievably early hour . . . on what we laughingly called my "bed of pain," I went on to think about my whole yearly income and where these expenses, and the hospital expenses which grew every moment that I lay there, would fit in.

My income for 1949 after deductions but before taxes, the figure which Form 1040 calls "Net Income," would be, as close as I could figure it in November, around twenty thousand dollars, which, for the show which I was running, was not a great deal of money. As I lay there I now tried to break it down in the same way as I had just finished breaking down the financing of Tinker's wedding.

First, from the twenty thousand I took away taxes, which would bring it down to about sixteen thousand dollars. Two installments had already been paid, but still the figure, the whole figure, had to be deducted from the yearly income. Then I deducted the nine hundred still left over from the wedding, but I called it a thousand because, figuring in my head, it was easier to subtract than would be nine hundred. That left me fifteen thousand dollars. Although the mortgage on our house was almost lifted, it was not quite, and the amortization would take away another thousand. Total, unexpended, fourteen thousand dollars.

Another thousand would go for premiums on the insurance policies which I carried. About four hundred would have to be deducted for house insurance, and insurance on the car, and the licenses on the car and so forth, another hundred. To keep the mental figuring easier I tried to take things away in blocks of five hundred. About three hundred would go for heat and light, two hundred for normal (not this special) medical expenses. That leaves my reckoning at about twelve thousand dollars.

Our maid cost us about fifteen hundred dollars, and incidental help perhaps three hundred, and repairs at least another two hundred. Remainder, ten thousand dollars.

Gertrude's clothes cost almost twenty-five hundred, although she claimed considerably less. My clothes cost perhaps five hundred. Tinker's (not counting the trousseau) perhaps a thousand, although there were a few special items in there including a ski outfit for the month she went out skiing in Aspen, Colorado, and the cowboy boots she insisted on buying when she was out there also. What does that leave? That leaves six thousand dollars.

It cost five hundred dollars at least each year to keep the car running. Liquor cost us almost a thousand, but we entertained a lot, and just two cocktails before dinner every night for two people comes to at least four hundred dollars, and one does not

always have just two cocktails. Just having a few friends in for
drinks can cost you almost ten dollars. My week's fishing trip
last spring cost me five hundred, and the vacation which Gertrude and I took for a week cost us a thousand. Total expendi-
tures to the moment, seventeen thousand dollars, balance on
hand three thousand dollars.

From three thousand, take away some twelve hundred for
food; laundry, three hundred; telephone, two hundred . . . I
know we made more long-distance calls than we should have
. . . gas and water, two hundred . . . I got to that point (the
point at which I only had a thousand dollars left) and then I
stopped, for as yet I had not counted in club dues, taxis, lunches,
entertainment, Tinker . . . although theoretically Tinker had
been working and paying her own way . . . tips, Christmas,
occasional gifts, flowers, charity, bets, debts, savings, although
that word sounds ironical after the list which I have just given.

Now at this point the reader may have cause to wonder.

I wondered a little bit myself, and I have not set any of this
down because I believe that it does me credit. I have set it down
because this breakdown of my expenses . . . although this was
not the first time I had done it . . . gave me my first understanding of what Doc Crocker meant when he had said: "You're
a big boy and if you want to live and be productive again it's
time for you to grow up now."

But this will not entirely satisfy the reader's wonder, for he
will undoubtedly be perplexed by the same thing which perplexed me, which was, if these were my normal expenses and
twenty thousand dollars my normal income, how in the world
did I ever come out even? And the reader's answer will simply
have to be the true one, which was that I didn't. Every year I
went in the hole a very few thousand dollars, and planned every
year to make it up in the next one, and in some years (1948, for
instance) I did that.[1]

---

[1] The reader may also wonder how Mr. Selleck ever managed to send
a son to Cornell and a daughter to an Eastern finishing school. These items
were financed by an inheritance from his father, Luke Selleck, who died

As I have said, this was not the first time I have made this accounting, but it was the first time I had made it when my earning power had been cut off, perhaps forever. As I have just said, I have not mentioned this because I am proud of this record, and I will freely admit that there have been many sleepless nights for me in the past when I have lain in bed making similar accountings. But, in my extenuation, I would like to say that a great deal of the money which I have spent I have not enjoyed, and have only spent because I had to. A man assumes a certain station in life, a certain picture of himself, and he must live up to it or else pull down his colors. And I will say this for myself, that nowhere in my life have I ever pulled down my colors.

However, although I have come to regard these matters which I have mentioned with equanimity, I will freely admit that at the moment at Saint Luke's I looked at them not with equanimity, but with something closer to panic.

As I lay there in the early morning (and early morning is not the best time for this kind of thinking) it occurred to me that I would have been more fortunate if I had simply died in that little parlor of the Town and Country Room at the Park Lane than I was now for having sustained the attack which I had suffered. In fact, had I died, I would not have left Gertrude in a too intolerable position. With Tinker well married, both children no longer needed to be supported. My life insurance would have taken care of my death and debts, and left perhaps thirty or forty thousand dollars from which, with proper advice, Gertrude could have realized annually perhaps a thousand dollars. I was leaving her two farms in a good farming part of the state, and our share of the income from these since the war had come annually to over twenty-five hundred dollars. And then my stock in the Yaw-Et-Ag Manufacturing Company, if she elected to

in 1934, also from money left to Mrs. Selleck when her father, John McCullough, died in 1930, the funds left in trust for education. Perhaps these are the reasons why Mr. Selleck was always considered a much richer man than he was.

keep it rather than sell it back to the firm, would bring in additional income of five or more thousand dollars. And all of that, along with a few securities of her own, would give her almost ten thousand dollars, which, for a single woman with a house almost completely paid for, would be more than ample. However, with me alive, as a nonproducing invalid, constantly incurring medical expenses, ten thousand dollars would be something considerably less than adequate for us to live on — that is, if we intended to live at all in the manner in which we had been living.

The reader may never have faced this kind of fact: that he is more valuable as a dead man than as a live one. Have you ever noticed how many widows buy new fur coats during the first year of their bereavement?

As I lay there, assailed by these very melancholy thoughts, I suddenly wished that I had not been put in a private room there at Saint Luke's, but in a ward rather, where there would be someone to talk to. During World War I, I had been in a large ward after I had been wounded, and it had not been so bad. There had always been someone around to play cards with or talk to. There had always been something funny happening to take a man's mind off his troubles. But now, alone in that room at Saint Luke's, there was nothing with which to occupy the time but thinking, and I have never been a man to occupy my time with thinking. But because of my position in life I had to be in a private room, and at that moment it was almost enough to destroy my faith in the system.

But as I have already said several times, I have not described any of this because I am proud of my situation or my reaction. Both situation and reaction to it leave a lot to be desired. I am describing this period of my illness as I have come to see it; while I have fought many battles, this one at Saint Luke's was the worst one. I was a big boy, and it was time for me to grow up now.

3

It was while I was still in this mood of depression and despair that first morning that Gertrude came in to see me, and while I did not think so then, I can see now that my whole reaction to what we had to say to each other was entirely jaundiced by my mood. And that in itself is a queer thing, the way in which a man can get the illusion of clear-sightedness in moments of sickness or more frequently of hang-over. The world, although completely hostile, seems also as clearly focused and lucid as the image seen through the wrong end of a telescope or field glasses. That this clear-sightedness is really illusion is one of the hardest things to keep in mind at such times. It seemed to me when she came in that morning that I had never before seen her in quite this fashion.

There she was, as handsome, as fashionable, and as young looking as she had been almost thirty years before, when we had been married, more handsome, more fashionable and younger really, for the fashions of today seem more fashionable and young than they did in 1920. She was wearing a severely tailored suit of dark material which, on a large woman, might have looked mannish, but which on a small woman like Gertrude made her seem more feminine, more childlike, and more help-less than anything else could have. With this, she wore a white blouse gathered around the throat, with a black ribbon with a cameo pin which had once belonged to Mrs. McCullough on the bow of the ribbon, and somehow this reminded me of a remark which Sam Zadina had once made about her and which I have never known how to interpret.

"Gertrude strikes me as helpless and confused," he had said, "but always remember she's right in the middle of the room, Jeff."

She was pretty that morning, appealing and pretty, and her hair, which had been turning white during the last few years, had a bluish tinge which emphasized, not age, but youngness. The irritating thing, which illustrates very well the jaundice of

my mind, was that as I looked at her it suddenly seemed to me
that it was I who had been doing the growing old, and the
getting worn out for her. And the unfairness of this observation
can be seen immediately when I tell you that also I could see
right away from her eyes that not long before she had come in
she had been crying.

"Oh Jeffrey," she said with a catch in her throat as soon as she
saw me. "Oh, Jeffrey," she said, and hurried to the bed and
kissed me.

I don't know how I wanted her to act, and the way she was
acting was certainly very normal, but somehow it all seemed
wrong to me at the moment.

"Oh Jeffrey," she said, "how are you?"

"I may have been hit," I said, "but I'm still in the ring and
still in there punching."

She sat helplessly on the edge of the bed for a moment and
then said: "Oh Jeffrey, what's going to happen?"

"Nothing's going to happen," I said.

"But," she said, and her hands kept fidgeting together as she
said it, "Doc Crocker said that you could die if you weren't
careful."

"Now listen," I said, "I may be taking a long count but, before
the bell rings, I'll be up and punching."

And what illustrates the perverted quality of my thinking as
well as anything else was that at that moment it suddenly seemed
unfair to me that I not only had to keep up my own spirits but
hers also.

Then suddenly she began to cry. "But Jeffrey, you're not. I've
talked to Doc Crocker and I know. You're not in there punching."

And then I became angry not only at her but at Doc Crocker,
for it seemed to me that he had had no business going behind
my back and alarming her unnecessarily. It was right and proper
enough to tell me, but there was just no reason to tell her what
the truth was.

I managed to pull myself up into a sitting position in the bed
and I said almost angrily: "Now get this straight, Missus S. —

I'm not dead yet, and Doc Crocker has no business going behind my back and telling you that I am dead."

"I made him tell me," she said, turning to face me. "I made him tell me because I had to know. A person has to know what the facts are."

"Well, set your mind straight on this," I said, "you're going to have to put up with me for a good many years yet. The Doc himself said that all I have to do to have years and years is to learn to take it easy."

And then again she started crying. "But you won't take it easy. You're not even taking it easy right this minute. You're sitting up and shouting."

"I am not shouting," I said. "I'm not even raising my voice, dear. If anyone is shouting and getting excited, it's you that's shouting and getting excited."

Well, actually she had not been shouting up to that moment, but now she stood up and did begin to let me have it.

"Now look here, Thomas Jefferson Selleck," she said, "you're a sick man. You're a very sick man, and don't try to tell me anything different. You're a sick man and you might as well face the facts. There's no sense in not facing facts, dear."

"I am facing facts," I said.

"You've never faced a fact in your life," she said. "You never have faced a fact squarely. And it's about time you started."

"And I suppose you've been the one who faced facts," I said. "I suppose you've been the one who adds up the stubs and comes out with the correct balance."

And I will admit that that was a dirty blow on my part because for years she had been unable to make her checkbook come out right, and almost chronically overdrew her account at the Gateway National.

It was a dirty blow and it made her so angry that she just stood there and clenched her fists by her sides and said, "Oh damn! Damn you!" And then suddenly, everything just seemed silly. Everything just seemed inane; two adult people, one of them sick in bed, shouting at each other.

"Oh hell, dear," I said, relenting. "I'm sorry. Let's face the facts then, if you want to."

"I'm sorry too," she said, and relented just as completely as I had, for what I had just seen she must have seen also. "It's just that I'm distraught and worried sick," she said, and walked over to the window and then back to the bed. "It's just that I'm scared to death and all filled with anxiety about you and don't know exactly what I'm doing." Suddenly she smiled appealingly at me and said: "Really, I'll try to be a good girl, Jeffrey."

And then I had the strange illusion which was also a part of the sickness of my mind. I had the illusion that we were just two little children like the ones in the fairy story lost in the woods, tired, frightened, and bewildered. But of course we weren't. We were middle-aged people in our fifties.

I reached out and took her hand, which she gave to me, and said, "All right, girl, let's face the facts now."

"Well, the facts," she said, brightening right away, "are simply that from now on and for quite a while we just aren't going to have anywhere near enough money."

I was glad then to realize that she must have been going through the same dismal kind of thinking which I had been going through myself that morning.

She said, "From now on, we're going to watch every penny."

"Life is going to be cheaper," I said, "now that we don't have to look after Tinker."

"Speaking of Tinker," she said, "George and Tinker called this morning."

"How did they sound?" I said, because, although I have not mentioned it, they too had been on my mind all morning.

"They sounded fine," she said, her whole mood lightening completely.

And my mind lightened then, too. "Not like you and me on our first morning," I said.

Gertrude said, "Not at all like you and me on our first morning." Then she walked aimlessly around the room again and sat down in the armchair which faced me and said: "Speaking of

George and Tinker, there was one thing about all the presents they got which has me bothered. They didn't get any service plates. Did you notice? I tried to hint to your sister that they needed service plates, but all she sent was a Mexican tin tray."

"Carrie should have sent more than that," I said.

"That's what I thought," Gertrude said. "But, as I was saying, there are some lovely service plates I saw at Beckerman and Chandler's, and I really think that you and I ought to give them to George and Tinker."

"How much are they?" I said.

Gertrude said, "For a full dozen, and they should have a full dozen, it's only a hundred and twenty dollars, and that's a bargain because the plates are really lovely."

And then, all at once, my earlier mood returned. How were we going to save money? How were we going to cut down on expenses? How were we going to face the facts if we wouldn't face them?

And I suppose that this showed right away in my face and manner, for Gertrude said, "What's the matter, Jeffrey?"

"One hundred and twenty dollars," was all that I said.

And then her mood returned to her also. "It's all very well to economize," she said, "and I know that we have to, but one just doesn't start economizing on one's children. The fact is that when Tinker gets back east to New Rochelle and entertains, as she will, I, for one, want her to be able to entertain in a way she won't be ashamed of."

"But damn it, dear," I said, "we've got to economize somewhere."

"There are plenty of places we can economize without economizing on our children."

"Where, dear?" I said.

"Well, for one thing," Gertrude said, "if you weren't too tight to sell the old car and get a new one we could cut in half the cost of operation. You can stop drinking, for another. And I can cut down on smoking. And not making as much money as you have will mean that you won't have to pay such awful taxes."

And then again I felt completely hopeless, and everything was as it always had been and always would be, which was that the more we got into things the more hopelessly we became entangled, and that, as always, there would be more peace of mind in going into debt than in trying to make the budget balance, and that the answer was the same answer which it always had been, which was that you couldn't cut down; you just had to figure ways to make more money. I felt completely discouraged because facts, as always, weren't facts but slippery things which you couldn't hang on to.

"We can't give up our membership at Sleepy Hollow or the Gateway Club," Gertrude went on. "But we don't have to go there as much, and that will cut down plenty. You won't be playing golf any more and that will cut down all your greens fees. And this year we won't take any vacation."

I cannot tell you how depressed I felt then. She went on talking but I seemed to stop hearing. A sort of numbness seemed to gather around me and all through me. It was wrong of me. I know that it was wrong. But although her visit had cheered me somewhat and given me someone for a while to talk to, I was almost glad when she left me.

The only bright spot in the morning had been that she had told me that George and Tinker had sounded happy, but even that was not too bright for mostly it reminded me of the automobile which I had promised them and which I could no longer afford to buy them.

4

After that, the girl who sticks hospital patients with needles came in, and after her the girl with the electrocardiograph machine which scared me with all its wires and electrodes. And then, finally, Doc Crocker, who was late that morning, came in to see me. And by that time I was deeper into the dark mood of despair in which I had started the morning. I was no good to myself and no good to anyone else, either. I was of more value dead than as a live person. I could see all the follies of my way of living and yet at the same time there seemed to me to be no way to supplant them with acts of wisdom. I could see the mistakes of my life quite clearly, but at the same time I could also see quite clearly that, were I able to live my life again, I would still make the same mistakes, because it was the way I was and there was no way to change me. And it angered me when Doc Crocker came in. He must have just come from outdoors for he was rubbing his hands to warm them. And he was so damn cheerful, and if I was unhappy I saw no reason why he should not be unhappy also.

My nurse was with him and the two of them studied my chart together. They nodded and talked to each other and kept their voices so low that I could not understand them. Then the nurse went out, and he turned to me and asked me how I was feeling.

And that was the point at which I suddenly exploded.

"Oh Christ, Doc," I said. "Who do you think you're kidding?"

"Take it easy, Jeff," he said. "Take it easy."

I said, "Look, Doc. I believe everything you say about me because I believe that you're a good doctor and know your business. I believe you when you tell me to take it easy. But what is there to stop me from not taking it easy?"

He took off his glasses and then said, "Staying alive," quite calmly.

"But what's the point of staying alive?" I said. "What's the point if I'm not really living? What's the point of keeping this old pile of guts going if it's no good to me or anyone else either? What's the point, Doc?"

He looked at me very quietly for a moment, then sat down in the armchair where he could look at me some more. Then he asked a question which was the last question I could have imagined.

He said, "Do you believe in atomic bombs, Jeff?"

"Why yes," I said, startled and bewildered. "I guess I believe in atomic bombs, Doc."

"I'm glad you do," he said, "because from the looks of things most people don't. But what you have to realize is that you have an atomic bomb right inside of you. As far as you're concerned your heart is as lethal a weapon as there is, and you can set it off so easily that it isn't even funny. You can do that if you want to, and then all your problems will be finished. It's one way to solve a problem. As far as you're concerned it's pretty damn effective."

"Why shouldn't I solve my problems that way," I said, "if I want to?"

He rubbed his hand up over his high bald forehead before he answered.

"You can if you want to," he said. "But just put the whole thing in a larger sphere for a minute. In a sense, the whole world today is suffering from coronary occlusion. And it's got all kinds of atomic bombs lying around with which it can blow itself sky-high and out of existence at any minute and solve all its problems. And you have to realize that that is one kind of solution. And that there's only one thing wrong with that solution, too, which is that things would be awfully quiet around here when it was over."

Then he stood up and walked over to the window and looked out of it and then back at me and said: "And do you know why people want to kill themselves, really? They don't want to kill themselves. They want to kill the whole world which has opposed them, and in killing themselves, as far as they are concerned, they do kill the whole world, too. I'm not a psychiatrist, but that's something like what one would tell you."

He stopped talking again and walked aimlessly around the room for a few minutes. Then he said, "When a man kills himself he kills the whole world — at least a little."

And then his manner changed and he became quite brisk and efficient. He said: "However, if you want to do it, I'll tell the nurse to get your clothes for you. I'll call a taxi for you and you can start down to the office." He paused only momentarily, and then said, "Okay, would you like me to call you a taxi?"

"No," I said slowly, for although I had not understood everything he had said, it had shaken me deeply.

"You sure?" he asked sternly.

"Doc," I said. "But Doc — what's the point in living?"

He relaxed again and said slowly: "I don't know any more than you do, but I believe there is a point somewhere. If I didn't, I don't see how I could be a doctor."

He left shortly after that, and I was deep in thought when he left me. What he had said about killing the world when you kill yourself I hadn't really understood yet. But the other part, the part about having an atomic bomb inside of me which I was carrying around all the time, had impressed me. If I had an atomic bomb inside of me, it somehow made me important, and at that moment it seemed as though it had been years since I had in any way felt at all important.

Tom

WHEN a man sits down to write his memoirs, that is when he sits down to contemplate his life, he finds himself repeatedly assailed by a desire to imply some kind of meaning to his existence, and repeatedly, very much to his chagrin, he finds that that meaning which he seeks eludes him. Does that mean, he begins to wonder, that there is no meaning at all or does he, as Doc Crocker said, know that, without knowing, there is a point to it somewhere? If Doc Crocker did not believe that, as he said to me, he could not continue to be a doctor. If I did not know that, I could not continue to be a man. Slowly, one seems to conclude that there are things which one must believe simply because life would make no sense without them. There is a meaning somewhere, although the area in which one seeks to find this meaning is continually shifting. I had thought at one time to find this meaning in my marriage. And at another time in business. Again it seemed to me that in politics and public service I might find the thing for which I was seeking, and then again in religion. But now I have to admit, if I am honest, that in none of these realms have I found this thing which is all-important. Logic tells me, however, that if I am to find it anywhere I am to find it in my children, for we live not for ourselves, but for the race which we bring into being. If we have any immortality at all, it seems to me we have it in our sons and daughters, although it would be nice to find that there was something else in store for us also.

This is the conclusion one comes to, but at the same time the subject of family, like the subject of marriage, is such a confused one that it is very difficult to say definite things about it. I look at Tom whom I created, and yet I see so little of myself in Tom that I sometimes wonder how I, Jeff Selleck, could have been his father, although it is quite obvious that Gertrude was his mother.[1] I look at Tinker, who is certainly everything I could have wanted in a daughter and who was certainly my child as much as Tom was Gertrude's, and yet here also I miss a sense of continuity between us.

The truth which I have to face is that my relationship with my children has not always been of the most satisfying nature. And Tom, although he is succeeding in his chosen profession in a way in which I certainly am proud of, nonetheless is in a profession which is not of my choosing and one about which I know nothing.[2]

I am sometimes bewildered at how Tom — at how my son — could have become an artist.

2

Tom was born June 15, 1921, at the Presbyterian Hospital, after a long and difficult delivery.

I shall never forget the panic I was in during those hours in which I waited. I do not suppose that my reactions were extraordinary in any way, but I would like to put them down as a part of my record. Curiously enough, for so much has been said and

[1] It seems to have been a continual bafflement to Mr. Selleck that Tom Selleck turned into a commercial illustrator rather than the business executive which Mr. Selleck intended. And the rapport which finally existed between the two of them during these last months, while satisfying, was not the rapport which he had really wanted.

[2] Mr. Tom Selleck says: "The unfortunate basis of Father's and my continual warfare, as I sensed vaguely from a very early age, lay in the fact which he has mentioned, that he looked on me as an extension of himself, his immortality perhaps, while I looked upon myself as myself and wanted to be an individual in my own right. And it was only when I became an individual that finally we became friends."

written concerning a man's paramount desire for offspring above
all things, during that time of labor Tom to me meant nothing,
less than nothing, and my only concern was for Gertrude and
the pain which he, and I too, had caused her. I hated him during
that time as a person torturing, perhaps killing, my wife, his
mother.

And I hated myself, for I could not help but think of myself as
the person who had initiated the whole business. Perhaps if
children were created more consciously than either of ours was,
a man's feelings would be different. If it were somehow more on
a contract basis, although I suppose that this is implicit in the
marriage bond, in which the wife willingly accepted, rather than
tacitly permitted, the ordeal of birth, a husband during those
hours of labor would feel different. In the case of both of our
children, however, I could not help but feel guilty of taking
advantage of Gertrude in her moments of weakness. And, I have
to admit, at both times, at the moment of conception the idea
of children was not paramount in my thinking.

However, this line of thought brings in its wake a consideration
which, to me, has always been one of the most mysterious and
marvelous facts of nature, that in spite of the pain of giving
birth, which must be greater than anything which a man ever
knows in the normal course of his lifetime, women invariably
seem to forget it within half an hour of its passing, while men,
who do not suffer it, sometimes remember it for a lifetime.
For women at least, the simple fact of parenthood seems to
banish everything else completely, and this in itself seems to imply that there must be a meaning of some kind somewhere.
However, I do want to say that while women bear the pains
of labor for a matter of hours, fathers, financially anyway,
bear the pains of their children's upbringing from that time
forward.

But at any rate, on June 15, 1921, after ten hours of labor, at
five minutes before nine in the morning, Tom was delivered, a
strong, healthy, eight and a half pound boy. And shortly after
that, I was allowed to go in and see Gertrude. I was shocked,

I remember, at the worn tiredness of her face, the transparency of her skin, and her absolute weakness.

"It's a boy, dear," I told her.

And then she said a very strange thing: "Count the toes and fingers."

I hardly understood her at the moment, but a long time afterward she told me that during her whole pregnancy she had had a terrible and utterly unreasonable dread that she would give birth to a monster.

"Count the toes and fingers," she said insistently to me after Tom's birth, and she would not be satisfied until I went out and came back and told her that everything about Tom was beautiful and normal . . . which was something of an exaggeration for, while he was normal enough, I have never seen a baby which was beautiful to begin with. And then, after I told her, she sank down into a semicoma. And it was only then that I could think of Tom as a person, although I certainly did not envision him then as he is today, an illustrator who has a cover on the *Saturday Evening Post* for the week of this moment in which I am setting this down here.

It is a picture of the Waubaunsee River in winter, the same scene and the same kind of a day on which I have frequently gone duck shooting out there. Although Tom claims (which I cannot understand) that he is not a really, truly artist,[3] that cover is a remarkable picture. The river is there and the cottonwoods and sand bar willows behind it, and an old car in the lower right hand corner which I suspect, although Tom cannot remember it, is our old Olds which made many such trips at one time or another. And there is a certain sadness to everything in the picture which is the same sadness I have felt when I have been out there.

[3] Tom Selleck's comment was: "Had I had the talent and the proper urge, I would have painted portraits of people, but there can be no painting of people today, for the age we live in is not interested in people and doesn't believe in people. But if father had been a painter he would have because if he believed in anything he did believe in people which was a fortunate anachronism in him."

But to get back to things in their proper order. Tom was born. He became a person. And although he was not beautiful to begin with, he very shortly became a very beautiful child. He developed blond hair, blue eyes, and a husky little body, which is like my side of the family, for all of us Sellecks have been blond, blue-eyed, and husky. He never became tall, though, as we Sellecks are, but, while tall enough, stopped a little bit on the short side. He was properly baptized, at which time I bought him a Government Bond to give him from the beginning a small fortune. He was presented with a silver porringer and a silver spoon by the McCulloughs, a rattle and a teething ring by my father and mother. A baby book bound in pink and white was started, and it began with a telegram which goes as follows:

DON'T DO ANYTHING UNTIL YOU HEAR FROM US. STOP.
THE OLD FORTY-SECOND DIVISION

Next there is a photograph of him taken at four months reclining inside a punch bowl. And on the opposite page is pasted a bit of his hair, very fine and almost white in color. After that is a photograph taken at thirteen months in which he is sitting on a cushion wearing nothing but a pair of diapers and a paper crown. He is holding a large spoon in one little hand as though it were a scepter, and this is perhaps indicative of the position he had assumed by this time in our household, for he had become the king, the master, a good deal more than I had.

Gertrude doted on him and it was almost frightening, the singleness of the love she bore him. I doted on him too, and so did Mrs. McCullough, and the nursegirl we had for a while did also. They used to like to dress him up in long dresses in which people used to dress their babies, but which were a little out of date by that time. And I, to tell the truth, used to give him my watch to play with. I mention this to point out the fact that so far as love was concerned, I doubt if any child on earth ever had a better start in life than Tom did; so why, in later years, for a long, long time he came to resent us I certainly cannot imagine.

He not only had love from the beginning, but from 1932 onward he had something which very few children have, which was the knowledge of a job and a business to step into as soon as he was ready, for after the Yaw-Et-Ag Manufacturing Company was founded I always fully expected that he would want to step into my shoes when I was finished.[4]

He grew up a rather temperamental child but, at the same time, possessed of a greater amount of charm than most people ever possess. And although I never envied him his charm, sometimes I have wondered whether great charm in a child is an entirely unmixed blessing. Things came easily for Tom right from the beginning, and I wonder now if it is not perhaps a disadvantage in later life for a child to have had things come too easily. He had the kind of charm which is entirely disarming.

The Ecleses have always lived on the north side of our house, but at the time I am talking about, which was when Tom was about four, there lived immediately on our south hand a very unpleasant couple named Dr. and Mrs. Spruley. In fact, the only nice thing about the Spruleys I ever knew of was their garden, which was very lovely. And a good many of our unpleasant connections with the Spruleys concerned that garden also, for our dogs would roll in the beds, and the children at times were almost equally destructive. Well, one day during an unwatched moment, little Tom made his way over there and into a border of tulips, which he began pulling out by handfuls. As was to be expected, Mrs. Spruley caught him. She ran out toward him from her back door waving a broom threateningly at him. He, however, disregarded the broom and ran to meet her with outstretched arms, embraced her around the legs and said, "I love you." She was completely nonplused, as might have been expected. Then she took him into her house and gave him cookies and told him to

[4] Tom Selleck says: "It was this expectation which filled me from the first with a sense of frustration. There is probably a Freudian explanation, but it seems to me that had I not always felt the plan for me I might have been quite contented to follow it unconsciously, for there were worse things I could have followed, and did. But, as it was, it was utterly impossible for me to do anything which Dad wanted."

come back and see her whenever he wished to. When a child has
that kind of charm, you have a problem.

I shall never forget his first words, or the circumstances in
which he said them. Gertrude had asked her mother and some
other ladies over for tea one afternoon in order to show off the
baby. Tom was brought out, and all of them made a great deal
of him, as you can well imagine. And up to this point, "Mama"
and "Dada" were the only words he had ever spoken. As the
ladies all looked down at him that afternoon (at the moment he
was in the play pen) he looked sweetly up at them and said,
"Dod damn," and I, for one, never blamed him.

"Well," Mrs. McCullough said, "that's one thing he doesn't get
from the McCullough side of the family."

But that was hardly true, for John McCullough was known for
his vocabulary on occasion, and his brother William had been
known to speak rather wildly from the floor of the United States
Senate.

Tom said and did a great many very cute things when he was a
youngster and, at the risk of pinning onto him a story of the kind
which I myself have so much resented, I would like to tell this,
which concerns his dawning understanding of sex in this world
we live in. We had two springers at the time, Rags and Mopsey,
and I believe I have already said something about them. Rags
was a male and Mopsey was a female, and when she was in heat
we used to keep her in the house and Rags outside in the garden,
an arrangement which could cause considerable confusion and
excitement. This was not lost upon young Master Thomas, aged
ten years at the time, and he went to his mother to ask her all
about it.

"Mopsey and Rags," Gertrude (who had rather advanced ideas
for the time concerning sex education) answered, "want to get
together so that they can have babies."

And quick as a flash Tom said "Did Daddy act that way when
you and he wanted to have Tinker?"

Now I think that was pretty cute for ten years old, although I
shall never forgive Gertrude's answer. "Tom, your father acted a

good deal more like Rags than you will ever be able to imagine."

As I have said, Tom was born healthy and husky, and he grew to be strong, well-co-ordinated and athletic. He took to organized sports, baseball, football and so forth, as a duck takes to water, but he never took to field sports, hunting or fishing, as I had hoped he would, for I have always wanted a son to take camping or hiking, and to whom I could teach campcraft and woodcraft. However, I certainly was not ashamed of his fine showing in football and baseball. They are both fine sports in which a boy can show what he is made of. He showed promise at the time he attended the Fleetwood public school, and definite talent for the one year he went to downtown high school. When he was fourteen, we sent him to Exeter Academy in Exeter, New Hampshire, because both Gertrude and I felt that if he were to go to an Eastern college, as we desired, it would be a great advantage to him to go to an Eastern prep school. And at Exeter he made good on our expectations. He played on his class team during his first year, and for the next three years played varsity football. In his senior year he was a real star, and I went East to see him play in the 1939 Exeter-Andover game which, for both of those schools, was the big game of the season.

I shall never forget that game. I shall never forget the moment in the last quarter when he ripped off his headgear and threw it high into the air and shouted: "Come on, fellows, let's really get those guys this time." And I shall never forget how, on the next play, he took the ball and ran through the whole Andover team for a touchdown. I was very proud, I can tell you, to walk about the lovely Exeter campus that evening with Tom and be pointed out by people as Tom's father. He was well liked at Exeter both by his fellow students and by his teachers. He was elected to membership in the Bootlickers, which is an Exeter fraternity, and both Dr. Perry and Mr. Kerr,[5] whom I talked to about Tom, said that they expected great things from him.

[5] Dr. Lewis Perry, who was formerly headmaster of the Academy, and Mr. Edwin Silas Wells Kerr, then and now dean of the Academy.

And curiously enough it was on this afternoon, or the Sunday afternoon the day after the game rather, at the very high water mark of Tom's career, that he and I had our first really serious conflict with each other, although already there had been small ones, I must admit, over trivial things like using our car or money.

Tom lived in Peabody Hall and he and I were up in his room talking over his prospects for the future. As we talked, he threw in a bombshell which was an announcement that he did not intend to go to college.

Now this was quite a shock, for Gertrude and I, while not completely agreed, were fairly well agreed upon Tom's future. Gertrude wanted him to go to Princeton, and I wanted him to go to Yale, for I have always felt that it is a fine thing for a man to be able to say he is a "Yale man." But I did not entirely object to Princeton except that for a boy who will do business in the Middle West the connotations of Princeton are not always quite to his advantage. But either school, in that respect, is preferable to Harvard, although Bert Bernstein did send his son to Harvard. However, the point is that both Gertrude and I very definitely intended that Tom go on to college in the East and make a creditable record.

"But, Dad," Tom said, in a rather arrogant way which he was affecting at the moment, "I said that I just don't intend to go to college."

Now had Tom been a dull boy this would have been different. He had a very fine scholastic record. He was a member of the Lantern Club, which is the Academy literary society, the Golden Branch, which is the debating society, and won the Glidden Latin Prize.

"Look here, son," I said. "If I get you right, I think you must have jumped your trolley."

"Dad," Tom said, with a little dark groove appearing between his eyebrows, "you don't seem to understand that I'm grown-up now."

He was seventeen then and would be eighteen the following summer.

"I'm grown-up now and I've had enough of formal schooling," he said.

"And what do you plan to do instead of going on to college?" I asked him, a little sarcastically, I imagine.

He said: "I want to get a job on a tramp steamer and go round the world and find out what life is."

I suppose if I had handled things differently, his whole reaction would have been different.[6] But, fortunately sometimes and unfortunately on other occasions, I have always dealt with things quite directly.

As it was, I said, "Son, your mother and I have not spent two to three thousand dollars a year on your education just for you to go out and see what life is. If we had wanted that, we could have given it to you for nothing."

Tom said, in that same lofty manner he had then, "I'm afraid that the automobile accessory business may perhaps qualify you in some things, but not concerning my life or how to run it."

And that, I'm ashamed to say, made me angry for I'm a little bit hotheaded. I said, "You're going to go to Yale, young man, or Princeton, and you're going to get into one of those clubs they have there and play football and graduate with flying colors and be a credit to your family."

"Can't you understand," he said, "that I just don't want to go to college? I want to get out and start living."

I said, "When I was your age I had to get out and start in living, and it isn't all it's cracked up to be, I can tell you. I worked on your great-uncle's farm in Illinois. I pitched hay and I followed the horses. Why, I would have given my right eye for the advantages you've had and are having."

Tom became so angry that he was almost on the point of tears, and I was almost as angry also.

"Don't you see that's what I want?" he said. "I want to pitch

[6] Tom Selleck's comment was: "It might have been very different. It was what I needed and I never got it until several years later when I was in the service, and I had made my bad mistakes by that time. If he had let me go then, I might even have been willing to go home afterward and work in his business."

hay and follow horses or do almost anything where there are living and breathing people. What do you know about life, you fat old bastard?"

Now I think that you must admit that when a son speaks that way to a father it's reason enough for the father to get angry, and I did get angry.

"You're just a seventeen-year-old punk," I said, "and you're not dry behind the ears yet. You don't know anything, and you might as well know that. You aren't going to tell me what you're going to do. I'm going to tell you, and you're going to like it. You're going to buckle down now and pass your college boards. Then you're going on to college and make a good record, and then you're coming home and go to work in the business, and then you may be able to talk a little about what life is."

What I said must have cowed him to some extent, for he did not answer, and until his Christmas vacation we left it at that point.

As I look back on this from the perspective of this moment, I can see I was probably wrong to have shouted at him in that manner. Perhaps I should have reasoned with him, but there is such a gap between generations frequently that reasoning is sometimes very close to an impossible thing to do. An adult has a wisdom which is beyond the grasp of the boy, and sometimes there is no way to make the boy understand this. Why, the adult wishes to say to the boy, should God have made you more capable of running the world at seventeen years old than your elders in their fifties? One admits freely that reasoning and persuasion are the right ways for producing action, but there are times when reasoning and persuasion seem to miss the point. And then you have a choice between the use of force and the allowing of the child to go ahead with mistakes of the most serious nature. Life for me has rarely presented clear-cut choices between right and wrong, but choices rather between mistakes of a larger or smaller degree in which I have tried always to choose the smaller. And especially has this been true in my dealings with my son. Even where reasoning might have been possible he was a difficult boy to reason with, for, as with all the McCulloughs (and he was at least half McCullough) he had a kind of reserve, a kind of secretiveness which would suddenly appear just at the moment when you had thought you were closest to him. And this is true even to this day, even now when we have finally reached a friendly, satisfying, affectionate, and even mutually confiding relationship. As an example, I can mention an occasion on which I congratulated him on one of his *Saturday Evening Post* covers. "Just some more of the old crap," he answered, which left me completely at a loss, for considering what they pay him, if that is not real art I must not know what real art is then.

But to return to the question which came up so unexpectedly that afternoon in the autumn of 1939 in Peabody Hall on the Exeter campus — we left the matter at the point at which I have just described until he came home for his vacation the following Christmas. We talked it all over again along with Gertrude, who felt as I did, that he must go to college. Whether a boy learns anything in college or not is not the point. The point is that a college degree is just one of those credentials a boy must have today if he is going to take any place in the world of business. Or even if he does not have a degree, it is a distinct advantage for him to be able to say that he has attended college and is a "college man," a member of a good fraternity, and so forth and so on.

That Christmas we argued this out through several sessions and finally came to an agreement which, although not a perfect one, was one from which all of us gained something.

He agreed that he would try college for one year provided it was the college of his choice, and that if at the end of that year he wished to drop out and get his job on a tramp steamer, I would freely allow him to do so. He further agreed to make a good scholastic record during that year at college.

Gertrude and I had expected that the college of his choice would be Yale or Princeton. However, he chose Cornell, which was a sensible choice, for if a man is going to do business in the Middle West it is in some ways better for him to be able to say

he is a "Cornell man" even than a "Yale man," inasmuch as the
implications are more democratic. There is quite a strong Cornell
almuni association in Gateway. Herb Johnson of the *Times Examiner,* in fact, is a Cornell man, and so is Charley Mason. What
Tom's reasons for that choice were, I don't know. Possibly it was
because Cornell is a coeducational institution.[7]

Be that as it may, both Gertrude and I heaved a sigh of relief
when all of us had arrived at this decision. And I was quite sure,
as more or less became the case, that once he was in college he
would not want to leave it.

However, I never anticipated the rebellion which would come
over him during his college years, for I can only interpret his
college behavior as rebellion. I never felt it in growing up and, as
I look back on it, I had much more to rebel against than he did.
While my upbringing was stern almost to the point of austereness,
his was quite lenient, and almost all of his desires were respected.
During my growing up I had had almost no spending money
except what I earned, while Tom, although chronically broke,
always had a very liberal allowance. I was the youngest of five
children, which meant that most of my possessions were inherited
after use by three or four others, while he, being the oldest,
always had things new and without having to wait in turn for
them to come down to him. I really am unable still to see what
he rebelled at, but all the children of his generation seemed to
have to go through this period of rebellion. And what can one
call his queer behavior at Cornell which culminated in a runaway
marriage in his senior year but rebellion of the most extreme
nature?

But I must say that during that first year at Cornell, his behavior was all that we could have wished. He played freshman
football, which was to be expected after his Exeter record. He
was pledged to the Chi Psi fraternity which is a very good one,

[7] Tom Selleck says: "My reasons were not very creditable when I think
them over. I wanted to go East but to assert myself I wanted to go to a
college which neither Dad nor Mother had thought of. However, had I
followed the logic of my convictions at that time it would have been the
University of Chicago."

and was to be expected also after his Exeter record, joined with the fact that Charley Mason, my very good friend, was an active Chi Psi alumnus. His scholastic record was as good as could be expected. There was really only one thing I could have complained about, which was the amount of money which he was spending, but, as Gertrude said, you can't send a boy to a good college and then expect him to act and dress as though he were a pauper. And then I myself have always believed in spending money. It gives a boy a kind of prestige which he cannot quite get in any other manner.

It was not until his second year at Cornell that the strangeness began to show up in his behavior, and what set it off I cannot imagine, unless it was the fact that he worked in a summer theater on Cape Cod the summer of 1940 which, although I considered it a waste of time, seemed harmless enough at the moment. Our first hint of his strangeness came when we learned that he would not go out for football in the autumn.

"Football is childish," he wrote me, "and I have decided that I am here primarily to get an education."

I was perplexed, and I wrote to him telling him that football for those who were fortunate enough to be talented at it was not only an important part of college but for some even the whole of it also. I wrote trying to explain to him what an advantage it was to a man in business to have a fine athletic record behind him, and perhaps a gold football to hang from his watch chain. I told him that *mens sana in corpore sano* was a very sound idea, and he wrote back: "I am trying to get a sound mind. I already have a sound body, and I can keep it sound playing tennis."

And that would not have disturbed me so much if he had gone out for tennis, for I think he could have made the team. But he would not go out for the team. He insisted on playing it for fun only. I wrote to him that he must realize that his career in college was not just that but the beginning of his career in life also, and that he must meet, rather than shun, the challenges which it presented. You cannot imagine how bewildered I was when he wrote in answer: "The challenge of the world today is reactionary fascism, not the goalpost nor even the diploma."

Well what can a father do about that kind of business? What could he do even if he understood it, and I certainly could not understand at all what had gotten into Tom to so warp his whole viewpoint. It is true that in my college days we talked about politics on a world scale, but we certainly did not let it interfere with athletics, and what we did talk about was certainly more American and healthy. We talked about people like J. P. Morgan and Andrew Carnegie, and Teddy Roosevelt, and about things like Christianity and success, and then, of course, later when things were making up toward the war, the Huns and freedom of the seas and so forth.

What was it, I asked myself over and over again, that had gotten into him? Was it the erratic streak which went through the McCulloughs,[8] or was it something about the times he lived in which, I will admit, were trying times for us all, what with the corrupting influences of the New Deal and the fact that England was in the war already. Neither of these things seemed to entirely answer my questions. The sons and daughters of my friends seemed to be carrying on revolts of their own, but very understandable ones compared to Tom's, for they seemed to run only toward staying up late at night and cracking up automobiles. But Tom . . . If I did not know and trust him I would say that he was almost Communistic in his behavior. And it was not Cornell, either, for I looked closely at Cornell, talked to my friends and their sons about it, and found it to be the very soundest kind of American institution. It would have been understandable had he been attending the University of Chicago. The only conclusion I could come to was that he was revolting against something somewhere of which we had no knowledge, and the only answer was to let it run its course, which fortunately it

---

[8] Mrs. Selleck had a brother, Maxwell McCullough, rarely mentioned by any of the family, who went to Paris to live after the First War, and became the organist in the American Church there. This is the erratic quality to which Mr. Selleck refers here.

seemed to do after we were in the war and he was in the service.

Instead of playing football and being a big man on the campus as he could have, he wrote essays and short stories for the campus literary magazine, and now and then made illustrations for it, and where he picked up drawing I have no idea, for there was certainly nothing of this in either Gertrude's or my family. He spent his time reading and listening to phonograph records. He drank more than he should have, although that did not worry me particularly. It was not that he drank, it was who he drank with that concerned me. The only thing he did which we could be proud of was to keep up an extremely high scholastic average, but what compensation is a Phi Beta Kappa average to a father whose son might have been an all-American halfback?

This strange behavior began, as I have said, in his second year and it progressed in violence from that time onward. During his third year he began going on week ends to New York as often as he was able, which is not alarming in itself, for when we are young all of us like to enjoy the pleasures of the city. The alarming thing was what he did when he went down there. He did not go to places like the Stork Club or Twenty-one as so many of the other boys did, but to plays, the Metropolitan Museum and the Museum of Modern Art, which is a queer place if there ever was one. And when he did go to night clubs he went to queer little places in Greenwich Village. It is all very well for a boy on a fling to go down to Greenwich Village or up to Harlem, but to practically live in the Village or to make friends of the Negroes up in Harlem is a completely different matter. Of course, one can say that all is well that ends well, but I could not say it at that moment. I am sure that Cornell did not approve of this, and I know for a fact that his brothers in Chi Psi disapproved of it completely. By senior year he was hardly on speaking terms with any of them in the lodge there.

In recent years, since Tom and I have become friends at last, he has tried to explain all this to me. "It was a normal enough way for me to go," he says. "Every son somehow has to kill his father, and father for me was not only you but business and

Gateway, and everything I grew up with." This, I presume, is
in the field of psychiatry, about which I know nothing, and the
explanation is just as bewildering as the fact, and it sounds a
little bloodthirsty into the bargain. The only thing I knew for
sure was that underneath, Tom was a good boy and would be
straightened out somehow when he grew older. It was two unfortunate facts which brought about the climax of all this which
I shall now describe to you: the war, which we were already in
during his senior year, and the girl he got mixed up with in New
York whose name . . . or rather, the name she went under . . .
was Dolores.

When Tom was at home for his vacation at Christmas time
during his senior year, he told us all one evening that it was his
intention to resign from Cornell and enlist in the Army Air Corps.
And this announcement again was a bombshell in the center of
our plans for him, although not an entirely unexpected bombshell.
It was natural enough, with the country at war, to have him wish
to fight, and I should have been disappointed in him had his
attitude been any different. For once I understood him completely for I had done the same thing in 1917, and I was also attempting to do it again at that moment, and it has been one of
the sorrows of my later years that I was not able to serve directly
in our armed services from 1941 to 1946. In fact, I tried to get
back in December 8, the day after Pearl Harbor, and continued
so to try from then on throughout the war.[9]

When Tom made this announcement, I did not lose my head
as I had on the other occasion when he had been so cursory
about a career in college. Very calmly, I pointed out to him that
he had only half a year left before he would be given his degree.
Very reasonably, I called his attention to the fact that a college
degree would enhance his attractiveness to the Army, or whatever service he chose, and probably would ensure a commission

[9] Mr. Selleck was frozen in his job at the Yaw-Et-Ag Manufacturing
Company which had been converted to the manufacture of hand grenade
fuses. Also, he suffered from an inflamed prostate which, in any case, would
have deferred him.

for him, which was a thing worth having. I did not want him to
be.an enlisted man as I had been in 1917 through 1919, not unless
he had to. I must have presented the case more effectively than I
have most cases, for he ostensibly saw the wisdom of what I
had said and went back to Ithaca apparently content to study
the year out.

So it was with considerable surprise and alarm that I received
a wire about a month later from the authorities of the university,
that he was missing from the campus. Inasmuch as Yaw-Et-Ag
Manufacturing Company was engaged in defense work, I was
able to obtain a priority on the air lines and fly to Ithaca on the
moment. I was sure, though, that nothing serious had happened
to him, only something foolish. I talked to the university authorities who felt that he was in New York City. From them, and
from his fraternity brothers, I obtained the names of some of his
close friends who, rather unwillingly, gave me an address on
Eighteenth Street in New York City where he had told them they
could reach him. I went to New York and went directly to the
address, which was between Irving Place and Third Avenue, a
brownstone which had been converted into apartments. In a wry
sort of way it was almost amusing how surprised he was when I
walked in on him, for he seemed to be under the illusion that he
had left no trail behind him.

He was alone in that one-room apartment when I walked in,
alone and wearing only a bathrobe. The girl was out, although
obviously it was a girl's apartment. And the apartment itself is
worth description.

It was a medium-sized room with an in-a-door bed fastened to
the door of the closet. The bed was up and hidden at the moment,
but, as I found out later, it would swing around and fall down
into the room at the slightest amount of excitement, which, on
the whole, must have been handy for them. Not that I object to a
young man's having his fling, but it just seemed like an awfully
sordid fling which he was having. There was a niche in one wall
which held a kitchenette, really nothing more than a sink and a
gas plate and an icebox, and some Venetian blinds which could

be dropped down over the niche to conceal it. The breakfast dishes were lying unwashed in the sink at the moment. In the far corner of the room was an open door leading into the bathroom, and I could see stockings, a brassière, and other bits of feminine apparel hanging drying from the rod that supported the shower curtain. In the center of the room was a card table which must have been the dinner table, and on which, at the moment, there was a portable typewriter with a sheet of paper in it. There were two straight, hard chairs at the table, and in a corner a large overstuffed armchair which was in bad and unclean condition. There was a bureau against one wall with a number of cosmetic jars and bottles on it. Beside it was an artist's easel, and there were one or two canvases lying face against the wall. The whole place smelled of stale perfume and powder.

Before Tom could say anything, I said very calmly: "Isn't it about time you went back to Ithaca and the books, son?"

I certainly was not going to make any moral issue out of it. Sowing wild oats, although I had had very little of it myself, is not necessarily a bad thing for a young man, I thought, although I changed my mind about that when I finally saw Dolores.

"Isn't it time to get back to the studies, son?" I said quite kindly.

"No," he said belligerently and then, "I'm now in the process of drafting my resignation from Cornell."

The resignation was the sheet of paper in the portable typewriter on the table.

"Look," I said, and sat down in the overstuffed chair in the corner. "I'm not one to criticize a young man for his diversions. As a matter of fact, it can be a darn good thing for him. But fun is fun, and there comes a time to buckle down to business."

"I'm resigning," he said, "in order to join the Air Corps."

I had a moment of anxiety then. "Are you already in?" I said.

"No," he said, "but I'm applying."

That made me feel better. "Let's look at all sides of this," I said.

"I have looked at all sides of it," he said. "I'm not learning anything at Cornell, and you are wasting your money in keeping me at it. And at best, it's only class education."

I didn't get that last, but I let it pass. I said, "Why don't you let me decide whether or not I'm wasting my money?"

"Because you don't know anything about it," he said. He lit a cigarette and elaborately blew smoke at the ceiling. Then he went on: "Logically, I don't believe in war, but under the circumstances I think it is every man's duty to come to the aid of our Russian allies." [10]

"Our Russian allies, God damn," I said, for that made me angry. "What about our own boys out there?"

"Well, however you look at it," he said, still superciliously, "I don't see how I can stay inside of ivied walls when there are other good men out there dying."

I said, "What the hell do you know about men dying?"

His face took on a very pained expression. "Please, Dad," he said, "don't trot in the old Forty-second Division."

And then, I'm afraid, I became very angry.

"Look here, you young pipsqueak," I said, "you get back to your school books and leave the war to men who know what they're doing. Just remember that I'm still your father and that I can still tan your britches."

I am ashamed of myself, of Tom, of everything about us both whenever I recall that moment.

Tom walked quickly over to the sink and dropped his cigarette butt into a coffee cup which was half full of dirty water. Then he turned back toward me and said quickly, "Would you like to try it?"

"Yes," I said. "I think it's time for me to try it."

And we would have been at each other's throats in another moment if the girl, the one called Dolores, hadn't walked in to interrupt us.

She was a sort of big-hipped girl, although with not too bad a

---

[10] Tom Selleck, when questioned concerning this, said: "No, I was never a member of the party. At that age I probably would have been except for the fact that the party was not interested in my kind of pinkness."

figure. She had dark brown hair, and she was wearing a tight black dress which emphasized her bosom. She was wearing open-toed pumps and black net stockings. Her hat was a sort of ribbon with a black veil that dropped down over her eyes, which were made up heavily with mascara. And although she looked clean enough, there was something about her which was dirty. She came from the Bronx, we found out later, but she had the crust to speak with a Southern accent.

"Why I do declare," she said, as she walked in and looked at me standing in a threatening attitude. "You must be Mr. Selleck, Tommy's funny little old daddy."

"Yes," I said, "but I don't think I know who you are."

"Why me," she said, "I'm just little bitty old Dolores. But you're Tommy's dear old daddy, and I declare, I feel that I know you already 'cause I know so much about you from Tommy. Yes, you're Tommy's dear old daddy."

And then a terrible realization came over me, the worst realization that I know of. I saw in a flash that this wasn't just some tart Tom had picked up for the week end. He was in love with her, which was something else to cope with.

Now all my life I have been handicapped because I have never been able to understand women, but this was one kind of woman that I understood completely. This girl I did understand from A to Z, from the first moment I saw her. And, as soon as I understood, I knew exactly what I had to do, although I had no liking for it. I sat down at the card table and pulled out my checkbook. Then I said, directly to her: "All right, Toots, how much do you want me to pay you?"

"Why Mr. Selleck!" said little bitty Dolores.

"How much, Toots?" I repeated.

"Mr. Selleck," she said, "maybe little bitty Dolores isn't very smart, but I just don't understand what you're saying."

Then Tom, who so far had been silent, got between her and me and said: "Of course she doesn't understand what you're saying. She doesn't understand because she's a decent, hard-working girl, and maybe you can't understand that. She doesn't understand because she doesn't know how low and filthy some people's minds are."

"I do declare," Dolores said, "I just don't think Mr. Selleck means to say what it sounds like he is saying, Tommy."

"He means exactly what he sounds like he is saying," Tom said, "and I won't let him say it. I won't stand here and let him insult you."

I disregarded Tom and kept looking at her, and I said again: "How much, Toots?"

"Why Mr. Selleck," she said then, with her eyes flashing, "I think that this is just downright insulting."

I admit freely that all of this was a very ugly business, but what do you do when your son's whole future is in the balance?

I said: "Just name your price to clear out of this, miss, because if you won't I'll have you investigated, and I doubt if you would like or can stand much investigation."

"Father!" Tom now shouted. "I suppose you think you're being pretty clever, but you just don't know anything about a fine, sensitive creature like Dolores. If it wasn't for the insult inherent in it I'd ask you to investigate Dolores because all that you would find out would be how fine and decent she is and how fine and decent is everything about her."

And at that moment that in-a-door bed swung around and fell down into the middle of the room, and Dolores immediately fell on it and started sobbing, but I didn't let that change my purpose.

I said: "For the last time, miss, I'm asking you to name your price. If you won't, I'll go into action."

Actually this about having her investigated was only a shot in the dark, and at that moment, in a strange city, I did not even know where to call to start an investigation. But having started with that lead I decided to play my hand all the way, and I have not played poker with the Chowder and Marching Society all these years for nothing. I stood up and went over to the phone which was lying on the floor under one of the windows. "This is your last chance, miss," I said, and then started to dial, but what number I was dialing I have no idea.

But before I could finish dialing she sat up on the bed and said, "Wait," and she said it with no trace of Southern accent.

I waited, and the feeling of relief coming over me was tremendous, as you can imagine.

"Mr. Selleck," she said, "I'll take five thousand dollars."

I almost hurrahed, for she had given herself away completely. I had her, and I knew that I had her. And, actually, she had held all the cards up to that moment. She should have called me and let me go on with the telephone and she would have had me, but she had chickened out at the most important moment. Girls like that are so smart and so dumb at the same time that it is awe-inspiring.

I put the phone back on the floor, and went back to the card table. I said: "Five thousand dollars is a little high. I'm making you a check for one thousand." Of course, I knew that I didn't have to give her a dime now, but I wanted to get my check back with her endorsement to show it to Tom if there should be any future trouble.

"Two thousand," she snapped at me.

"On second thought," I said, "I'm making it out for five hundred."

That stopped her, and she knew she was beaten. "Make it out," she said, "to Dolores Schummic," and then she fell back on the bed and again started sobbing.

I made it out and handed it to her. She stuffed it inside her brassière and, still crying, ran out of the room . . . to cash it, I imagine, and Tom and I were left alone, not looking at each other.

"I guess it's time to go back to Ithaca, son," I said, finally breaking the silence.

"Yes," he said, his voice sounding very brittle. "Yes, I guess it is," and without saying anything else he pulled his valise out of the closet and started packing.

I doubt if anyone who has not gone through something like this can have any idea of what it means. A man has to save his son's future, but it is hard to do it consciously knowing the way in which you have to do it may make him hate you forever. I know, because a long time ago I hated my father for something of the same nature.

After he was packed and dressed, we took a cab together as far as Grand Central, which was where we parted. He took a train for Ithaca. I went across the street to the Air Lines Terminal and managed to get a flight to Chicago which would connect with another to Gateway City.

3

(Inasmuch as it has seemed to the editors that an understanding of the conclusion of this episode depends as much, if not more, upon an understanding of Tom Selleck's attitude at the moment in question, we include here a passage which Mr. Tom Selleck, who has co-operated in every way in the compilation of this volume, has written for this purpose.

Tom Selleck said, apropos of this:

"As I grew up, I thought of myself as different completely from Dad, but in one respect we were alike. Both of us had to learn everything the hard way.")

Although I never knew that Father knew it at the time, I did hate Father after this moment. I might even have hated him forever after that, as he feared, had it not been for the war and the fact that I was in the service so soon after the business happened, and once in the service other matters overwhelmed everything else, all of my life before becoming a sailor somehow taking on a dreamlike, unreal nature.

I think that in the whole affair the check which Dolores took and cashed was the most humiliating and intolerable fact I had to cope with. It made not only Dolores but myself and Father seem completely sordid, especially the way they had haggled over the amount of it. Had it not been for that check, the fact that it had a physical reality which could not be denied, I think that I might have been able to go back to Cornell, forget Dolores and the whole episode, or, if not forget it, transform it in my mind into something romantic, maybe even beautiful, for I had the kind of mind which could accomplish that kind of thing, and lost forever. However, the gnawing knowledge that the check was somewhere with her name written on the back of it made it impossible for me to do that. Therefore, I had to find some other way to erase the ugliness which had been forced upon me, and the way which seemed logical to me then was for me to go back to Dolores and ask her for an explanation. Father had not counted on this because he did not know how my mind worked although I doubt if it was any different from the way his mind would have worked under similar circumstances. Within a week or so of the misadventure on Eighteenth Street, I was back there ready and eager to believe anything she would tell me.

What she told me was that she had taken the check because she desperately needed the money to pay for hospital expenses for her mother who had cancer. I believed her and wanted to go see her mother and help her in every way I could, but she was very reluctant about it and felt that it would be inconvenient inasmuch as her mother was in Richmond, Virginia, which, of course, she wasn't.

It was about then that the idea of our getting married came into the foreground, for, up till that time we had not believed in marriage, and considered it only a bourgeois capitalistic custom. We were married secretly, and then I tried to get into the Air Corps, lying about my age, which did not seem to be much of a sin for actually I would be eighteen in June. The Air Corps turned me down on account of asthma from which I suffered. I then went away to the Navy and then Coast Guard, where the recruiting chief told me that with my education and background I could "write my own ticket." He also said, "But you will also have to be willing to start at the bottom." And I, in my naïveté, said, "Is there any other place I can start, sir?" He said that he liked my spirit, and that was the last I ever heard about my getting a commission.

But I do not regret this, for the experience of being an enlisted man was what I had needed and known I needed from the time when I wanted to work on a tramp steamer.

However, to get back to Dolores . . . We were married secretly, and I was enlisted in the Coast Guard and after a short wait assigned to Algiers, Louisiana, for my Boot Camp. And this, I think, fills in the gap between the episode on Eighteenth Street and the next episode which Fathers tells.

But — to conclude this letter . . . I would like to say that today I fully realize that whatever Father did, no matter how clumsily he did it, he did do it unselfishly and for my good. In fact, in all the quarrels Father and I used to have he was always motivated by a desire to help me. Perhaps it is easier for me to say this now since his death, but I am glad of one thing which is that in his last year, especially after his illness, we became good friends and he did many little things which touched me then and touch me now as I remember. He was a good man, and that is why I especially want to see this book of his well edited and published.

(*And now, as our radio commentators say, we return you to Mr. Selleck.*)

I heartily wish that the whole Dolores incident could have been concluded with that moment down on Eighteenth Street, but unfortunately it was not. And I heartily wish that the nonsense of Tom's joining the Armed Forces could have been concluded at that time too, but unfortunately neither of these affairs was ended. His wanting to get into the service I can fully understand, but his going back to that girl after what happened eluded me then and still eludes me.

It was a matter of less than two months when again the authorities at Cornell notified me that Tom was missing. The only thing he seemed to have learned about anything from the earlier experience was to cover up his trail, for at this time no one knew where to find him. All in all it was something like three weeks that he was missing, and what his mother and I went through I shall not attempt to describe here. It was on a Sunday morning that he finally did appear at our house in Fleetwood. He was in a secondhand automobile and Dolores was with him, and I knew as soon as I saw them drive up (which I did happen to see from my bedroom window) that they were married.

I went immediately to the front door to meet them and I already knew exactly my course of action. I opened the door, and Tom was standing there looking frightened, but Dolores was standing out at the curb by their automobile.

"Are you married?" I said to Tom.

"Yes, sir," he said, "and I'm enlisted in the Coast Guard."

That was all I wanted to know. I turned and went to the telephone in the front hall and began to dial Bert Bernstein, for here I was on my own ground and knew what to do, and Bert was the man to start an investigation.

Dolores must have guessed immediately what I was up to, for by the time I had finished at the phone and gone back to the front door she was back in the automobile. Tom was standing by the door trying to tell her something, but whatever it was he was saying went unheeded. She put the car in gear and went off at a great rate down our street, leaving Tom standing at the curbing. And that was the last any of us saw of little bitty old Dolores.

What Bert's investigation brought out was that she was already married to a sailor, a soldier, and a Marine, and getting allotments from all of them under different names. The Coast Guard, although Tom denied it, was her suggestion, for she liked to have her husbands in different branches of the service to keep the records from getting tangled. The annulment of Tom's marriage was a very simple business, but we were not able to divorce him from the Coast Guard. He became a member of the amphibious forces and served with distinction in the South Pacific.

As for Dolores, today I feel rather sorry for her, and I can feel sorry for her inasmuch as she no longer has any connection with our family. As I said before, girls like Dolores always amaze me because they can be so smart and so dumb in one and the same moment. She was smart enough to wind Tom around her little finger and at the same time, after once meeting me and finding out the kind of man I am, she thought she could get away with marrying not only him but three other men also. How on

earth could her mind have been working? The only possible way
she could have gotten away with it, even if I had not been in
the picture, was to have had at least three of her men die in
combat. But at the same time, one cannot help but admire a little
bit of her crust in trying.

Tinker

ALTHOUGH all's well that ends well, Tom, as I have already said, was not an unmixed blessing to us, but Tinker, if any child ever was an unmixed blessing, was one to me. If Tom had been Gertrude's child in a sense, Tinker was mine. Tom was a bright child but in some ways not a really happy one, while Tinker was always happy and sunny in disposition. If a parent looks for meaning in life through his children, Tinker was a child to convey that meaning. The old saying is that it is love that makes the world go round, and I believe it except that I would say that it is the kind of love a father can have for his daughter which does it rather than the kind of love one sees in the movies. In some ways, I think that Tinker has always been closer to me than Gertrude has been.

One cannot help but wonder over the difference between two children. How can two little people born of the same mother and father be so totally unlike? The difference, it seems to me now, lay in the fact that at the time of Tinker's birth we (I mean Gertrude and I) were more settled, more married, so to speak, for people don't, in spite of the ceremony, get married all at once, but slowly, the business sometimes taking years and years. In fact, it sometimes seems to me that Gertrude and I are still in the process, still have not arrived yet, and it has been thirty years now.

But at any rate we were more married in 1925 when Tinker was born than we were in 1921 when Tom was. We were in the

new house. Business was good. I was on the House Committee of
the Sleepy Hollow Club, although how that happened after the
Kangaroo Golf Match of the summer before I cannot imagine.
Both Gertrude and I had learned that we had to have separate
lives from each other along with our lives together. I was beginning to be active in the local Republican Party, and she was interested in her Junior League work. There was a little group of
them making puppets and, while they never got as far as putting
on a puppet show, it was a good, healthy interest for them, and
for quite a while they had their puppet stage set up out in our
garage and we had to keep the car in the driveway.

But what I am trying to say is that by 1925 we were much
more settled. And then, too, I think there is something about
just the fact of having a second child, more even than having the
first one, which makes you know that for better or for worse and
for richer and for poorer you are really and truly for keeps in the
business. You are committed, and you realize that you must spend
the rest of your life working out those commitments. I suppose
that every married couple has thought of divorce or separation
at one time or another, but one learns after a while, too, that
while divorce exists, by and large it is for other people and does
not concern you. I think only very special people are able to
really achieve a divorce, for I have seen really successful divorce
almost as rarely as I have seen completely successful marriage. People always somehow seem to keep hanging onto each
other.

But to return to Tinker, I think it was this more settledness
of our home which accounts for her happy and placid behavior
which was so different from Tom's.[1] We were not only settled,
but the whole country was. Coolidge was in the White House. A
man was allowed to make money if he cared to. There was optimism in the air. The world was like an orchard with fruit

[1] Tinker Selleck says in comment: "I do not remember myself as placid
at all, and I really think that Tom and I were very similar in temperament.
The only difference was that Tom fought back while I hid from unpleasant
matters."

hanging around ripe for plucking, fruit of all kinds and descriptions.

Tinker was born May 29, 1925, at the Presbyterian Hospital by Caesarian section. She weighed ten pounds, and was as healthy and beautiful as Tom had been. Both of us had wanted a girl, so you can imagine she was more than welcome. And we began right away to spoil her completely. But with a girl baby you feel you can spoil it, for girls are supposed to be spoiled at least a little.

She was blue-eyed and blond, as Tom was, but as she grew older she was not husky, but rather slight and delicate as was Gertrude. She was a wonderful, wistful looking little girl who lived for a long time in a sort of dream world. For example, she had imaginary playmates, one in particular whose name was Charley. I remember Charley well, for on one occasion he created a very difficult situation. We were driving the children to Minnesota where Gertrude used to stay for the summer, and we had gone about fifty miles along our journey. We stopped for gasoline, I remember, and Tinker suddenly discovered that we had forgotten to bring Charley with us. Gertrude wanted to ignore the absence of the imaginary person, but that threw Tinker into hysterics. Then we tried to tell her that Charley was going on the train and would meet us at the lake, but she would not believe it. And the upshot of the matter was that I had to leave Gertrude and the children in a hotel in the next town and drive all the way back to Gateway City. It seems silly, but what else could I have done in that situation?

She was about five then, and I have a snapshot taken of her that summer, a snapshot which I have had framed and which is on my desk down at the office. She is sitting in a swing. She has those big, wistful blue eyes. Her fine, whitish blond hair is in curls. She is wearing a paper crown on her head and a little ballet dress with a tarlatan skirt. She is carrying in her hand a little wand with a paper star on it. The whole getup was what she called her "good fairy costume." When she wore it, she used to talk thoughtfully about granting people their wishes but warning them when she did so that they must be very careful what they wished for. She had just been read the story about the Three Wishes in which the sausages were wished onto the man's nose, and she didn't want to be responsible for any such thing happening.[2]

Her good fairy costume was not her only costume, for she was a great one for dressing up and imagining herself one thing or another. Sometimes, she would be Queen Marie of Rumania. Sometimes Mrs. Spruley who lived next door. Once, as I remember, the Virgin Mary. As a little girl she was very religious and liked to pray out loud before she went to bed in the evenings. And sometimes I had to pray with her, for she worried about my soul, which touched me, although what would happen to Gertrude's soul did not seem to alarm her. She was really always my girl. When she had nightmares, she would come to my room and slip into my bed for comfort.

I have already mentioned a number of the cute things which Tom said and did. Well, there were cute things she said and did, also.

One time, at a cocktail party . . . we always had the children down for a little while when we had a party, for we felt that it was a good way for them to learn social poise, and because they were handsome children so that it was a pleasure to show them off. But one time at a cocktail party, as I was saying, she volunteered to a stranger the information that she was not born but that Doc Crocker brought her in a suitcase. Then, when asked who Doc Crocker was, she said, "He's the man who comes to our house when Daddy goes down to the office."

Neither Doc nor I have ever lived down that one, although it was true that for a while there during the long period when

[2] Tinker Selleck says: "I remember this very well, and one terrifying result which I have never mentioned. I gave a wish to Mr. Boardman, who was the man who mowed our lawn. He said, 'My wish is that I come to an end of all my troubles,' and two or three days later he was killed accidentally while cleaning a pistol. It convinced me of my magical power which up till then I hadn't been sure of, and gave me a sense of guilt which even now I can remember."

Gertrude suffered from headaches Doc used to drop in almost daily to see her.

That was one of the cute things she said, but probably the cutest was the yell she learned at Camp Carefree where she had gone during the summer when she was twelve. The yell is quite complicated, but I had her give it for us so many times that I have never been able to forget it:

> One, two, three, four, five, six, seven;
> All good children go to heaven.
> All the rest stay down and yell,
> One-a-zippa, two-a-zippa, three-a-zippa, *zam.*
> We don't give a razzle-dazzle, shazzle-dazzle,
>   sis, boom, bah;
> Susquehanna Tribe girls, rah! rah! rah!

You see the little girls at Camp Carefree were divided up into two Indian tribes, the Susquehannas and the Potawatomis. Tinker was a Susquehanna, and the little Ecles girl was a Potawatomi, and for a while they were very contemptuous of each other. The Ecles girl used to give her yell, which I have forgotten, at cocktail parties too, but she was never anywhere near as cute as Tinker giving hers. I used to give Tinker a dollar when she would do it for our guests, and it was really a treat to see her stamp her little foot in time as she shouted: "One-a-zippa, two-a-zippa, three-a-zippa, *zam.* We don't give a razzle-dazzle, shazzle-dazzle, sis, boom, bah; Susquehanna Tribe girls, rah! rah! rah!" [3]

She had another little stunt which was almost equally amusing. It was at the time the Yaw-Et-Ag Manufacturing Company was first making those air horns which I have mentioned. She learned to sing, "Just around the corner there's a rainbow in the sky," and she could sing it for company and do a little time step [4]

---

[3] Tinker Selleck says: "I was not the wistful child Father called me, but a shamefully exhibitionistic one. And even then I sometimes hated Father for encouraging me in it. I always desperately wanted the dollar I would get for the show, but sometimes I was ashamed of the dollar once I had it. And later, I came to be ashamed of Father for enjoying this kind of thing."

[4] "This must have been a rather horrible thing to see," Tinker says, "and my own children will certainly never do anything like that. It's undignified, and a child knows it."

which she had worked out to go with it. I used to give her a dollar when she would do that, too.

When Tinker was born, just as with Tom, I bought her a United States Treasury Bond to start her fortune. It was a coupon bond, and when she was older I used to take her down to the vault in the bank where together we would get my box out and her bond. She would clip it herself, which she loved to do. Then, with me holding her on my shoulder, we would go upstairs in the bank and cash in the coupon, and all the people behind the bond counter would make a great fuss over her as she very seriously counted her money. Later on, I opened a little savings account for her, and we would go in together once a week to deposit fifty cents or a dollar in it. She came to know all the tellers by name, and all of them knew her, and old Ben, the guard, used to keep candy in his pocket to give her on those occasions.

Yes, Tinker and I had grand times together. While she was attending Miss Darling's School,[5] she used to play hooky frequently, and would show up at my office alone or with another girl just before lunchtime. I would take her and whoever happened to be with her to lunch at the Gateway Hotel and give them money to go to the afternoon movie, which would have been the reason for their truancy. It was always great fun to do this, but it usually took considerable ingenuity on my part to write the right kind of note to Miss Darling to explain their absence. I suppose that was very wrong of me, but I see no great harm in showing a little bit of indulgence toward a daughter.

Next to seeing Tinker married, I think that the greatest pang she ever gave me came at the moment when we sent her away to school at Miss Bennett's School in Millbrook, New York. I suppose that, on my own, I would never have sent her away at all. It was always such a pleasure to come home from work and

---

[5] Except for the Catholic Convent, Miss Darling's School was the only private girls' seminary in Gateway. We suspect that attendance at it represented a class distinction for the Sellecks in the same way that "Eastern education" seemed to.

find my Tinkerbell there when I came in. And I also came to enjoy thoroughly all the young people whom she was beginning to bring home with her, all the embarrassed little boys and the giggling girls who would be sitting in the living room playing phonograph records, or ping-pong in the rumpus room in the basement. No, on my own I do not think that I would have given up all that for the sake of her education.

It was Gertrude who first saw how important it would be for her future to go East. And Gertrude was quite right. Going East to school gives a girl or boy a kind of assurance which does not seem to come in any other manner.[6] It isn't knowledge a girl seems to get really, but a realization, rather, that nothing has been skimped on her background, the unmistakable kind of thing Gertrude has always had, and I have not had.

Tinker was not particularly anxious to go away when we sent her, but there were several other little girls from Gateway who were going, and once she got there she loved it. Millbrook is a beautiful spot, nestled up there in the Berkshires, a healthy, out-of-doors sort of place where a girl could not help but be happy. Tinker took to it like a duck takes to water. She seemed to be in everything that was going on, as far as I could make out, and especially in dramatics. I fully believe that, had Tinker cared to, she could have made a career of the stage, for she had genuine talent.

She took part in several plays while she was at Miss Bennett's, and in her last year she took part in the "Greek play" which, at Miss Bennett's, is quite an occasion. I went East at the time and enjoyed her performance very much, although the play was something called *Medea* which was rather dull and did not make much sense, to my way of thinking.

After Tinker graduated, I took her to New York for a few days, where we saw several plays, *Life with Father, Lady in the Dark,*

[6] Tinker Selleck said: "I did not get assurance from Miss Bennett's but a terrible inferiority complex, which sometimes happens when girls go from places like Gateway City and meet other girls who come from really rich families. But I guess when I came back, I looked as though I had assurance, which is the thing that matters."

Arsenic and Old Lace, and others. I took her to the Stork Club one evening for dinner, and she was quite thrilled because Sherman Billingsley gave her a present of a bottle of perfume and introduced her to Walter Winchell. Another evening, we went to El Morocco, and both evenings after the theater we went to Sardi's, where I introduced her to Joe E. Brown whom I once met at a World Series.

I had hoped that after Miss Bennett's, she would want to come home to Gateway for a while, but she had other plans. She wanted to stay in New York for a year to study secretarial work.[7] And while I suppose she could have learned typing and shorthand in Gateway, she did prevail upon me to let her spend the winter of 1942 in the city studying at the Katharine Gibbs School and living at the Barbizon for women. It was all good for her, I know, but it worried me, too, for of course it was during wartime. Actually she met George Manelle that winter, who (although she did not know it at the time) would not so much later become her husband.

I think that New York for a year can be an excellent thing for a young girl if she can be trusted. There are the advantages of the theater, and the concerts, and there is the indefinable something which, like Eastern education, makes a girl into a very finished product. Tinker was a very big-city little girl when she finally came back into our household.

It was wartime then, and it has sometimes seemed to me that wartime is a very unfortunate time for girls in their late teens. There is a feeling of excitement which seems to charge the air, but yet there are very few ways in which a nice girl can share in the excitement. And then the boys who should be coming calling at the house are all away somewhere fighting. Of course, there are servicemen around, but with servicemen (and this is in no way considered a slight against them) you are not always

---

[7] Tinker Selleck says: "Actually, the whole idea, and one I could not say, was to get away forever from Gateway City. I felt the same way Tom did. Gateway represented to me the dreariest kind of living. It never excited me the way it always seemed to excite Father."

sure about what they are after. I suppose that it was fortunate that George Manelle was stationed for a short time in Gateway, for it gave her a more fixed point for her emotions than she might otherwise have had then, but strangely enough I never met George until a long time after.[8]

Tinker came back to Gateway, as I was saying, and it was wonderful again to have her with us, and occasionally again to take her out to the Hotel Gateway for luncheon. She got herself a job selling records in the record department at Beckerman and Chandler, and in the evenings she did USO work. She wanted to go abroad with the Red Cross, but this was one of the few things in life which I have had to deny her. I heartily approve of the Red Cross but I just could not see sending my daughter into danger, especially when my son was already in the South Pacific. She was quite angry with me over it, but there was nothing I could do about it, and that was one of the very few times when she and I ever had any harsh words with each other.

"Father," she said, "you have ruined Tom's life, and now you want to ruin my life."

I did not answer, for whatever it was she was thinking about, I could not imagine.

There was nothing very important in her life after that until George came back, and she, after a long courtship, consented to get married.[9]

[8] Tinker says: "I was careful that Father didn't for I was still at the age where one is ashamed of one's parents, and I hated to think of him calling George off into a corner to ask him what his intentions were as he had with one or two other boys who were in the service. I know that everything Father did he did with my best interests in mind, but he could be impossible on occasion. He was not subtle, and I desperately wanted a subtle father."

[9] Tinker Selleck says: "Actually, it was not a long courtship, not on George's part, that is, for I accepted him the first time he asked me. He wanted to get himself established in business after the war before he would ask me, established in a way which, he said, could support me, for he seemed to think that I was expensive. It was a long, frustrating, heartbreaking time of waiting."

2

The greatest pang which Tinker ever caused me was certainly a natural enough matter on her part, a thing also in every way to be desired, a matter for which I thought I had been preparing myself for years. It was simply that she got married as she should, and I should say also that in George she found as good a man as any of us could ever have picked out for her. And yet it is still difficult for any father, I imagine, to give over the responsibility of almost twenty-five years to someone else who is still almost a stranger. There was a life there which had belonged to me [10] and then it suddenly was someone else's.

I have come to wonder now whether or not my heart attack could not have had something to do with Tinker's marriage, for after all the two events did happen almost simultaneously. I'm not talking about the work and worry of the wedding, either. I'm talking about something deeper, the same kind of thing I felt the first time I met George Manelle. On sight, I disliked him, a thing which had never happened to me with any of her other suitors. It is enough, when I think about it, to make me wonder if a man can love his daughter more than he ought to, for George was just exactly the kind of man that I had always wanted her to marry.

It could not have been that I resented her being in love with someone else, for I had not felt that way about any of the boys she had been in love with, not even about the one who played professional hockey for the *Yaw-Et-Ag Red Men*,[11] or the Communistic one who lived in Greenwich Village and who hitchhiked out to Gateway one summer, or the one who was a writer. With all of them, in spite of Tinker's very obvious infatuations, I never worried, and always knew that nothing serious could

[10] Tinker says: "This was what Father could not understand about either Tom or me. Our lives didn't belong to him. They were ours; and after my marriage my life didn't belong to George then either, although maybe it should have."

[11] The Yaw-Et-Ag Red Men were the Gateway City professional hockey team.

happen. But with George I knew as soon as I saw him that he was going to be a young man to cope with. I think it was because he wore garters that I knew this, for all of Tinker's other young men had always had socks bunched up around their ankles. I think it was those trim silk ankles over well-shined shoes which alarmed me more than anything else did.

They had met, as I have said, during Tinker's winter in New York and again when George, as an ensign, had been stationed in the Gateway City Recruiting Office. It was the summer of 1949, however, when he came from New York to ask her to become his wife that I first met him. It was late one summer afternoon, and I had come back from a particularly hard day. Feeling hot and tired I came in and found him sitting in the living room in my favorite corner of the sofa. Tinker was sitting on the hassock as though she were at his feet. Gertrude was sitting across the room from him in the big chair in a worshipful attitude also. They were all very politely drinking highballs, and I could tell that the occasion was very special, for the silver ice bucket, the soda siphon, the bottle and so forth, were all on a tray on the coffee table, and generally when we drank we mixed the drinks in the kitchen.

He was a big young man in his early thirties. He had sandy red hair and big freckled hands. I suppose you might have called George handsome, but I thought of him first of all as a man whose mind was working, who was taking in everything about Gertrude's deferential attitude, everything about Tinker, everything about our house and its furnishings and translating them into their meaning about my income, our position in the world, and what pigeonhole we fitted into. And I do not mean to say that I felt he was interested in money or anything like that, simply that here, suddenly, was a man who was observing. And that made me angry because it made me observing too, made me dissatisfied with the setup I lived in, with all the junk which Gertrude and the interior decorator from Beckerman and Chandler had put here and there around us. And I don't really mean that this junk was bad stuff, either, for all of it, all that

French period stuff, had cost one whale of a lot of money. I was mad because none of it said anything about me; because there was nothing in that room which I had ever picked out or wanted; because all of it seemed to say that I didn't count and was just a person who came in in the evenings from the office. I was mad at George because he had made me see this and because he saw it too.

He was wearing a gray flannel suit, a red tie with polka dots in it, and trim silk socks, neat but just careless enough to make you respect him.

And what he actually was, I found out later, was just exactly what he looked like. He came from a good, solid family in Montclair, New Jersey; his father was an underwriter for a marine insurance company and had done very well for himself during the last war.

George had been educated at St. Paul's School, which, I am told, is a very good one; he had gone to Yale and Harvard Business School. He had worked for his father until December 7, 1941, and then gone into the Navy, in which he already had a Reserve Commission as an ensign. He had been stationed briefly in San Francisco, then on a destroyer, and had eventually become a full lieutenant and the executive officer of a destroyer escort. He had been in everything in the Pacific which anyone else had been in on.

At the end of the war, he had gone back to New York and gone to work in a rather unusual business. It was a firm which made a business of buying up other businesses, which they would build up and then sell again at profit. He was making almost as much money as I did. He belonged to the Yale Club in New York, the Montclair Country Club, and the Yacht Club in Larchmont. He was buying a house in New Rochelle, and men who are buying houses by and large have serious matrimonial intentions. Well, I suppose that any father is bound to be jealous of any young man who can give his daughter everything he can. It was alarming, really alarming, for there was nothing about the young man to object to.

"Father," Tinker said, as I came into the living room that late afternoon, "this is George." That was all she said, but that was all I needed, for just that told me the whole story.

"George is from Montclair," Gertrude said, "from Montclair, New Jersey."

And from that I knew right off that they had already been given (whether they had asked for it or not) Gertrude's blessing.

"George," Gertrude said, "let Jeffrey fix you another highball." She purred at George just like a kitten.

"George," she said, turning to me, "is in the most fascinating business. He, his firm, buys up other businesses, little ones like Yaw-Et-Ag which aren't making any money, and then he makes them make money."

"Look, sir," he said, squirming uncomfortably on the sofa, "don't get me wrong, I'm not out here to buy up your business."

"No," I said to myself, "just my daughter."

"Go upstairs and get cleaned up, Jeffrey," Gertrude said. "George is staying for dinner."

As I went into the hallway, Gertrude came out with me and whispered: "Run down to the drugstore in the car, will you, and get some ice cream, some pistachio and almond. We don't have anything on hand for dessert for dinner. And why don't you pick up some white wine? We really should have some wine for dinner."

Well, what am I saying here now? What I am saying is that George, and everything about Tinker's engagement, just suddenly overwhelmed me.

I had always thought that when Tinker did get married things would take place a little bit more slowly. I had expected it to be more like it had been when I had married Gertrude and gone, in fear and trembling, my bank book in my pocket, to see old Mr. McCullough, who had given me quite a grilling. But now I could see that if I was asked at all it would be about something that was already settled.

Actually, I was asked, and I am glad that I was because after it was all over I liked George a whole lot better. But the way that I was prepared for the interview did prejudice me against him.

Gertrude, in priming me, said, "Now Jeffrey, you mustn't be harsh with George because if you are you know Tinker might not get him."

That made me angry and I said, "Is he such a prize then?"

"Yes, he is," Gertrude said, "and he's a step up in the world for her also."

And that made me laugh because I had never heard Gertrude . . . or any of the McCulloughs . . . admit it was possible for them to take a step upward.

"You must be very nice to George," Gertrude said, "because he comes from a fine old Montclair family, and he's been terribly successful, and she'll have all kinds of advantages living in the East, advantages which Gateway City just can't give her."

I said, "All I want to know is do they love each other?"

Gertrude said, "Of course they love each other."

It would have been easier for me to like George at first if Gertrude and I had not had that little conversation.

The actual interview took place at my office, and I appreciated his coming to me there, for at the office I was on home ground while home was only home ground for the women. I remember Helen Flanagan eyed him up and down as she brought him in to see me, and I made a mental note to ask her afterward for her reaction.

He came in and sat down in the chair across the desk from me. I offered him a cigarette, but he had his own with him. We were silent for a moment and I saw his hand shake a little as he struck the match, and that made me feel less nervous.

He frowned after a moment and then plunged in: "I think you know why I'm here, sir. I want to marry your daughter."

I said, "Does she want to marry you, George?"

He swallowed and said, "Yes. Yes, sir, I think so."

I said, "Don't you know so?"

And that little bit of meanness on my part, rather than em-

barrassing him further, seemed to snap him out of all embarrassment and into a serious directness.

"Yes, Mr. Selleck," he said, in almost a military manner, "I
know so. We want to get married, and I have here some facts
and figures and budgets to show you that we know exactly what
we're doing."

He reached into his coat pocket and pulled out a whole sheaf
of papers. He had his current bank statement there, his bank
book, a list of investments, his insurance policies, his baptismal
certificate even. And I will say this for George, that when he
set about selling any proposition, he briefed himself completely
and came with all the documents pertaining to the subject. He
was a young man who (and I admired it in him) had trained
himself to think up all the questions and be ready with all the
answers, the kind of young man, in short, whom I wished I had
somewhere within my business. He was so well prepared on this
occasion that I became quite bewildered.

Finally, I said, "Now look George, all I want to know is, can
you make her happy?"

He stopped his sales talk then and looked down at his hands,
and there was suddenly a kind of boyishness in him which was
appealing.

He said, "All I know, Mr. Selleck, is that I awfully want to
marry your daughter."

And when he said that, I was suddenly all for him.

"She's expensive," I said.

He said, "Yes, I know she's expensive. Otherwise, I would
have been in a good deal sooner."

I said, "She's kind of a spoiled child."

He said, "She'll be all right, Mr. Selleck."

Then both of us were silent for several moments.

Finally I said, "If I should not give my permission would it
make any difference?"

He said slowly, "I think we would get married anyway, but
that isn't the same thing as saying that it wouldn't make any difference."

What more was there to say? Naturally, I gave my blessing.

After he had gone, I asked Helen Flanagan what she thought. I don't know on what she based her judgment, but she said: "We could use a young man like that, Mr. Selleck, in the business."

I couldn't quite make up my mind whether I liked the idea or disliked it. It takes a long time to get to know a son-in-law, longer possibly than any other person.

I wonder again whether any of this could have had anything to do with my coronary occlusion. After all, the heart is not the seat of the emotions, but why had so many people for so many years thought so? The heart is an organ like any other organ. It's a muscle with blood vessels which feed it. In one of these vessels there occurs a stoppage like a stoppage in a gas line. The pump stops working and then you die or else it keeps on working feebly and you sit around writing your memoirs until new gas lines grow out around it. It's mechanical, just as mechanical as an automobile. And yet, emotions do seem to have something to do with it.

3

To announce the engagement we gave a large cocktail party in September, and the wedding itself was scheduled for Saturday, November 12.

Gertrude said to me, "Jeffrey, this is one time in our lives that we have to shoot the works even if it breaks us."

I agreed with her, for it was true. When you marry off a daughter there isn't much you can stint on. Although I don't like to think so, I think that Gertrude was right when she said: "When you put on a wedding people are watching you. You know yourself that when you get a wedding invitation you rub your finger across the letters to see whether it is really engraved or not." And that's true, for while I have never done that myself, I have seen Gertrude do it a hundred times at least. If you don't have your colors flying at the time of a wedding when else would you fly them?

"Gertrude," I said, "how much do you think that it will cost us?"

"About five thousand dollars," she said, and while I did not believe her then, that was almost exactly what it came to.

"At least five thousand dollars," she said, "The Ecleses spent over four thousand when Shirley was married and that was during wartime and before inflation."

"We aren't trying to live up to the Ecleses," I said, but in a sense I think we were. The Ecleses are in about the same bracket as we are. They live in about the same kind of house. Tinker was a bridesmaid in Shirley Ecles's wedding, and Shirley was to be matron of honor in Tinker's. We never in anything ever planned to live up to the Ecleses, but for some reason it always seemed to work out that we had to.

"Of course the Ecleses had to," Gertrude said, "because, after all, Howard is a little *nouveau*. But I think that five thousand is just about the least we can get by on."

"I'll be more convinced," I said, "when I see it down on paper."

We sat down and planned the wedding then the way we wanted to have it; and the way things figured up, to my amazement, the total came closer to ten thousand than to five thousand dollars. So then we started cutting. We cut the invitation list to the bone, to only very close friends, people we had to invite, and people who might send nice presents.

For the reception, we had wanted to take over the whole Sleepy Hollow Club, as the Herb Johnsons had done when Marcia Johnson had married the young man from Peoria in the Caterpillar Tractor Company. We had to abandon the idea of the club in favor of the Town and Country Room. We had to cut down the bridal dinner to just the wedding party and one or two friends and relations. Helen Flanagan stuffed and addressed the invitations, which saved us from having to get a professional to do it. For the reception, we didn't use as good champagne as we did for the bridal dinner, and I was able to get a rate through the influence of some friends of mine on the State Liquor Commission, and a special rate on the flowers through

George Jerome, the undertaker, who sometimes goes hunting with us.

But cut as we would, it was still an expensive business, and there were all kinds of things which came up that I had not anticipated. The bed which George and Tinker picked out was a seven foot by seven foot one, and I found out that when you get into the oversize sheet department you really get into something. Boy, that percale was expensive! Then there were nightgowns, and I had never known before that a nightgown today can cost as much as fifty dollars, which I still don't understand because the ones I see in the stores seem to be labeled around twelve-fifty or seventeen dollars, and they look just fine. And even that is more than I would pay for a whole pair of pants. And in the whole business I hadn't figured telegrams and telephone calls which, when the two lovebirds are separated by a thousand or fifteen hundred miles, can add up to something really whopping. I had some bonds tucked away to sell to cover the occasion, but, as I have said already, they didn't cover the total.

But at any rate Tinker was married right, and that is something. But it has seemed to me always that, considering the cost, a wedding really should have more than one performance. Everything took a month or two to prepare for, but finally everything was ready. We arrived finally at the evening before the wedding day, and a moment at which I was dressing for the bridal dinner. I was in my room and I was in the middle of getting my stiff shirt on. I was putting in the studs, to be specific, and the shirt had been so stiffly starched that the holes for the studs would not open. I was exasperated about that.

And it was at that moment that Gertrude came in in a distraught manner. She was in her slip, but otherwise dressed for the party, and in one hand she was holding a hairbrush.

"Jeffrey," she said, "you've got to go in and talk to Tinker."

"What's the matter with Tinker?" I said. "Damn it."

"She's hysterical," Gertrude said, "and she says she won't go to the bridal dinner and doesn't want to get married."

"What in hades is the matter with her?" I said, and I am afraid that I shouted, for, like everyone else, I was very much wrought-up at the moment.

Gertrude said, "She says she hates George and can't stand him."

"Tell her," I shouted, "that he probably can't stand her either, at the moment."

"No," Gertrude said, "you've got to go in and talk to her. She's your daughter."

Now I suppose that every father has to go through something like this at the time of his daughter's wedding, for while the women seem to love excitement they don't seem to be able to stand it. And then, there seems to be something about a big wedding which makes everyone temporarily loco. No one gets enough sleep, I imagine, and all the rich food at the parties beforehand gives everyone indigestion, and then getting married is actually a big step, such a big step, in fact, that it even starts people who have nothing to do with it to crying.

"Jeffrey," Gertrude shrieked at me as we stood there, "do something! Don't just fumble with those studs, but do something. Do something quickly!"

I left the shirt where it was and went down the hall and into Tinker's room without knocking, for the door was standing open. And as soon as I saw her, all my irritation turned into the deepest kind of concern, as you can imagine. She was lying in her slip on her bed and sobbing into her pillow. She seemed so young, so childlike at that moment that it was heartbreaking. Her room was in complete disorder. Her dress for the party was lying crumpled across a chair, and there were several pairs of shoes scattered about. In the center of the floor was a silver Paul Revere bowl which was a present, and not far from it was the box it had come in with the paper spilling out on the carpet.

All of this not only gave me concern but it almost put me in a panic. If she didn't want to get married, did she have to? But it suddenly seemed as though the whole thing was now my decision, and can even a parent make a decision in a case like this?

Was it just hysteria which always happens? Or was this something serious and different?

"Look, honey-baby," I said, going over to the bed and trying to keep my voice as calm as I could keep it. "Honey-baby . . . Tinkerbell . . . what's the matter?"

"I don't want to get married," she sobbed, her face still in the pillow.

"Honey-baby," I said, "you don't have to do anything you don't want to."

And then Gertrude shrieked again from behind me: "Don't be a fool! Of course she has to get married. It's too late now to do anything about it."

She was almost as hysterical as Tinker.

"You don't seem to realize," she went on in the same hysterical way, "that everything is all arranged. You don't seem to realize that we have sent out a thousand invitations and the house is full of presents, and that you don't just call off weddings at the last moment."

I lost my temper, too. "God damn it!" I shouted. "If Tinker doesn't want to get married she doesn't have to get married."

"Don't shout at me," Gertrude shouted.

"You go to hell!" I shouted back.

I am ashamed of that now, for it was a rather terrible thing to have shouted, but it did have the effect of quieting Gertrude. Then, lowering my voice, I turned back to Tinker and said: "Look, Tinkerbell, tell Daddy what's the matter. That's what he's here for. He's here so that you don't have to do anything you don't want to."

"I can't," she sobbed. "I just can't do it."

"Why not, Tinkerbell?" I said. "Why not, honey-baby?"

"I'm not" — she almost choked with her sobbing — "I'm not good enough for him."

I don't think she could have said anything more unexpected. It was so absurd it almost made me laugh. Not good enough for him, when there really wasn't anyone quite good enough for my honey-baby.

"What do you mean, not good enough?" I said, and patted her hand to soothe her.

"I'm not what I pretend to be," she sobbed on. "None of us are what we pretend to be. We're all just Midwestern and common."

It was the damnedest thing I had ever listened to, and I didn't know how to answer.

"Look, honey-baby," I said soothingly, "if you go on that way you'll make me real angry."

"I can't," she repeated. "I just can't do it to him."

"Do you love him?" I said.

"Oh, yes," she said, "I love him."

I said, "Then you've got to get married. If you love him that's the only thing that matters."

She stopped sobbing then, and sat up and looked at me, and she looked so wretched that it was heartbreaking. Then she said another thing which was jolting.

"Dad," she said, "do you love Mother?"

I said very softly, "Yes, dear, I love your mother."

Then she looked at Gertrude who was still standing behind me and said, "Mother, do you love Dad, too?"

And then Gertrude started crying, and she said, "Yes, I always have and I always will love your father."

"You see," Tinker said, "I just don't want my life to be the way yours is."

"If you love him," I said, "it's the only thing that matters."

Then I went to the bathroom and dampened a washcloth and took it back to her.

"Here," I said. "Wash your face, dear."

It was funny, but from that moment on, she became quite normal again and went through everything right on through the wedding, not even shaking on my arm the next day when I led her down the aisle.

Tinker Selleck, upon the request of the editors, makes her comment upon this passage which concerns her, and we have printed it here in part.

"Inasmuch as the things Father says here are his, and, as you say, necessary to make up his portrait, I don't suppose that I can ask you to eliminate anything, much as I would like to have you do so. But I would, as you suggest, like to say something for myself.

"First of all, although at the time he describes I may have appeared very grown-up and self-reliant, I was very immature, and, I am very sorry to say, unable to appreciate my father. That he was kind, that he was a pillar I could always lean against, that he was good, were matters that I knew but which I took for granted. That he spoiled me, I did not know. That he was unhappy, I dimly realized.

"My only wish now is that he could have lived long enough for me to let him know that I appreciated him, and that the horrible ties (hand-painted some of them), the ventilated shoes, the red feather in his hatband, were not matters of great importance. And a part of this wish is the desire to thank him for saying, no matter that it was said blunderingly, the right thing at a crucial moment. But honestly also, I suppose I must admit that, were he still with us, I would still be embarrassed by the hang of his trousers, the drape of his coat, and his hearty, Rotarian manner.

"It seems to me a strange thing that one should be bewildered when it comes to saying anything about one's parents, and especially when one of them has unexpectedly become articulate and said things completely unexpected. But one is bewildered. I suppose the hardest thing children have to learn is that their parents are possessed of feelings."

Here at the beginning of the last major section of Jeff's book, I am reminded of a story he used to like to tell on many different occasions.

A motorist, the story goes, is driving in a remote area of Colorado. Observing a native sitting by the roadside, this motorist stops to inquire directions.

"What's the name of the next town?" he asks the native.

"Don't know," is the answer.

"Where is the nearest gas station?" asks the motorist.

"Don't know," is the rejoinder.

"Strikes me," says the motorist, "that you're not quite bright."

"No," says the native, "I ain't quite bright, but I ain't lost, neither."

I don't know whether Jeff Selleck, when he died, was lost or not. If his book could have gone on further we might know, but here, in this last cycle of his story, we do see indications that he was arriving at some kind of answer to all the intangibles which oppressed him.

Saint Luke's Hospital . . . Continued

On Friday morning, November 25, while I was still at Saint Luke's, two very important things happened, three really, for that also was the first day on which I was allowed to "dangle." Dangling was the first exercise allowed me since the beginning of my illness, and dangling consists of sitting on the edge of your bed and letting your feet hang in the air, dangling and wiggling as they please.

Now to a person in the normal, active ways of life this may not seem to be an exercise at all, but to a man who has been lying on his back for two weeks it is not only an exercise but also a sign of progress, a reason for hope that someday you will again be on your feet and in there punching. At least, that was what it was for me, and Doc Crocker told me that I was right to look at it in this fashion.

The other two events were these: Helen Flanagan was allowed to come in with papers for me to sign concerning my business, and Tinker and George visited me on their return from their honeymoon, for they had gone to Colorado and had come back through Gateway on their way East to New Rochelle where they would be living. I had not seen them since the wedding reception, for I had not wanted to see anyone really on that first day of my illness, which was the only day after the wedding that they had been in Gateway.

These were the two events of the morning of November 25,

although, at the time, I did not realize their importance. I shall deal with them in the order in which they happened.

1

What Helen had to say to me disturbed me in a vague kind of way, for it is always disturbing to find that things with which you have been intimately concerned are still going along without you. But it did not really surprise me, for I had known, after a fashion, the way in which Jake Brawn's thinking had been going ever since the Yaw-Et-Ag Manufacturing Company had manufactured hand grenade fuses during the war and had been awarded a Navy "E" for the job we had been doing. I had known that his mind had been running toward weapons and explosives, for, even back in '43 and '44, he had started talking about how antiquated were the ways in which the war was being fought. They never seemed antiquated to me, but Jake had the kind of mechanical mind which saw almost anything outdated by the time it was in blueprint. It was bombs which bothered him mostly, and I remember in particular one conversation.

"Can you think of anything more impractical, Jeff," he said, "than dropping a bomb, or dropping anything, and expecting it to hit the target? Try it yourself," he said. "Try dropping a marble from three feet in the air into a glass of water. It's only blind luck if you do it more than once in ten trys."

I remember that this was at luncheon, and I laughed at his seriousness. I remember that I answered: "Well, I guess our boys in Europe and the Pacific seem to be able to do it."

He had become quite excited, and replied: "But only through all kinds of correction devices, and then only because the burst of the bomb is bigger than the glass of water. They talk about 'pin-point' bombing, but there is really no 'pin-point' bombing, and there can't be as long as they stick to this antiquated principle of dropping."

It seems strange now to think back on those times which, actually, are not so long ago, strange to think back into the way we were, and had to be, thinking. It is a hard time to recall at all, in the same way it is hard to remember a dream, although the dream may have been ever so vivid. It is odd to think of two, on the whole mild, businessmen sitting at luncheon so seriously discussing destruction.

"Well, how are you going to get a bomb down," I said, "if you don't drop it?"

He lit his cold cigar and said: "You have to build intelligence into it. You have to give a bomb a brain, and then you are beginning to get modern."

And when you think about that, it is a very frightening idea.

"How do you give a bomb a brain?" I said.

He said: "Well, these proximity fuses are a step in the right direction, but they are just the brain of a caveman compared with the brain of the twentieth century which could be put into a projectile. All the proximity fuse has is ears, but you could put eyes into it too, eyes which would guide the missile right into the target even when it's dodging."

Well, of course what he was talking about was a guided missile, although at the time the name had not come into popular usage.

"Shooting," he said, "of course is better than dropping. Shooting is like throwing, and a pitcher can throw a ball to a very small target, but shooting is really antiquated, too. What you have to have is something that not only has eyes and a brain, but its own means of locomotion. Then, Jeff, you got something. And the funny part of it all is that all the principles you need to do all that, we already got. All you really got to do is combine things we already got now."

I remember thinking: "You've come a long ways, Jake, since one winter evening in 1932 in a shed with a couple of air horns." I don't know why it scared me, but it did scare me, and I suppose that it was because an ordinary person like me doesn't have anything to do with such matters. We leave that to special people like the du Ponts or whoever the people are who think about such matters.

I suppose, though, I was wrong to discount him, for after all our whole American tradition (which is a great tradition) has been one in which little people like Jake Brawn actually have made world-shattering discoveries in homemade laboratories and back-yard machine shops.

And I don't know why a weapon should be any different from any other mechanical thing. The same process makes them all, and there are very few things today which are not weapons in wartime. I don't know why a weapon should be different, but it does seem different. And even everything Jake had said had scared me. The idea of a brain built for just one purpose, and which destroys itself even when it's accomplished its purpose, to me somehow seemed shocking, but after all, that is what you do frequently enough with a soldier.

It was funny, too, because I thought when the atom bomb came in 1945 that it would please Jake, but it didn't. "Same old antiquated principle," he said, "merely a very gross method of solving a problem in precision."

And in spite of everything Jake had said I never, until that morning when Helen came in to see me, quite realized that the whole thing he was thinking about was "homing devices" of one sort or another, a natural thing for him to think about since we at Yaw-Et-Ag had to build small things which had to go into other things, everything today being like that. No one makes a whole thing any more. Everyone makes parts, essentially, and then somewhere the parts are assembled.

But all that I am trying to tell here is why what Helen told me that morning at Saint Luke's disturbed me, but did not particularly surprise me.

"Well, they're at it again," Helen said to me when I had finished signing the papers.

"Who is at it again?" I said, although I knew without asking. It would be Jake Brawn and Bert Bernstein who, as the years had gone by, had found it harder and harder to work with each other. They were both men of temperament. Their wives did not get along with each other. And then, during the war, Bert had suspected Jake, because he was of German extraction, of being

a Nazi sympathizer. And Jake had come to be strongly anti-Jewish.

"Mr. Brawn and Mr. Bernstein are at it again, Mr. Selleck," Helen answered.

And it gave me a sort of heavy, tired, and sick feeling.

More and more in the course of years, my job, or a large part of it, had become a matter of keeping peace between Bert and Jake, which Helen knew, and which all of us knew was essential to the business.

"What is it this time?" I said, leaning back in my pillows.

She said, "It's Mr. Brawn's invention."

I said, "I didn't think it was far enough along to be a bone between them."

She said, "Mr. Brawn thinks it's far enough along to approach the Army." And I could see she was as tired of all this as I was.

I said, "Doc Crocker says I'm not supposed to concern myself with such matters."·

Helen was sitting in the armchair which was in the room, and she had dragged it up beside the bed. She was sitting erectly with her dictation pad on her lap and her pencil poised above it, but, as she spoke, she gave way to one of her very, very rare demonstrations of emotion. She put her pencil down on the pad and said, "Oh, damn! Damn, Mr. Selleck!"

"Well, Helen," I said, "what do you think?"

She picked up the pencil and bit the end of it, and then said: "Oh, damn! I know you need a rest. I know you shouldn't be bothered and I get so mad at the two of them for acting just like children."

I said: "But about the invention, Helen? About the invention, what do you think?"

She recovered herself completely and answered matter-of-factly: "About the invention . . . I think it's awfully important. In the model he's working on he's got it built into some kind of a bazooka, and he says it will just automatically home into a tank at least a mile away."

Well, to hear her say that frightened me and bewildered me in the same way Jake's conversation back during the war had bewildered and frightened me, too. To hear Helen, with whom I had once (although neither of us ever mentioned it) ridden on a summer streetcar back in the days of gas street lamps, mentioning bazookas and tanks and things like that gave me a sensation of seeing everything out of focus, a sudden fear that, after all the different eras of change I had lived through, I was about to go into still another.

"But look," I answered in irritation at all of this, "President Truman himself says that the world was never nearer to peace than at this moment."

"The President's a fool," she snapped, in quick irritation also.

"I grant you that," I said, "but he does have more information at hand to work from than anyone else."

"Now," she said, "you're talking like Mr. Bernstein."

"Helen," I said, "do you honestly think that there'll be another war and that you and I will see it?"

She frowned and bit her lip and then said, "Yes, Mr. Selleck, I think so."

And then that sense of going into something new again overwhelmed me, for I was a man with a heart attack, not a man ready for new things. It, strangely enough, overwhelmed me in that same way that this fear of death which I described as coming the first moments of my illness had overwhelmed me. Only this time, the resilience, the thing which makes a man stay alive, didn't seem to follow. All that seemed to follow was tiredness, tiredness which made me perfectly willing just to lie there in that hospital bed which I hated.

I didn't seem to spring back at all, and all of this which was purely a matter of business seemed like a world issue with which, as with the rest of the world issues, I was too tired to cope. I suppose that all of this was merely a symptom of my illness, for I did eventually overcome it, but I describe it here because, bitter as it was, it was all a part, a very important part, of my recovery.

But it did seem wrong, it did seem unfair that, sick as I was, I should still be expected to cope with new things. But I suppose that that could be said about the whole world, too, for the whole world right then was too tired and sick to cope with new things, either. Guided missiles, bazookas, homing devices with electronic brains just weren't in my department, or at least I did not think so.

"Look, Helen," I said, pulling myself up into a sitting position, "I'm not supposed to think about these things. I'm all through. I'm done and finished. I don't like to think so, but I'm beginning to realize that whatever I've done, from now on someone else has got to do it."

I was looking straight ahead of me at nothing at all while I said that. And then, when I looked back at her, I was amazed to see that she was crying.

I have put this down here now, not because any of this settled anything, but because it serves, in a sense, as a prelude to some very important things which did happen later.

2

I did not look forward on the Friday morning to George and Tinker's visit. And there were several reasons why I did not. Helen's visit had left me depressed and disturbed in mind. There was the matter of the Ford convertible which I had promised Tinker which was in the Ford garage at the moment, but which I could not see how I was going to pay for.

There was the fact that no man wants his children to see him lying in bed and knocked out of the running. And, most of all, there was a question which I desperately wanted answered which they, during their visit, would possibly answer and which I was as afraid of as I was anxious to be enlightened. After two weeks of marriage were they, or were they not, happy?

While I waited for them to arrive, I was as nervous as a young man waiting in the anteroom of an office for an interview about his first job. I just lay there sweating and saying to myself: "Snap out of it, Jeff. Just remember you've got an atomic bomb inside of you."

"Company, Mr. Selleck," my nurse, whose name was Jane, said, smiling at me from the doorway.

And then there were George and Tinker in the doorway smiling at me also.

Tinker was wearing the fur coat I had given her for a wedding present and she looked very well, very pretty, very smart in it. George was wearing a tweed overcoat which made him look even bigger than he was, made him seem to entirely fill the doorway. In his arms he held a green wax-paper cornucopia of flowers.

"Hello, Father," Tinker said.

George said, "Hello, Dad," and I was glad he said that because he had always called me "sir" before that.

He laid the flowers down on the dresser and produced from somewhere else a paper box and then said: "Tinker and I brought you a present."

I opened up the box, and it was a little miniature toilet which held cigarettes in the flushbox, and popped one out every time you pulled the flusher. I have always been delighted with mechanical toys, and, although I was no longer smoking, I was particularly delighted with this one.

And what delighted me most of all was that it showed me that my son-in-law and I at least had the same kind of humor, for I knew very well that the toilet could not have been Tinker's idea.

"Well, George," I said, relaxing, for I suddenly had the feeling that everything was going to be all right now, "how is everything in the matrimonial department?"

"Everything is under control, sir," he said, and the way he said it made me feel that everything really was under control, for that matter, maybe under control for the first time ever in our household. And the way Tinker suddenly blushed and looked off and out the window then made me envy this young man who knew all the answers.

"If you've got Tinker under control," I said, "I think it's the first time it's ever happened."

She looked at me and said, "That's just the awful part. I think he has, Father."

Yes, I envied him. I wished that I had been able to say that in that way after two weeks of my own marriage, and that Gertrude had been able to say what Tinker had just said as she had just said it at that time, too. It suddenly seemed to me that if we had, why everything would have been somehow different. Everything under control? It had been almost thirty years for us, and even now things weren't quite under control yet. I felt choky as I thought about it, and I wanted to change the subject.

"Look, you kids," I said, "it's damn nice of you to come and see me when you've got other things to do more worth doing."

"Well, you've got to stop doing them and do something else once in a while," George said.

Then, right at that moment, there came to me the idea which must have been in my head somewhere without my knowing it all along, the idea which, if it worked, would be the answer to all my problems. What did I need and what did Yaw-Et-Ag need but a young man to keep juggling the things which I had been juggling for such a long time now? A young man with some experience, a lot of energy, one who could stand between Jake and Bert and keep them in order, and best of all, one who was in the family. There he was, standing right before me. I suppose the idea had been in my mind somewhere ever since the day he had come into the office and Helen Flanagan had so oddly said, "We could use a young man like that in the business."

"George," I said impulsively, "did you ever think of leaving those people in New York for a smaller company which might be your own sometime?"

"Yes," he said slowly, "sometimes I've thought about it."

And I was sure, absolutely sure, that he understood me.

"Tell me," I said very seriously, "just what does the job you now have offer?"

He looked at me very keenly and pursed his lips in thought before he answered.

"What does it offer?" he said slowly. "Well, a lot of fun in the first place."

I knew just from his manner that he was answering lightly, and that what he would say after that would be a little bit more than the words used. I knew that he knew what was in my mind, and would try to answer my question without making me ask it.

"At the moment," he said, "we have twenty big oil tankers which we bought from government surplus right after the war was over. Now, we're selling them, and I don't have to tell you that oil tankers are getting to be important." Then he let his eyes meet mine. "You see, this whole deal has been my deal. Do you know how much an oil tanker costs? Several million dollars."

Well, he had answered my question completely, and we were right back again where we started. He had answered it very completely, for the whole of the Yaw-Et-Ag Manufacturing Company didn't come to anything like several million dollars. But this I appreciated deeply about his answer, it had never forced me into the open to ask the question.

"It sounds like fun, George," I said.

I was more deeply depressed than ever, for everything, it suddenly seemed to me, just seemed to point out that there was no one who would do my job, ever, that there would never be a time for sitting back even a little bit and resting, nothing much left, really, but my illness.

I think that George sensed my feeling. He was very acute in sensing feelings. I think that he had sensed everything that I was thinking for he changed the subject very quickly.

"Look, Tinker," he said, "you take the flowers and take them down the hall to the nurse and ask her for a vase. I've got some things to talk over with your father."

When she was safely out of earshot, George said, "Now, Dad, I want to talk about the car."

"What car?" I said, although I knew very well what car it was that he was mentioning.

He said: "The one you've promised Tinker. We went down this morning to look at it, and she likes it all right but I don't think we ought to take it."

"Why do you say that?" I said, and I imagine that I said it very strangely.

He was suddenly embarrassed, but obviously bound on saying what he was saying. He took a pack of cigarettes out of his pocket and offered me one and, when I shook my head, took one himself and lit it.

Then he walked about the room smoking as he spoke in a jerky fashion. "Now don't get me wrong," he said, "and maybe it isn't my business, but it occurred to me . . . well, it struck me that, all in all, in all the expenses of our wedding, well . . . you didn't plan on being in a hospital when you promised us the car."

That was the thing that frightened me about George, he always knew what I was thinking.

"Don't be silly," I said. "I want Tinker to have it."

"Damn it," he said, "she doesn't need it. I've got a car. And you didn't count on retiring quite yet, did you?"

"Have you said anything to Tinker about this?" I said.

"No," he said, and put his cigarette out in the ashtray. "I thought that, first of all, it was yours and my business."

"It's true that I'm temporarily a little strapped," I said, "but if she wants it I want her to have it."

I suddenly felt like a small boy before him.

"Of course she wants it," he said, "but why not face it? If you can't afford it, it's a hell of a way for us to start out our marriage."

"But Jesus God," I said, and suddenly found myself sweating, "what will you tell her?"

He said, "Why, simply that you can't afford it."

I don't know which I felt most, fear of him or admiration.

"Did you ever try telling a woman that?" I asked him.

He grinned then and said, "Not yet, but I don't see how for very long I can escape it."

And at that moment Tinker came back into the room with the vase of flowers.

"Tinker," George said, "I've been talking it over with your father and telling him that we don't want the convertible he promised."

"And just who are 'we,'" she said, "when you say that?"

"You and I," he said, quickly and without retreating.

She said, "Well, that's what you think."

Do you know what he did? He reached out and slapped her. What had we gotten into our family, I suddenly thought, a husband or a Tartar, but the most amazing thing of all was that before I could protest, I saw that she liked it. "Yes, George," she said, after her shock was over, and she put her arm around him. Then she said to me: "A long time ago, you should have done that to Mother."

This incident, like the one just before it, is really of no importance in itself, but as is also the case with the other, I mention it as a prelude to something which comes later.

What Remains Then?

WHEN a man sits down to write his memoirs, he cannot help but wonder why, in the last analysis, he is doing what he is doing. Is it because he wants to leave behind him some sort of memorial, a tombstone, in effect, which he has carved, or is it that he hopes that in the process he may finally arrive at a conclusion? I think it is this latter. A journey, no matter how long and devious, is not a journey unless it has some sort of ending. It is with endings that I must now concern my thinking.

Politically, I have always attempted to be a middle-of-the-roader, a conservative perhaps, but not a reactionary, as my son Tom used to call me. However, if to be of the political party of Abraham Lincoln, William McKinley, Teddy Roosevelt, and Herbert Hoover is to be a reactionary person then I suppose that I am one. And if to be a New Dealer is to be a middle-of-the-roader, then I am no middle-of-the-roader. But, still and all, I actually am a middle-of-the-roader, or at least I have been as often as I have been able. But one does not always live as one wants to. Sometimes, one lives only as one can. My experience has taught me that to be consistently in the middle of the road presupposes that you are strong enough to shove the other fellows off toward the gutters.

But suppose that I am a reactionary, as Tom called me, I still think that in reaction, at least of my kind, there is some value. The world moves too rapidly. It turns too fast, and the conservatives keep the brakes on. I feel that if I have helped at all to slow things down, then possibly I have served a function.

But actually as I look back on my life, I do not feel that slowing or speeding the pace has been the job I have been employed in. I have not had much to do with the policy of the world, but, if I do say so myself, I think that I have had something to do with the maintenance of it.

Most men must be content with tightening the bolts, replacing the packing as it wears out, oiling the bearings and sweeping the shop out. Perhaps for men less humble, there is another function, but slowly I have come to doubt it. I suppose that now and then even a man with the power of Joseph Stalin sees humanity, which I assume is me, moving in an incalculable direction.

But there are many other matters one must come to terms with, and the first of these, it seems to me, is work and business.

Business can be fairly and easily defined, simply as making money, but work, I think, is something different. I have often wondered what is the difference between work and play, inasmuch as frequently enough both of them require equal amounts of physical and mental effort, both can be equally constructive or destructive, and one not necessarily pleasant and the other not necessarily unpleasant. Work, I have come to think, is activity with the idea of continuity in it and, as such, is a kind of faith, or the expression of one, that the world will keep on turning. Work then is not unlike religion and . . . I would like to pass this on to Tom and Tinker . . . I have found in work salvation frequently enough when all else has seemed to fail me.

And this leads me to another matter, which is that it is claimed that a man should live mostly day by day and minute by minute, which I think is a very attractive philosophy except for one objection, which is, that a man simply cannot do it. It throws the continuity out of the world, and a man without continuity is a lost one. (This, again, for Tom and Tinker.)

Now, of the imponderables of life, love is perhaps the most imponderable of them all. It has been asked whether or not a man would ever fall in love if he had not read about it in a book, or seen the business in a movie. One cannot argue this,

but one can say . . . and I say this also for Tom and Tinker
. . . that it, love, does exist because I have seen and felt it. I
believe that it is as natural for two people to love each other
when they are brought together as it is for them to be hungry.
And I say this because, while I am not at all sure that Gertrude
and I loved each other at the time of our marriage, I am quite
sure that now it would be extremely difficult for us to live without one another.

Is love, then, simply habit? Is love only the habit two people
form of depending on each other? I suspect that this is what it
is, but in time the habit becomes so strong that one cannot fully
exist without it. In addition to that, it must be said that there
are people with whom one could never form the habit. And this
may be an unromantic way in which to regard the matter . . .
I would have liked to have had the kind of love one reads about
and occasionally suspects exists, but I have never had it . . . but
it is a way which makes possible a long-range basis. And, even
where marriage has been incomplete, which has certainly not
been the case in mine and Gertrude's, there are compensations,
good times, rewards, which I do not think are known to single
or promiscuous people, not the least of which is family, which
again is the expression of faith in a continuity of existence.

It is not a good thing to think of oneself as being alone, but
it is a good thing to think of oneself as at least, if nothing more,
one member in an infinite series.

What is the principal reason a man gets married? Because
he is tired of being lonely, and there is a kind of loneliness which
is not satisfied simply by being with a number of other people.

One comes eventually to the subject of religion, and here one
finds that one has less to say than one had expected. I was born
a Baptist, became a Presbyterian upon my marriage. I like to
think that I am a Christian.

I know the Bible as well as do most men of my generation, for
I had a rigidly biblical childhood, and yet, upon examination, I
find that I know very little about it. I have to confess that I
would have been a Mormon or a Hindu or a Moslem if I had

been brought up in a Mormon, Hindu, or Moslem family. I mean that I have never been vouchsafed the vision, and I regret this, for, in my experience, those who have been so favored have had a strength which I, at least, have only been able to pretend to or manufacture.

Does God exist? One cannot help ask the question. The kind of God which I could believe in is very difficult for me to imagine for, at one and the same time, He would have to be all-powerful and at the same time cognizant of me. But yet a God who would upset the whole order of His universe because of a prayer in which I requested Him to do so, I could not respect as a being of good judgment.

And yet, I pray. I pray almost unconsciously, and certainly earnestly, when I am in trouble. A theologian might say that I could not pray unless there was something, somewhere, to pray to. But at the same time I suspect that it is possible to pray to nothing.

Then why go to church? I believe in going to church, although most of the time I do not do so. I believe in the Church, for, by and large as I have seen it, I think that it is a good thing. And I believe that, since it is a good thing, I should support it. Outside of this, I find I must admit that I can say very little. And no one can say much more unless vouchsafed the vision which from so many of us these days seems to have been withheld. And although I cannot, I wish that I could say a great deal more about these matters.

What remains then? The only thing which remains then, as I see it, is courage, and to me courage is one of the few things in the world which are absolutely lovely. Courage for what? Courage to keep the whole show running. That, I believe, is the really, truly atomic bomb inside one.

2

This next section is one which may not properly belong in this book for, although Jeff is responsible for it, he did not intend

*it for a part of his memoirs. But in the just preceding passage
I, for one, find a disturbing kind of sadness, and Jeff was not a
sad man although I am not prepared to say that he was a happy
man, either.*

*The reverse side of his sadness is shown in the optimism preva-
lent everywhere within a little notebook which he got up and
distributed to his friends and customers every Christmas, and
what was in that notebook I want to include here at this moment.*

*The book itself was about three inches by two inches in size,
bound in red imitation leather, stamped in gold with "Yaw-Et-Ag
Mfg. Co." on the front cover. On the edge of the back cover was
a fold of binding into which a pencil could be inserted. The
first few pages contained several useful tables of weights and
measures, postal rates, and so forth. After this came a day-by-day
calendar of the current year, and then several pages for miscel-
laneous notations. After that were a few pages of jokes which
had, at one time or another, caught Jeff's fancy, one of these
being sufficient to give the idea:*

BARTENDER: Have you ever had any Truman beer?
PATRON: No, what is Truman beer?
BARTENDER: No head on it.

*But what is more important is what was printed inside the
back cover:*

"F" is for the funny face on father.*
"A" is for the alcohol he drinks.
"T" is for the things he throws at mother.
"H" is for his heart so black like ink,
      so black like ink.
"E" is for the empties in the cellar.
"R" is rong and wrong he'll always be.
Put them all together, they spell my old man,
      Don't bite the hand that feeds you.

* A parody of "M-O-T-H-E-R (A Word That Means the World to
Me)." Lyric by Howard Johnson. Music by Theodore Morse. Copyright
1915, copyright renewal 1943 by Leo Feist, Inc. Used by special permission copyright proprietor.

The thing which is important about that is that that song was Jeff's favorite song and that, while it may under the circumstances contain the same sadness as the preceding passage, he never thought of it in that manner. Jeff's hand was bitten many times while feeding others, but I don't think he ever held it against them.

3

It would probably be unfair to leave these matters without some kind of record of Jeff's achievements in Gateway City . . . that is, achievements not mentioned heretofore in his memoirs:

1927 . . . Commander of American Legion Post No. 1 of Gateway City.

1930–1936 . . . Board of Directors of Gateway City Masonic Boys' Home.

1934 . . . President of Junior Chamber of Commerce of Gateway City.

1938 . . . Head of Gateway City Community Chest Drive.

1942–1945 . . . Air Raid Warden.

In 1945, he accompanied the Governor of our state on a tour of occupied Germany. In 1949, which is not generally known, he was considered for the honor of Sachem of Yaw-Et-Ag but felt unable to accept the distinction inasmuch as he could not afford financially this and the marriage of his daughter both in the same year.

Christmas

In THINKING it all over now, it seems to me that Christmas 1949, in spite of, or perhaps because of my illness, was one of the most important days of my life, and I think it is a good thing to be able to say that such an important moment arrived, not in my young manhood, but in my middle fifties.

It was important because it was probably the best Christmas I ever had, and because, what is more important, it was on that day that I finally arrived at the state of mind which allowed me to get well again and finally back at the office.

On that day, I suddenly realized that my illness need not be only a kind of payment for a physical debt I had built up in the past, but actually an investment toward a new and larger life in the future.

One cannot help but be reminded of the poem, "Build thee more stately mansions, O my soul," for truly the most stately mansion of them all was opened up to me that day.

Christmas 1949 was very different from any Christmas I had ever known before, and to show how different it was I will have to describe how Christmas had always been before that. We had always had it at Mrs. McCullough's house, and Christmas at Mrs. McCullough's house was almost like a business.

Although Mrs. McCullough thought about Christmas all year round, and bought cards and presents in midsummer, or even early spring, the intensive part of it began as soon as Thanksgiving was over.

On the Monday after Thanksgiving Day she would begin making cookies. That is, Thelma, her cook, would begin making cookies under Mrs. McCullough's direction, and that big, old-fashioned kitchen of theirs, in which they still kept the coal range, from then on would be devoted to all kinds of baking. The cookies would be made and then decorated with little bits of citron and candy shot. Then there was a special kind of Christmas bread which Mrs. McCullough always made and sent around to friends for presents. In addition, she made plum puddings, gingerbread men, and peanut brittle. That is, Thelma made all of these, but Mrs. McCullough was constantly in supervision.

After the cooking stage of this business the packaging stage got started, and Gertrude would have to go over and help with it. Boxes had to be decorated with colored papers and scraps of paper doilies. Then they would have to be filled with assortments of gingerbread and cookies, and finally wrapped decoratively, tied with red ribbons, and tagged with cards.

And the same thing would have to be done with the loaves of Christmas bread which went to a special list of Mrs. McCullough's cronies. At the same time Christmas cards would have to be gotten out also. Then Mrs. McCullough would begin on the stockings, which she made out of red felt stitched together with green yarn and decorated with gilt thread. The stockings went to innumerable grandchildren, nieces, and nephews. And after they were made, they had to be filled with oranges, apples, nuts, candy bars, and ten-cent-store presents.

All of this was a very fine thing for the old lady to do, but I must add that it was something of a burden upon Gertrude, who had to help her, and who had Christmas responsibilities of her own to tend to. It was a burden on me too, for on the afternoon of Christmas Eve, in addition to trimming Mrs. McCullough's tree and our tree, I had to drive around the city delivering the bread, the boxes of cookies, and the stockings.

As you can imagine, the afternoon before Christmas Eve was a frantic time, and for me it began as soon as I could get back from the office. I would have a hurried lunch at our house and

D

DEAR READER

It is a great pleasure to send you the accompanying volume, as a book-dividend, to which you are entitled by reason of your recent purchases of two Book-of-the-Month Club selections. We hope that you and all the members of your family will enjoy it.

BOOK-OF-THE-MONTH CLUB, INC.

Meredith Wood PRESIDENT

then drive down to Mrs. McCullough's big old house at Twenty-eighth and Pike which, as I have said, was the only one of those old houses down there which was still kept up in the condition in which all of them should have been. There I would meet Horace, who was Mrs. McCullough's driver. Horace and I would drive down to the wholesale district to Glidden Brothers, the wholesale grocers, where the tree which Mrs. McCullough would have picked out a week or so before would be waiting for us. We would always drive down in my car rather than in Mrs. McCullough's old Pierce-Arrow, for Mrs. McCullough believed that the business of bringing back the tree might scratch the Pierce. And she was probably right in that, for it always did scratch my car.

At Glidden Brothers we would pick up the tree, a big crate of holly wreaths, and some ropes of evergreen to hang about Mrs. McCullough's mantel. It would be about two o'clock by the time we would get back, and then came the business, which was always the same, of cutting a foot or so from the bottom of the tree. There were twelve-foot ceilings in that old house, but the tree which Mrs. McCullough would pick out was always a fourteen-foot blue spruce with the most prickly needles you can imagine. Once we had the tree cut off, we had to fit the base to it, and that was always a tricky business, for the old base Mrs. McCullough had had for so many years was a very poorly designed one which would never stay on solidly at first and was too small anyway to support a tree of those proportions.

Horace and I always got to swearing while we did this job, for we would prick our fingers and get our hands covered with resin. Finally, we would take the tree into the house and set it up in the living room in a corner where Mrs. McCullough would have put a sheet down. Then Horace would leave me on my own and go back to his other duties.

My first job would be to secure the tree to a curtain rod on one side and a lamp fixture on the other, using picture wire to do so, for the tree with that bad base would never stand steadily without some kind of guy wires to hold it.

After that, I would get the lights out. And they were probably the worst Christmas tree lights in existence, for I think that they were the first set of electric Christmas tree lights in Gateway City. They were wired in series rather than in parallel, which meant that one faulty bulb would blow out a whole circuit. And almost all of the bulbs were, somehow, faulty. They were different in socket size from the ones used today, too, and modern bulbs could only be used if you wedged them in at an angle. It always took a long time to find which of the old bulbs were no longer any good, and a longer time to wedge in the new ones. But once the lights were all on and burning, the job with the tree was temporarily ended, for the actual trimming was always done after supper in the evening.

After I had the lights going, I would join Mrs. McCullough and Gertrude, who would have arrived by this time, in the job of hanging wreaths in all the windows. That would take time, and time would be pressing, for I would not yet have even started on delivering the cookies, the bread, or the stockings.

A holly wreath went into every window, and behind every wreath we had to set a candle, for on Christmas Eve Mrs. McCullough always had a candle burning in every window, which was really very lovely if you drove by the house and saw them. I rarely did, however, for I always seemed to be doing something else almost every moment. And then putting up candles can be an irksome business, for in no household are there ever enough candlesticks. A good deal of improvisation always has to be gone through with. Then, when you do have enough candlesticks, there is always the job of getting something high enough to put them on, then the making sure that they are all far enough back from the wreaths to eliminate a fire danger.

Now in what I say here I do not for one minute mean to say that I am in any way against the real, old-fashioned Christmas, for I am not against it. I believe in our Christmas traditions completely, especially when there are young people to be considered, for all of these traditions are important in giving a boy or girl a sense of the continuity and the stability of the world he lives in. And I do not grudge the work involved, either. I am merely saying that at times it can become a little irksome, especially when so much of it fell on me. How John McCullough managed to escape it, I do not know, and I have always intended to ask him the secret.[1]

After the wreaths were finished, I could get to my deliveries. Horace and I would set out in the Pierce-Arrow in the gathering gloom of the later afternoon and work as fast as we were able. He would stop the car at each house and I would run in, ring the bell, mumble "Merry Christmas", and gallop back, so that we could get on in a hurry to the next place.

When that was finished, I would get Gertrude and we would hurry home to have supper with the children and take the nurse girl we had in those days out to her parents' house in North Gateway where she would always spend her Christmas. Then, pretty weary by that time, we would go back to Mrs. McCullough's, taking the children with us, for the trimming of the tree, which Mrs. McCullough believed was one of their Christmas duties.

It took most of the evening to trim the tree, and I will say that it was always particularly lovely when it was finished. Mrs. McCullough had all kinds of beautiful ornaments made in Germany which are impossible to get these days. There were birds with spun-glass tails, gnomes, and angels, icicles made of glass, and a crèche which was very handsome. When the tree was finished, we would put the children temporarily to bed . . . we would have to take them home later . . . and then sit around the living room listening to Christmas carols and old records of Alma Gluck and Caruso played on Mrs. McCullough's old-fashioned Victor.

We would sit and listen until it was time for all of us to go to the special Christmas Eve service at Mrs. McCullough's church which was the last chore of the day. Once it was over, and we

---

[1] This would be John McCullough, Jr., Mrs. Selleck's brother. John Sr. died in 1930, which meant that most of the time Mr. Selleck knew her, Mrs. McCullough was a widow.

had the children back home, we could go out and get a drink somewhere, which would be what, by that time, we most wanted. That would be Christmas Eve, but we still had Christmas Day before us.

Christmas morning started for us a bit before daylight. That is, when the children were little it would. Before it was even light they would come running in, wild to see their stockings which sometimes Gertrude and I would have filled the night before, although sometimes we would not have. We would try to get the children to go back to bed so that we could either sleep a little more or else frantically fill their stockings. But no matter what we did, by daylight we would have to take the children downstairs so that they could get their stockings, which would be hanging from the fire screen in front of a fire which would have been lighted also. The stockings would be filled with fruit, candy, and foolish little presents, for the main presents were given and received later in the day back at Mrs. McCullough's.

After the ordeal of the stockings would come the ordeal of breakfast, which Gertrude would have to get for us, for our servants, unlike the ones Mrs. McCullough had, always had to be let off for Christmas to go home or to wherever it was they made their celebrations. Gertrude, still in her wrapper, would make breakfast, and I, still in my pajamas and bathrobe, would try to stuff oatmeal down the already overexcited Tom and Tinker.

When we were finished, all of us would be covered with oatmeal, and so would the dining room table. After that, we would have to bathe and dress ourselves, and bathe and dress the children, which I have never been able to understand, for, as I remember, I myself at a very early age was completely self-sufficient. The bathing and dressing was quite a job, for everyone had to be spotless by the time we went back to Mrs. McCullough's.

It was always about ten o'clock when we got there. We would get in the Packard . . . we had a Packard when they were little

. . . and drive over there, and I would leave them all at the side door under the porte-cochère, and then put the car in Mrs. McCullough's garage, which was really her old carriage house and stable. Then I would have to sneak through the kitchen door and prepare for what, for me, would be the worst ordeal of the occasion.

In the kitchen where Thelma, the cook, and Olga, the maid, and Mary, the girl Mrs. McCullough would have in for the day, would all be busy already with cooking the turkey, making rolls, stuffing celery and so forth, I would find a Santa Claus suit laid out on a chair waiting for me. And I don't know why I always had to be Santa, for John McCullough could have done it just as well, and he would have fitted the suit better. But everyone seemed to think that I was the only one who could do it.

I would put the suit on in the kitchen with Thelma, Olga, and Mary laughing at me. I would adjust my beard, put the pack on my shoulder, and then take a great big breath. Then I would run in through the dining room to the living room where everyone would be by that time. I would run in "Ho! Ho! Ho-ing!" and "Ha! Ha! Ha-ing" and, like as not, slip on the carpet which was in the center of the double doors that led in from the hallway. Then, after I had picked myself up, I would take my place beside the tree and begin passing out presents to Tom and Tinker, and Gloria and Gladys and Lawson, who were the John McCullough children.

But I don't really know what good I did, for while I would be handing out a present to one child, the other four would be dragging presents for themselves from under the tree or out of my pack and making general bedlam. And the way they tore the wrappings off those presents was savage and frightening, with Mrs. McCullough nodding and beaming at them. And that was very big of Mrs. McCullough, for she valued Christmas wrappings highly. She saved them from year to year, the day after Christmas always being occupied by her having Olga iron the wrinkles out of the papers with a flatiron.

But there was one fortunate thing about the bedlam and that

was that presently I would be forgotten. I would be able to sneak back to the kitchen and get rid of the red suit and white beard and the hat which made my scalp sweat.

I would go out the kitchen door again and come back in through the side one and pretend I had missed all the fun. I really did not have to do that, for the children would not be paying any attention to me by then, and more than likely one of them would be crying.

Gertrude would give me a nod, and the two of us would sneak out, this time to the carriage house over which Horace lived, and where I would have left a bottle for just this moment. We would have a few stiff ones with Horace. If Mrs. McCullough had ever known about it, poor Horace, after all those years, would have lost his position. We would stay there and have stiff ones for as long as we thought we could. Then we would chew some cloves and go back into the house. And by that time it would be almost time for Christmas dinner. Christmas dinner was always promptly at one o'clock at Mrs. McCullough's.

In the house, we would find the guests all assembled in the living room, which would have been cleaned up again after the ravages of the morning. The guests would be holding little glasses of tomato juice which Olga, in black with a white apron, would have passed. Old Henry Burton, who was Mrs. McCullough's lawyer, would be there. He had shared Christmas with us since Mrs. Burton had died in 1923 of a kidney infection. Mr. and Mrs. Sidney Courtney, also members of the old guard, would be there, and they would be talking about their great adventure which was when they had almost gone down on the *Titanic*. In addition to them and all of our family, there would always be two or three lame ducks whom Mrs. McCullough had picked up somewhere and who always looked uncomfortable at being surrounded by so much family.

After the festive tomato juice, a special sweetish kind which Mrs. McCullough and Thelma put up every summer, had gone round, it would be time for the Christmas dinner.

The conversation would be flowing fairly easily for everyone

except the lame ducks, because the conversation was the same
every year, and all of us would go through it without thinking.

Mrs. McCullough and old Henry would get to talking about
investments and the future of the country.

"Helen," [2] old Henry would say, "I think you're too much in
rails."

Mrs. McCullough was well provided for with Union Pacific.

"You need," he would say, "a little more diversification."

And Mrs. McCullough would say: "But Union Pacific has always been so good to me, Henry. In fact, they've all been good
to me, Henry."

"But," he would say like a Dutch uncle, "you do need more
diversification."

"You may be right," she would answer. "Mr. McCullough always did say that the Panama Canal would ruin railroading in
Gateway." She would think for a few moments and then ask:
"Why is it, Henry, that we can't get those good safe 7 and 7½
per cent bonds the way we used to?"

"Because," Henry would say, and wink at the rest of us, "they
don't make them any more, or anything else quite as good as
they used to."

I was always sure that he came to these dinners well liquored
up in advance, but you could never smell it. "They don't make
anything as good any more. Women, for instance. You, for example, Helen. They don't make women like you any more,
either."

That was one conversation which always happened, and another was the one about politics which I was supposed to take
part in.

"Jefferson," Mrs. McCullough would say to me, "what do you
say to this man Willkie? He seems like a nice man. Do you think
that he is a sound one?"

"A very nice man, Mother McCullough," I would answer.

"Do you think," she would ask, "that we could ever get the

[2] Mrs. McCullough's given name was Helen. She should not be confused
with Helen Flanagan, who could not be present here.

Republican women behind him the way we got them behind that poor Mr. Harding?"

But it was about then that tomato juice would have been finished and Olga would have come in to announce dinner.

We would all get up, and two by two, children leading, form a procession and file into the dining room, the double doors of which would have been opened. And it was a very impressive sight, that dining room, especially if you had never seen it before.

It, as did all the rooms downstairs, had a twelve-foot ceiling with black-walnut beams across it, and the walls had black-walnut wainscoting to waist height also. Between the wainscoting and the ceiling moldings there was a green brocade with a design of flowers and cornucopias painted on it. There were pictures, too, those heavy old elaborately framed oils people of the McCulloughs' generation used to collect after they had arrived at a certain amount of wealth. One of some cows in a field, and another one of old John McCullough himself, busy thinking. But on Christmas Day you did not see these things at first. The thing you saw first was the table.

With all the leaves in that table, and they would all be in on Christmas, it stretched fifteen feet long. And Mrs. McCullough actually had single tablecloths which would cover it all with a proper amount still left over. So what you saw first off was that long expanse of whiteness, with the places set around the edge, knives and forks, service plates, goblets, napkins, place cards and favors. And in the center was a decoration which was always the same one. It was a round mirror laid down to look like a lake, and there would be cotton snowbanks and little Christmas trees around it. And skating around the lake would be figures made of pipe cleaners, who were all supposed to be members of the family. At the end of dinner you could take yourself home if you cared to. Two silver candelabras were centered on the lake, and these massive pieces gave everything a very rich appearance.

We would file in and take our places around the table but not sit down at once, for there was a little ceremony to go through before we did so. On each place card was written a Bible verse, and each guest had to read his verse before we could sit down to dinner.

"I have a little Christmas custom," Mrs. McCullough would always announce for the benefit of the lame ducks who did not know what they were in for. "Each person will find on his or her place card a Bible verse, and it is our custom for each person to read his or her verse in order. Jefferson, will you start, and Gertrude can read the verses for the children."

I don't know why I always had to start, but I always did start. "Psalm One, First Verse," I would say, and clear my throat and then go on. "Blessed is the man that walketh not in the counsel of the ungodly, nor standeth in the way of sinners, nor sitteth in the seat of the scornful. But his delight is in the law of the Lord; and in his law doth he meditate day and night."

The verses which Mrs. McCullough picked out, I might say, had no special reference to the people who read them, although one might think so from the fact that one year the verse which old Henry Burton drew was: "O ye sons of men, how long will ye turn my glory into shame? How long will ye love vanity, and seek after leasing?"

The verses, I think, were actually picked out at random except for the last one to be read which was always the same one and read by Mrs. McCullough when everyone else had finished. "And the angel said unto them, Fear not: for, behold, I bring you good tidings of great joy, which shall be to all people. For unto you is born this day in the city of David a Saviour, which is Christ the Lord. . . . Glory to God in the highest, and on earth peace, and good will toward men."

Then we would all sit down at the table.

Those dinners of Mrs. McCullough's were stupendous, and I always am amazed when I think of how much food was brought in and how much we ate of it.

We would start with some decorative little melon balls in goblets, and then move on quickly to the soup, which was usually a clear soup with a slice of lemon or a dab of whipped cream floating on it. And then, after the soup, with no more formality, in would come the turkey, a huge eighteen- or twenty-pound bird, golden brown and steaming, and you could smell the sage in the dressing. Old Henry always did the carving, and had done it even in the days when old John McCullough was alive. He was an expert carver. It was lovely to see the fast, clean way he could lay off thin slices of breast, or take a drumstick from the second joint without any awkward hunting for the parting.

"A noble bird, Helen," he would always say to Mrs. McCullough, "and will you convey my compliments to the kitchen?"

After that, he would pause as he quickly flicked the carving knife across the steel. Then he would say: "And many a noble bird or joint have I seen in this house." Then he would pause again and make the joke he made every Christmas. "And speaking of joints, all that I know of importance in this world I learned at my mother's knee and other joints."

Then he would serve out the plates and Olga, or Mary or Horace, who doubled in a white coat on these occasions, would bring them to us. They would also bring in mashed potatoes, sweet potatoes, two or three kinds of vegetables, gravy, hot rolls, cranberry sauce. There was always much too much to eat, but somehow we always ate it.

For dessert, there would be Christmas pudding brought in on a platter. It would have been doused with brandy in the kitchen. (Mrs. McCullough objected to drinking liquor but she would always eat it.) It would come in set on fire and blazing. In addition to the pudding there would usually be homemade vanilla ice cream brought in in a large silver bowl, and we would put the ice cream on top of the pudding. After the pudding came fruits, nuts, cheese, and finger bowls. Coffee would be served in the living room after all of this was ended. Cigars would be passed to the gentlemen, but no cigarettes were ever passed to the ladies. By this time the climax of the day would be over, but the day itself was not yet over by two or three hours.

The children would all be put to bed in various upstairs bedrooms but we older people were not allowed to get off so easily.

We would sit in the living room and make conversation while Mrs. McCullough would bring out various curiosities which she and Mr. McCullough, in the years when they had traveled, had collected. We would look at these things, some of them very choice and lovely, and then discuss which ones of them Mrs. McCullough should will to various members of the family. This would take us into a general conversation of objects in the house and which objects should go to whom when she was dead and buried. Mrs. McCullough was very interested in her will, and hoped to make a good one. It should have been a good one, for Henry had to revise it almost weekly.

It always seemed strange to me that these discussions did not bother her, for they bothered me very much.

Mrs. McCullough would say: "Gertrude, do you want the sofa? It's got good springs in it and good hair, and could always have the arms rebuilt to make it more like your things. But remember, if you get it, John gets the piano."

I know that all of this was very prudent on her part, but it did depress me. I would want to scream when Gertrude would say: "Mother, I wish your things were just a little bit more modern. They'll just never fit in our house."

This would go on for an hour or two, but finally it would be late enough for us to leave. We would collect the children and all their presents and load them into the Packard. By the time we got back to our house the day would be finished and we would be too.

And that is the way Christmas always was for us, and I really have described it at this length so that the reader may see clearly how different the one in 1949 was.

But before going on I would like to repeat a thing which I have said already. This is that in no way do I wish to disparage the old-fashioned Christmases such as we always had at Mrs. McCullough's. I approve of such Christmases, especially when there are young people concerned, for to the young people we have a duty. I approve of such Christmases, I repeat, and have even on occasion enjoyed them immensely. But at the same time they sometimes remind me of an old proverb which goes something like this: "Even the Lord gets tired of too much Hallelujah."

2

The unusualness of the Christmas of 1949 began as soon as I woke up that morning. And it must have been six o'clock or earlier when this happened. I was at home by this time although I was still pretty much confined to the floor that I slept on. One trip downstairs and one back again was all the stair-climbing allowed me.

It was six or earlier when I awoke, as I said. It was dark still, and the room was black except for the square of deep blue which was my west window, deep blue with a star in it. I could see this without raising my head from the pillow. It was cold in the room, too, that sleepy kind of coldness of the early morning, and it made me think of waking in the night sometimes when I was a child and when I was lonely for my mother. But it was not quite that, either, for this was an easy and pleasant kind of awakening. At one moment I had been asleep and in the next I was fully awake but in no way at all alarmed or angry. I had been unconscious and then, with no transition, aware, and aware of my awareness. There was that deep blue square of sky in front of me with the pale star in it, night light upon which I could focus, not at all like waking up in complete darkness devoid of points of reference. It was exciting, but not an exciting excitement, something peaceful rather like the thing in the poem "Abou Ben Adhem" when the angel gave "a look made of all sweet accord." But I am nothing of a poet and must leave it at that now.

What it was at first, I have said, was just an awareness of an awareness. I was in my bed, in my room, in my house, in my precinct, in my county, state, nation, and so forth. There I was in the center of things, I mean, with breathing rings of it around me. The house seemed to breathe like a sleeper, but then houses, as long as people live in them, always seem to breathe in one way or another. But the neighborhood around the house and the city around the neighborhood seemed to be breathing, too. "Christ the Lord is risen today. Hal-le-lu-oo-jah." But it wasn't quite that, either, for there wasn't anything religious in it.

One sometimes wonders if there is not a part of a man's mind about which he doesn't know anything at all. And, one also wonders, if there is such a part of the mind, whether it may not be working all the time, absorbing things for you which you don't know you're absorbing, and arriving at conclusions at which you don't know you're arriving . . . conclusions which don't pop out to where you can see them until they are all concluded nicely. I think that that must be true, for where do a man's ideas suddenly come from? Or why should something you haven't thought about for twenty years unexpectedly pop out at you? Now, whether or not any such ideas are true, of course I can't say, but it seems to me as I think about it that it must have been something like this which started happening to me early that morning and kept on happening from then on.

In other words, all the elements of your salvation may be right around you, but you don't put them together until a special moment arrives and the special moment only arrives after that part of your mind about which you don't know anything has come to the conclusions it has to about them.

One feels odd and frightened when trying to put down these things in writing, for, in the first place, one knows one doesn't have too many words with which to say them, and in the second place all of this is in a department about which a man like me knows nothing.

At any rate, I lay there in the blue dark with this awareness and an excitement something like that of being dealt a hand of stud, one card up and the four which come slowly, which finally tell you what your hand is. And the funny feeling of this was the feeling that I, myself, was also the dealer, that part of me which I don't know, all the time shuffling, dealing, and putting bets down. It may seem odd, but I had never before had the feeling that I was my own dealer.

Perhaps a man should not try to write down these things, for they are not really events in the sense the other things which I have mentioned are. But then, at my age, I suppose a man can write down what he feels like.

And furthermore this wasn't at all the way I usually thought when I woke up early in the morning, for usually I worried, thought about money and how to get some, about Gertrude and our life together, or Tom and Tinker and whether or not they were or ever would be happy.

This time, while I was right at the center of everything, I seemed to extend out to the edges, too, out through all those rings of city, county, state, and country so that the outside was just as much me as was the inside. Everything, I mean, seemed to breathe together in that slow, regular, early morning breathing.

I keep trying to account for all this, and maybe it was partly that in that part of my mind I don't know about there was the idea of Christmas. And that's not unnatural, for, after all, it was Christmas morning. And the idea of Christmas, no matter what happens to it in practice, is the idea of "all sweet accord," too, and right in the middle of everything we believe we believe in, although whether we really do believe what we believe that we believe may be a different matter. But, be that as it may, I think that it must have been the idea of Christmas which was working on me partly. And then another part of it must have been my illness, for illness, too, can make a man abnormally sensitive sometimes.

But there must have been other parts also, one of them that I had been thinking so much about myself and my life lately, another that with Tom in New York and Tinker married, Gertrude and I were alone now, for I did not know at the moment that they were both going to make a surprise visit home for Christmas. And the idea of Gertrude and I being alone at last without the children between us seemed to mean that, although we had always been well married, we were going now to have to be married more completely. And there must have been all kinds of other parts, but I have not been able to dig them out and find them.

The way things came first was simply a matter of hearing, of hearing sounds which had always been there but of which most of the time I had been unconscious. For instance, I heard our oil burner kick on deep in the house below us, and the regular automatic succession of the sounds was comforting to me. First, the thermostat kicked on the motor which had a high, regular hum, then the fan turned on, and after that the motor turned off. Then the whole business repeated, and all of it seemed to say to me:

"Look, Jeff, things are really running very nicely."

After the sound of the furnace came the sound of a car coming up our street and shifting into second. And it seemed to me that I hadn't heard anything so mysterious or exciting since I was a boy and heard the caller calling off: "Omaha, Grand Island, Cheyenne, Julesburg, Salt Lake City, Ogden, Sacramento, San Francisco," in the old Union Station.

And after the sound of the car . . . the night was now turning slowly into daylight . . . came the sound of the newsboy on a bicycle delivering the paper which was not only the Christmas morning paper but the Sunday morning paper too, so that it made a heavy, solid thump against the front door as it struck it. Then I waited for a sound I wanted to hear, which was the sound of the milk wagon and the rattle of milk bottles in their wire basket, and it was with a keen sense of disappointment that I realized that the milk would not be delivered on Christmas morning.

That was the way things came at first. They came through my ears completely.

But after I had become accustomed to hearing, for it seemed as though this were the first time that I had heard in years, I started seeing, too. The sun came up and I raised up in my bed so that I could look out of my window to the west at the far-stretching farm lands out beyond Fleetwood. In that slanting morning light, they were all a frozen dead gray or brown color, for we had had no snow yet to speak of. But those dead brown, rolling fields of broken corn stalks with cold-looking cattle or horses standing in them seemed to me to be as beautiful as anything I had ever looked at.

There was a farmhouse on one of the hogbacks, with a rutted dirt road leading up toward it, and a windmill beside the barn with the vane rattling around wildly. What I am getting at is that I not only saw the deadness of it, but the life within it, also. "Christ the Lord is risen today. Hal-le-lu-oo-jah," and it seemed as though it should have been Easter rather than Christmas.

But maybe this is misleading, for, as I have said many times already, I am not a religious man, never have been and never will be. But at the same time I must say that I could not help but think of things like, "Hallelujah," or "Rejoice! Rejoice! Emman-u-el shall come to thee, O Israel."

The final awareness which came to me after hearing and seeing was smell, just one odor, but it was as acrid and penetrating an odor as exists, the odor of cigarette smoke in a cold house in the early morning. It told me that Gertrude was awake in her room in this early morning and perhaps aware of everything that I was aware of. The thought excited me more than ever, and made me feel that something, something as important as the birth of Christ even, was about to happen, and to happen to me in person. I expected it might happen right away, but that wasn't the way it came. It came slowly, all day long, nothing all at once, but in little but building pieces.

Now it was Gertrude's habit when she woke in the morning to smoke a cigarette and then lie for a long time in bed before rising. The length of time was always about long enough for me to bathe, shave, and dress in, so as soon as I smelled the cigarette smoke I decided to get up and make myself presentable before she should see me, for by this time I was allowed to bathe and shave myself without assistance. Everything seemed to time itself perfectly that morning, for when I came back from the bathroom in my dressing gown and clean pajamas and climbed back into bed, in the distance I could hear the church bells ringing.

When I was in bed again, I heard Gertrude get up, and I knew that it would be about half an hour before I would see her, for she too hated to have anyone see her before she was presentable in the morning. She hated to have even me see her before she had rid herself of sleep completely. And, on the whole, while there have been moments when I desperately wanted to see and touch her in the early morning, I think her way was probably a good one. Probably no one can stand much of being seen when his or her wits are not yet working.

So I sat there for that half hour, and actually it was as pleasant a half hour as could be, for I just sat there surrounded by this new feeling that something good was bound to happen.

I suppose that it was about eight-thirty when she finally came in to say "Merry Christmas," and "Good morning." She looked so clean then. She had bathed, too, and anyway everything about her was always immaculate and dainty. The only thing lacking was that she was wearing no make-up, but I have always liked that, for I grew up before women used it. Then, too, a woman's face unmade-up is a sort of special face which hardly anyone ever sees except her husband.

She was wearing a pink quilted dressing gown which was belted around the waist and fitted, too, so that it was more like a dress than something you would throw on in the morning. It gave her the well-turned-out look which she always had, no matter where she was or what she was doing.

She came into the room and over to my bed and leaned over and kissed me. This, in itself, was a rather unusual thing, for she did not generally like to kiss me in the morning. She kissed me and then looked at me very seriously and said, "Merry Christmas, Jeffrey."

I don't know why this should have been a moment of such particular emotion, but it was, and I have never known how to deal with emotion, either. There seems to come a certain outgoing feeling which is clear enough wherever it is, which starts but which gets all mixed up before it gets to the surface. You almost want to cry, but men don't cry, so you cough instead, and how can you expect your wife, or anyone, to understand you?

I coughed and said, "Merry Christmas, Gertrude."

But that morning Gertrude must have been thinking a great many of the same thoughts which I had been thinking, for she said: "We're alone now. . . . It's you and I now, isn't it, Jeffrey?"

It suddenly made me think of that moment at the old Gateway Hotel the first night of our marriage when she had said to me "Jeffrey, you've got to be good to me because I feel so alone and frightened."

"Yes," I said. "And it seems like the first time since almost 1920."

We sat in silence for several minutes, both of us thinking of all the years since that time.

"You know you've been good to me," she said suddenly, "and I don't think I've ever said so."

And then again I had that rush of feeling which there is no way of expressing, so I coughed again and said, "If you look on the top shelf of my closet I think you'll find something there for you." For, with Helen Flanagan's help, I had managed to do my Christmas shopping, and for that matter Helen had done it for me for so many years that she knew the tastes of all of us better than I did.

Maybe Gertrude was having trouble showing her feelings, too, or maybe she didn't feel anything for that matter, but she seemed glad to have something to do to fill the silence. She hurried over to the closet and took the big box, which Helen had had Christmas-wrapped, down from the shelf, and it amused me the eager way she tore off the wrapping.

My present to her was a black velvet dressing gown with a white satin lining. Helen had found it in *Vogue,* showed me the picture, which I had liked, and then ordered it for me. It had cost a lot of money, but it really was a knockout. It swept the floor like an evening coat, and the lapels showed the lining, and the sleeves were so full that they did too, and Gertrude, who put it on right away, looked wonderful in it.

"Oh, Jeffrey!" she said. "Oh, Jeffrey, it's lovely." And then she did what a man never can do to show his feelings. She started crying. "It's lovely," she said again, "but Jeffrey, can we still afford it?"

And although I knew that we really couldn't, I coughed again and said "Well, I guess so."

And then I was glad that, although I had known it was too expensive, it was the thing I had gotten, for Helen had shown me several times several less expensive presents. I was glad because it seemed to mean so much to Gertrude. Clothes always seem to mean so much to women. A new dress which she may wear only a dozen times can make a woman more excited than I could get over a new shotgun. Gertrude pirouetted around the room in that dressing gown, looked at herself in the mirror on the door, and then went to her room and put on some earrings to go with it.

When she came back she said to me, "Your present is downstairs and I can't bring it up because it's too heavy."

"You can tell me what it is," I said.

It was a television set, and Gertrude said, "You can sit here at home and see all the things you aren't allowed to."

Well, that too was more than she should have spent. But she got it on time, she told me, and I was glad she had. There's something about spending more than you ought to at Christmas time which is like keeping your colors flying or your shoes shined in muddy weather. And then I did want a television set, for not only would it enable me to see all sorts of things, but in a way a television set seems to me to be a symbol of something — the future, I suppose — and proves that at least you are keeping up with the present.

"It isn't connected up yet," Gertrude said, "but the man is coming on Monday."

I don't know why, but I too was then very close to crying.

"And best of all," Gertrude said, still admiring herself in her new dressing gown, "this is one Christmas we won't have to go to Mother's, and that's one thing your heart has done for us."

It was odd, but I had never known before that she felt the same way about Mrs. McCullough's Christmases as I had. I had never said anything for fear of hurting her feelings.

"God," she said suddenly sitting down on my bed, "I hate family dinners."

And this was the first specific manifestation of all the mysterious things which had been on my mind since daybreak. I mean that this may not have been the first time, but it seemed like the first time Gertrude and I had ever been completely and unarguably in agreement. It was more than that, really, for it seemed suddenly to push us over into a region in which we had never before existed.

She lay back on the bed and began to laugh. Then she sat up abruptly and said: "There's a surprise in store for you, and I think I'd better warn you." Then she frowned oddly, and added, watching me as she did to see how I would take it, "The children are flying in this morning for Christmas."

And my reaction to that was as curious as anything else that morning. "Look," I said, before I had thought, "let's not let them spoil it for us."

I don't know why in the world I said that.

Christmas . . . Continued

"BUILD thee more stately mansions, O my soul." I cannot seem to help recalling again and again this passage from Holmes's poem as I think about that Christmas Day of 1949. All day long, it seems to me, I, like the Chambered Nautilus, moved from one room into another, and then another, each one larger than the one before it.

I have dwelt on the first of these rooms at some length, for, as I grow older, it seems to me more and more that what goes on in a man's mind is almost as important as that which goes on outside of it. The first room of that morning was one, as I have tried to say, mostly of awareness. And then there came that moment with Gertrude which I have just described which again was something different, something very distinct and large to me, and this may have been why I felt that momentary alarm when she mentioned the visit of the children.

Of course, I was delighted that they were coming, but I do think that at that moment I thought that somehow they might disturb this new mansion into which Gertrude and I had suddenly moved, for in some ways the moment which I have just described did have the dimensions of a mansion.

Gertrude said, "The children are flying in this morning for a surprise visit."

"Look," I said, as I had said before, "let's not let them spoil it for us."

There was that moment of alarm which I could not quite understand, but it was followed almost immediately by a wave of pleasure, for I realized what a big thing it was that they were doing, not so much for Tom who, being an artist, could come and go as he pleased, but for Tinker and George a very big thing really. They had a household of their own now, all kinds of expenses of being newly married, and George's parents in Montclair, who had all the same claims on them that we did. I realized all this, and it touched me very deeply. And then right after that, another emotion touched me.

"How soon are they coming?" I said, again alarmed but this time over something different.

Gertrude said: "They ought to be landing almost at this minute. They're coming up by taxi, so we could expect them in about half an hour."

"Then I've got to get dressed," I said, throwing back the bed-clothes. "I've got to be dressed and downstairs when they get here."

Gertrude began to object, as I had known she would, for at that point I was only allowed one trip down and up a day. But there was something more important about it than that. My mind, my feelings, whatever you would call all those things happening to me that morning, told me without any question that there was another mansion into which I could move, and that to do it I must be downstairs, dressed, and eating breakfast at the dining room table when Tom, George, and Tinker arrived. Does that take some explanation?

Well, no man wants his children to come home and find him looking like a sick man. But there was something else. When a man does anything he wants to do it, if possible, with his colors flying. And then, in addition to this, that part of my mind which I didn't know anything about must have already known that the big conclusions, the final salvation which the day was going to bring, depended upon the children as much as it depended upon Gertrude or on me.

Very simply put, as I can see it plainly now, life was waiting for me downstairs, and somehow, without knowing it, I knew it.

I knew it distinctly, although Doc Crocker called it "euphoria" later when I tried to tell him all about it, but what that meant I don't exactly know.

But I do know that, in a very slow way during the last month, I had been going through the same successions of feelings which I had gone through rapidly during World War I in the moment which I described in the early part of all of what I have been getting down here. I had been through the sick feeling of death, then the moment of being about evenly balanced between wanting to live and wanting to die, and was at last filled again with that strong rush of returning energy and, somehow, power. This last, though, was going to fluctuate up and down during the day before it found its right direction and allowable outlet.

"You can't get up yet," Gertrude said, looking frightened. "You haven't had your breakfast."

"Gertrude," I said sternly, "go downstairs and put my breakfast on the dining room table and I'll be down directly."

"But Jeffrey," she objected.

I cut her off. "Today," I said, "I'm spending the whole day downstairs. I can do my resting on the sofa. But I've got to be downstairs when they get here."

Since then, I have been told that what I did at that stage of the game was foolish. But while I will admit that I did not exactly know what I was doing, I must say this, that a great many important things in the world have looked foolish and been done by people who did not know exactly what they were doing, either. The decision to go downstairs, I now fully believe, was the turning point, the true turning point of my illness.

Gertrude seemed to sense my seriousness, for she left the room and went directly down to the kitchen . . . we never seemed to have help, as I have said, on Christmas.

I was already bathed and shaved, so it was only a matter of ten or fifteen minutes before I was dressed. Then, remembering to take it slowly, I went down to the living room, and here again I experienced a thing which touched me.

The television set which Gertrude had mentioned was in the

bay window, and beside it was a Christmas tree which Gertrude
had had brought in and had decorated herself in order to surprise me. It was not a big tree, but it was a very lovely one with
presents piled up underneath it. And this again gave me the sense
of flying colors. Life is not lived on facts alone, but just as much
on symbols, and a Christmas tree to a family is a symbol which
is important, as important, perhaps, as a uniform to a soldier or
a football team to an educational institution.

Gertrude came in from the dining room and looked at the tree
as I stood looking at it, also in silence.

"I didn't expect you to come down and see this till afternoon,"
she said, "and I wanted to get a little more tinsel on it."

Then I thought of something else.

"If the children are here," I said, "what are we going to feed
them?"

She looked down at the carpet and said, "I'm going to try to
roast a turkey."

And that was the most affecting thing of all, for, curiously
enough, because we had always gone to the McCulloughs' for
all family functions, Gertrude had never cooked a turkey, and
it had been a joke in the family for years that "next year" she
would roast a turkey.

"There's a place," she said, still looking down, "where you can
get them so that you don't have to do anything but put them in
the oven."

And a turkey, I think, is also a symbol. A turkey also in a
sense is flying colors.

"Look," Gertrude said, "you must sit down and eat your breakfast and rest now until they get here."

2

Curiously enough, as I recall all of this which was so completely satisfying as it happened, I suddenly want to pause, for
the business of being very happy is sometimes as frightening as
anything I know of.

What is happiness? And what does it consist of?

All of my life, it seems to me that I have been looking and waiting for happiness. And everyone else, I assume, has been looking and waiting for it also. And yet, in the moments when I have known it, a kind of shyness has come over me.

Something which I cannot understand has always made me tongue-tied.

Happiness, I mean, has never made me entirely happy, and there is always the suspicion in it, to use a word of Gertrude's, that I am being "corny" . . . either that, or I am being mistaken.

And that was the way it was with both of us suddenly that Christmas morning before the children arrived, as I ate my breakfast.

There was the Christmas tree, the presents underneath it, the turkey which I could also see through the open swinging door to the kitchen from where I sat, the turkey on the kitchen table, Gertrude in her new dressing gown, everything so perfect that I could feel my eyes misting.

I put my arm around her as she stood near where I was sitting.

"Oh, God," she said suddenly and angrily, "I feel like an illustration by Norman Rockwell."

3

I had finished my breakfast and gone back to the living room by the time the doorbell rang and the children were at the doorway full of all that excitement and sense of well-being which people always have when they arrive from long distances: coldness, excitement, and confusion.

They came in, calling out "Merry Christmas," surprised and pleased to find me dressed and not looking like a sick man.

"Merry Christmas everywhere," Tinker said, dropping into an armchair before she even took her fur coat off. "Did our presents get here?"

"Hello, Dad. Hello, Ma," George said, and went over and kissed

Gertrude, which pleased her because she always likes to have young men kiss her.

"When do we have to go to Grandmother's?" Tom said.

Gertrude, very flushed and excited, now said: "We don't have to. We can all do just as we please this Christmas."

"Thank God!" Tom and Tinker said together. Then Tinker said to George, "You don't know what you're getting out of."

And George said: "Yes I do. I've got a family in Montclair, just remember."

I don't quite know what it was that came over us, but suddenly all of us were completely carefree. All of us were as excited as children playing hooky. And that was strange, because all of us, in our hearts, really did believe in an old-fashioned Christmas like the one going on at that moment over at Mrs. McCullough's. In a way, it shocks me when I think of how emancipated we all felt over the knowledge that we were not going to take part in that great big family dinner.

"You know," George said, "I think we should all have a drink just to get the day in motion."

And that startled me at first for it was only a little after ten o'clock in the morning.

Gertrude looked a little startled too, and said, "Before you even get your presents?"

"Yes," George said without being embarrassed as I would have been had I been in his position, and again I had that odd, almost fearful feeling of wondering what actually had come into the family. "Yes," he said, "because it's Christmas."

And then an idea came to me which had never come from any of my own children. I had long known that my children, and perhaps all the young people, were in some kind of rebellion, but the idea that came now from George was that, not only were the young people in some kind of a rebellion, but that Gertrude and I were also young people also in a rebellion, and that was a new idea added to all the other ideas which had come to me already that morning.

I have already spoken of the seven or so different eras which I have lived in, and also of the new one which I think that we are moving into. The thing about George which frightened me, and flattered me, too, was that he seemed to be something of that new era and not any of the old ones, and that he was taking me by the hand, even though he was twenty years my junior, and leading me, pulling me into the future. "Rejoice," he seemed to say, "and get in there pitching."

"Yes," I heard myself say, startling myself as much as any of the others, "I think it would be a good idea for everyone to have an old-fashioned." Of course, it made no difference to me for I was only allowed two drinks a day which I always had in the evenings. "Tom," I said, "you know where things are. Make everyone an old-fashioned. And I'll have another cup of coffee."

It is very strange to recollect this, too, for while on hunting trips and vacations with the Chowder and Marching Society we have all certainly started drinking frequently enough in the morning, for Christmas Day, which always before we had spent with Mrs. McCullough, it seemed shocking and, as Gertrude said later, "rather heathen."

As I have said, I had the feeling of being included in the future, an exciting future, too, it suddenly seemed to me, in which a man with a weak heart might find many problems. I suppose that it was only the problem of new wine in old bottles that I was facing.

And it is curious to me now how I fought against the future which was actually going to save me, fought against all this new energy which George seemed to represent and which was so different from the symbols, Christmas tree and roast turkey, which I have mentioned. And at my age, when so confronted, I cannot help wonder about the future, if George in some mysterious way really is its symbol.

And, as far as that goes, what difference does it make if George liked to drink in the morning when he was on a vacation? And anyway, neither George nor the future is the subject of this passage.

Tom made an old-fashioned for everyone but me, and it was

very pleasant to sit surrounded by my family as they drank them. And, as everyone drank, we exchanged presents without rushing into the matter as it had always been rushed into when the children had been children. Their presents for Gertrude and me had been sent on ahead so that they were all beneath the tree, and all of mine for them, which I had instructed Helen to send to them, were under the tree also.

I gave Tinker a traveling clock and George a barometer, which was what Tinker had written to Gertrude that George wanted. I gave Tom a check because I never knew what Tom wanted or needed. Tinker gave George a set of military brushes, and he gave her a pair of diamond clips which must have cost more than he could have afforded. George and Tinker together gave Gertrude a silver desk set which was very handsome. To Tom they gave an album of prints of the work of some artist I had never heard of whom he seemed to value highly. Tom gave them an old-fashioned music box which may not have been George's speed but was very much Tinker's. He gave Gertrude a Wedgwood pot which she liked and me the recording machine which is the reason for this book here. That was everything. No . . . George and Tinker gave me a very impressive-looking corkscrew.

We had finished our old-fashioneds by the time we were through with giving and receiving presents, and then Gertrude jumped to her feet and said: "Good heavens! I've forgotten all about the turkey, and even if I put it in now it'll be three or four o'clock before it's ready."

"Look, Mother," said Tinker evenly, "you don't have to cook the turkey. You could send out for something and not spoil the day with cooking. There must be some place open. Some Chinese place, maybe, where we could get them to send out some chop suey."

"Yes," said George, "you can always get chop suey."

It was one of the most curious suggestions I have ever heard as a dish for Christmas dinner.

"But it sounds so heathen," Gertrude said after a moment.

But here again I could suddenly see the beckoning of the fu-

ture, although the whole idea of chop suey for Christmas seemed
as ridiculous as . . . well, as if someone had said that we would
go to war with China, or that flying saucers really existed.

And I think that if I had not had all those startling and
mysterious experiences that morning, even the idea of it would
have disturbed me.

Tom, who had not said anything yet, said, "Yes, let's have
chop suey with a sprig of holly."

Actually, it was only Gertrude who seemed highly confused
by the idea, which was strange, for in our family as far as food
goes she has always been for innovations. And also she has never
liked to cook and always been the first one to find a way to get
out of it when she has been able.

"Look, Mother Selleck," George said, "you said that we can
all do as we please this Christmas."

All in all, I think that Christmas dinner was the most curious
event of my lifetime. We had old-fashioneds first. That is, everyone except me had them for I found that if I saved my two drinks
for evening, all day I could look forward to them, while looking
back on them, if I had them earlier, was no pleasure.

We had old-fashioneds first, then chop suey which Tom and
George went out and got, and champagne left over from Tinker's
wedding with it. And for dessert, we had a fruit cake which my
sister Caroline had sent up from Kansas City to us. Then all
of us took naps in various parts of the house, I on the sofa, and
I had scarcely lain down before there returned to me more of the
queer experiences of the early morning, the queer, enhanced
awareness.

It was not an awareness of seeing or hearing or anything like
that, however, this time, but an awareness of me, whatever that
means. I lay there and began doing something which I had not
done since I was a child, which was to repeat my own name
over and over to myself: "Thomas Jefferson Selleck. Thomas
Jefferson Selleck. Thomas Jefferson Selleck." I repeated it over
and over again as I had as a child, until it had no meaning.

But who was Thomas Jefferson Selleck lying there on a sofa,

ringed round by his family, his city, his country, the world for
all he knew? Who was this man? And then I remembered another childish thing I once had done, which was to write my
name in my textbooks back at the Stephen A. Douglas Grade
School, with my address after it, then after that the name of the
county, then the state, then U.S.A., the World, Solar System,
Universe, and finally, Space, which had been as far as I could
take it. But who was Thomas Jefferson Selleck of the U.S.A.,
World, Solar System, Universe, and Space, who had come to believe that he carried an atomic bomb around inside of him? This
was the kind of awareness which now struck me.

And it was a torturing business like the other questions one
asks when one is a child: "Where does the sky stop?" "What
number is the biggest number?" "Is there anything in the next
room when the door is closed?" "And if there is, how would I
know it?"

This Christmas, although it was a very good one, was a very
peculiar one for me, I can tell you.

These are not questions a man can answer. These are questions which have to be answered for him and for which he must,
at least in that part of his mind which he doesn't know much
about, wait for answers. However, as I lay there in this awareness, the answers did not come any more than they had when I
had been a child, for even now I cannot say that in life I have
ever arrived at anything which is final. I am mentioning these
various awarenesses though, because they were the things that
jolted me sufficiently to see the answers to my more specific questions, when those answers, later in the day, were presented.
For, while I have not dwelt on it much so far, I was still worried about how we, who had lived on twenty thousand dollars,
were going to make a go of it on something a good deal less than
ten, or if the Yaw-Et-Ag Manufacturing Company was completely
out of balance as it seemed to be from what Helen Flanagan had
told me. And this, too, was added to my awareness as I lay there.

4

One has to start bringing together the things one has mentioned, for without the conclusions which the afternoon brought, most of this would not be relevant to anything whatsoever. While the others took their naps in various parts of the house, I lay on the sofa, awake part of the time, half asleep at other moments, but all of the time with this troubling awareness, this feeling of something about to happen, staying with me, the vague future somehow hanging over me like a cloud, a disturbing sort of shadow.

And for me, my future seemed depressingly plain, for Doc Crocker had outlined it to me frequently enough for me to know all about it. For a month more I would go on living for the most part on one floor of our house. I would probably make my one trip downstairs a day and my one trip back upstairs, and, if things progressed as we hoped, I might be allowed to make two trips daily up and down shortly.

I would sit, for the most part, where I could look out of a window upstairs with my binoculars, which were the only means I had of stalking up on far-off objects.

When spring came, I might be allowed to be taken for automobile drives in the country. By April or May, I might be able to go now and then for a half day at the office.

And the thing Doc Crocker had in mind for my permanent future was a kind of vegetable life with maybe a little light work in the garden to entertain me. I could go back to work possibly, he felt, but I would have to have someone to carry the whole load of it for me, which, with Tom so settled in his profession and no interest in the business anyhow, I could see no way to accomplish.

My personal future was easy enough to foresee, but a personal future unlinked with the general future can hardly seem like very exciting business. And while I could not know much about the general future, I could hardly think that it would have much in common with gardening or looking at the landscape.

There really should be some kind of an exciting business for men whose active lives are finished. Perhaps there is, but, as far as I am concerned, I have never found it. Hobbies? The trouble with hobbies is that they are only hobbies, and furthermore, a hobby must be learned early in life for a man to have sufficient skill to enable him to enjoy it in middle age.

Reading? Reading is all very well but it is not a thing in itself, and is only killing time unless it has a purpose.

Religion? What is religion unless you have been vouchsafed the vision? There is nothing more impossible than an old man battened down inside a Bible. And I have never had any inclination in that direction.

Sports? You are denied them. These memoirs? Even they have sometimes appalled me. I did not realize, as I lay there in this temporary slough, that life was about to once more claim me.

It was about five o'clock in the afternoon when the doorbell rang, and I, being the only one downstairs, answered it. It was Jake and Mrs. Brawn, who made a practice of calling on friends at Christmas, usually on us late in the afternoon, for the rest of the day we usually would have been spending with Mrs. McCullough. I let them in and then called Gertrude for, while I felt that I could talk to Jake, the effort of talking with Mrs. Brawn was much more than I was up to.

They came in and, leaving their wraps in the hall, sat down in the living room on the sofa, and then this awareness of mine began acting on them, and it seemed to me that, for the first time in years, I was seeing them, reacting to what they looked like. And this depressed me because it suddenly made me wonder if the years had acted on me likewise. It seemed to me that the last time I had looked at Jake had been away back when we had first been associated and he had been a young, stocky, pleasant-looking mechanic, and Mrs. Brawn a slim girl wearing a shawl and smiling in a nervous manner. It was a shock to realize that neither he, nor she, nor I was what we had once been.

He had grown into a heavy, middle-aged man with a bald,

round German head, who wore an expensive if very conservative dark blue suit, and scratched a kitchen match across his heavy shoe sole to relight the cigar which he was smoking. She had grown into a heavy, complacent, middle-aged woman who sat on the sofa with her knees spread. Jake still had the heavy-fingered machinist's hands, and that was the only thing about either of them which I now remembered.

Perhaps he was thinking the same thoughts, for, after he had his cigar going, he said heavily, "Well, it's been a long time now."

I said, "Yes, it's been a long time now."

I kept a bottle of schnapps in the house for his very infrequent visits, and Gertrude came into the living room with it on a tray with some glasses.

"Well, *Gesundheit*," he said as he drank, and I said *"Gesundheit"* although I was not drinking.

Then he put the glass carefully down on the coffee table which was in front of him and Mrs. Brawn and, looking up, said, "Has Miss Flanagan reported to you about my invention?"

"She mentioned it," I said, "but she didn't say much about it."

But I saw at the same time that the matter of the invention was the primary purpose of this visit. And to tell the truth it was the last thing I wanted to discuss at the moment, and that is another example of just how bitterly a man will fight against the thing which eventually saves him.

"We are about ready," he said slowly, and looking at the end of his cigar as he said it, "to show our results to the Army." While my greatest desire was to get back into business, somehow I didn't want to get into this business. Not that there was anything wrong about it, and not really that I objected to dealing with the Army, for it could not be too different from dealing with the Navy as we had in World War II when we had made hand grenade fuses.

It was just that instead of some kind of homing device for projectiles, I wished he was still inventing things like air horns which played "Just Around the Corner, There's a Rainbow in the Sky" . . . for it suddenly seemed to me that was what our time needed again, not guided missiles. And even President Truman had said that we were never nearer to peace than we were at that moment.

"We have come to the point," Jake said, "where I have a device which will work, which is practical, and which we should not only manufacture but which should be protected in a way which only the Army or some kind of authority can do it."

I didn't feel at all like discussing any of this, and in addition it alarmed me. I said, "You haven't gotten into anything too hot for us to handle?"

He smiled. "Well, this device could also be used for steering a lawn mower while you sat on your front porch." He let his smile fade. "But it also could steer a projectile into a plane which is traveling at six hundred miles an hour."

"If this is something we can make," I said, "I'd rather make it for lawn mowers."

He sucked his cigar and frowned and said, "I think that it is fairly certain that if we put it on a lawn mower the Russians will put it on a rocket or a bazooka."

Then that awful sense of an impending future returned. Why always the talk about the Russians? Why always the talk about war when the President himself kept telling us that peace was just around the corner? Why (although I have no belief in Communism at all and utterly detest it) always assume that the Russians are different from what we are? You would have thought that they would have had a bellyful of fighting. And you would think that the man-on-the-street Russian, the boy-outside-the-corner-drugstore Russian, the wife-in-the-kitchen Russian, would feel just as we did.

"My inclination," I said, "is just to bury the whole idea."

Jake smiled in a sort of superior way which, in the last few years, he has come to use more and more when we have had to argue a point of business.

I didn't want to talk about it at all. And there should have been no reason for me to talk about it, either, for Doc Crocker had told me that I should not think about such matters, and the world, if it had had a heart attack, should not think about such matters either. And no one wanted to think these things. Everyone, and the Russians too, I imagine, just wanted things to settle down so that what was probably the biggest boom in history could go on booming.

"Look," Jake said, "I've invented this thing, and you can't ignore it. You've got to make up your mind about it."

And that was another thing which now depressed me. People were always inventing things which you had to make up your mind about, and why, I suddenly wondered, although I have always believed in progress, did they have to do it? Why couldn't you just have a moratorium on inventions? That was something which the U.N., which didn't seem to be getting anywhere, could put its mind to. Why did there always have to be more things, more people, more ideas?

"Jake," I said in exasperation, "don't you realize that today is Christmas?"

He didn't get a chance to answer, however, for George, up from his nap, walked in at that moment and I introduced him, and again I had that sense of the future. Gertrude took advantage of the moment to go into the kitchen under the pretext of there being something out there she wanted to show Mrs. Brawn, but the maneuver didn't quite work for Mrs. Brawn went with her.

And as soon as George was seated, Jake started in on him. "Mr. Manelle," he said, "do you think peace or war is coming?"

"Why war, of course," George said without even batting an eyelash.

The future! Oh, the future!

"And," Jake went on, "if you had a device which could steer almost anything into almost any target, including fast-moving airships, what would you think?"

"I'd be very interested, of course," George said, folding one leg over the other, and looking at Jake in his serious, sizing-up manner.

The new phase! The new era before us!

"Well," Jake went on, getting excited now, "the Yaw-Et-Ag Manufacturing Company has a device, or one which is ready to be adapted with the right kind of work on it, to do that."

"How does it work?" George said quickly.

Jake hesitated and then said, "Do you know anything about electronics?"

Oh, more stately mansions!

And much to my surprise, although nothing about George really surprised me, he said, "Enough to follow."

And apparently he did, for almost immediately they plunged into a discussion so technical that I could not follow.

And again I found myself becoming disturbed and angry with the future into which George and everything else were going to drag me, a future which seemed to be filled with things which I could not cope with, for why should any man be expected to cope with electronics? What business did I have with nuclear physics, with electronics? What business did I have with nuclear physics if what they were talking about was nuclear physics, which it might have been although it might also have been pig Latin. They talked and seemed to understand each other and then drew pictures for each other on an envelope which Jake took out of his pocket, pictures of circuits, or I suppose that it was circuits. What all was a man supposed to keep up on these days, I had to wonder.

They talked in this fashion until Gertrude and Mrs. Brawn came back from the kitchen which put an end to the conversation. Then Jake and Mrs. Brawn left, and Gertrude went to lie down again because she said that she was exhausted. George and I were left there in the living room looking at each other.

"Well, George," I said, "what's your reaction?"

He rubbed his chin slowly with his hand and said: "I think he's got something. And I think he's right. From this point on I think you should be in contact with the Army."

Oh, land of hope and glory!

"Something big?" I said.

"Damn big," he answered.

"Too big," I said, "for Yaw-Et-Ag to handle?"

"No," he said slowly, very slowly, for George was a serious young man in these matters, "not too big if Yaw-Et-Ag wanted to expand a little."

But then the flash of light came.

As he said that I felt a return of the excitement which had been fluctuating up and down all day within me, for the idea, the idea that put everything together, was arriving.

"We could manufacture whatever this thing is?" I asked him.

Then came the dawn.

He said: "I don't see why you couldn't. The idea is complicated but the actual thing is simple the way I get it, and this thing you could make. The way it gets adapted would probably be someone else's problem."

Then the sun rose.

We were silent, but the idea within me was growing to the point where I was almost bursting.

I broke the silence, saying, "Do you really think that there will be a war with Russia?"

"With Russia," he said carelessly, "or some of her puppets."

I said, "Then the invention could be important?"

He said, "Damn important."

"So important," I said slowly and hardly daring to breathe, "that it would appeal to almost any really able young man to be in on it?"

Then screamed the eagle.

He wheeled around sharply, and our eyes met so that I knew he had not failed to understand me.

"As you can see," I said, "I'm not in any shape to do much more with this than keep in contact. Jake has invented it but he's no kind of a salesman or promoter. Bert Bernstein could, but all of what we're talking about has always fallen in my department, but even I wouldn't know how to get to the Government in this kind of a business, for in the last war they came to us, which is something different."

It was like walking on a wire!

"And my problem, Dr. Anthony, is . . ." he said, looking down and then up again at me sharply.

I said: "My problem is that I need a young man, preferably a member of our family, who knows something about this kind of thing, to start out acting as my assistant, later perhaps to take over my position. Am I making any sense in what I'm saying?"

Then time stopped!

He put his hand to the back of his head and walked the length of the room twice before he answered. "Yes," he said, "you're making sense in what you're saying."

"From watching you and Jake talk," I said, "I'm sure that he would be agreeable. But of course you would have to talk to Mr. Bernstein. I'm not asking you to say anything on the spur of the moment. All I'm saying is that if you would like to talk to him I could probably arrange it so that the two of you can have lunch together tomorrow."

And breathing.

He walked back and forth in silence several times more and then said: "I don't want to say anything on the spur of the moment, either, but I think I would like to have lunch with Mr. Bernstein whenever it's convenient."

I could suddenly draw a breath again. The answer he had given was the best answer I could have hoped for.

"It'll be nice," I said, "to have a son-in-law in the business."

It would seem as though nothing more of importance could have happened on the Christmas, but one thing more did happen.

As I lay in bed that night just before I was going to turn out the bed lamp, Gertrude came in and sat down on the edge of the bed beside me.

"Tinker isn't quite sure yet," she said, "but she thinks she is going to have a baby."

The passage just ended was the last passage that Jeff dictated, and it completes the material he left to us. The untouched-upon part of his life was a matter of a few months only. Fortunately, from my conversations with him during the spring of 1950, I have some idea of what he intended to put into his book beyond this part. There was to be a brief history of his family, its origin in New England, its migration to Illinois where members of it still farm the half section of the original homestead, his father's migration finally to Gateway. This was to be followed by a description of Jeff's battle with the C.I.O., when it tried unsuccessfully to move in on Yaw-Et-Ag. After that were to come further details concerning the new developments at Yaw-Et-Ag and comments on George Manelle's negotiations in Washington obtaining government contracts. It is our misfortune, I feel, that these matters have been denied us.

In place of them, I have tried to round out this book by an inclusion of letters, communications, and so forth, which contain matters of interest.

Loose Ends

On the morning of May 22, 1950, Tom Selleck in New York, and Tinker Selleck Manelle in New Rochelle, received duplicate telegrams.

COME HOME AT ONCE STOP YOUR FATHER PASSED AWAY QUIETLY IN HIS SLEEP THIS MORNING STOP SERVICES ON WEDNESDAY STOP THINK YOUR MOTHER WOULD APPRECIATE A CALL BY LONG DISTANCE.

DOC CROCKER

The following is from Tom Selleck:

Actually, Father did not die in his sleep. Mother found him early the morning of the twenty-second lying on the floor of the upstairs bathroom in his pajamas. Death must have come during the night, for he had apparently been there for some time. Death must have come very rapidly, however, for he had made no effort to call out. Disregarding the aesthetic part of it, for I think it would have disturbed him to have been found as he was found, I think he died the way he preferred to, mercifully, quickly, and with a minimum of fuss about it. He had his own ways of being dramatic, but in important matters he did not care for fuss, and most of all it always embarrassed him to be the center of attention.

I was notified on the morning of the twenty-second, and I called Mother immediately. It was an unsatisfactory call as all such calls are, but I found out that everything was being taken care of already by his friends, Sam Zadina and Doc Crocker and, in particular, by Helen Flanagan whom he mentions so frequently in this book. It was very suitable, it seemed to me, that Helen should look after the details, for all during his lifetime she looked after the details also.

The services were held at the Second Baptist Church, which was strange, or at least seemed strange, for he had not attended that church since the time of his marriage. It happened that way because he had requested it in his will which was made only a month or so before his death. Why he wanted it that way can only be a matter of conjecture, but, after reading over his book which you have put together so intelligently for him, I have formed my own ideas on this subject. I do not think that he was returning in any religious way to the faith of his childhood. But I do think that symbolically (and he did believe in symbols), he was trying to, in one tremendous stride, reach all the simplicities which his childhood represented for him. But this is enough of this. I am enclosing in this letter the last letter he wrote to me in hopes that you may find it of some value to you in getting out his book.

The letter which Tom Selleck enclosed follows:

DEAR TOM:

I am soon to be allowed to go back to the office for a visit which, as you know, will mean a great deal to me, not as going back to the place where I have worked in the past but as a return to the place where, with the help of your brother-in-law, I expect now to be able to work in the future. Big things, I might say, are in the offing.

But to get down to the purpose of this letter, I have been cleaning up a number of odds and ends lately. I have made a new will, for instance. And don't let that alarm you because I have no intention of dying for a good long time yet. But in the course of taking care of this sort of thing I have come across my guns which I will have no use for in the future. As you know, they include a Browning "over and under," a 30.06, and a .22 target automatic. There is also a Police .38 which I am keeping, for I have always felt that it is a good idea to have a gun in the house.

It occurred to me that you might like to have the shotgun, for on occasion I believe that you have gone duck hunting although I know you are not particularly interested in field sports. I would like. to give you the shotgun and George the rifle. George has told me that he does go deer hunting in Maine in the autumn and would like, after coming west to live as he plans to this summer, to try his luck in Colorado or Wyoming. I thought that I might also give you the pistol and, to keep things fairly even, him my rod and reel and the other fishing gear. Will you write me your ideas about this division? Is it all right with you, I mean?

Now there is one other thing I want to mention. When you were home at Christmas time, and at other times since the war, I have heard you express discontent with what seems to me the very fine artistic work you are doing. For one thing, you said something about wanting to become "a serious artist," which I do not understand, for if those *Saturday Evening Post* covers, considering what you say they pay you for them, are not serious art I doubt if I know what serious art is. But even without understanding, I want to say that if something else is what you want you ought to do it. And the reason you don't do it, I take it, is a matter of money.

While I am a little short at the moment, I think I can figure out a way to finance this thing. I would like to give you five thousand shares of Yaw-Et-Ag Manufacturing Company, that is about three thousand dollars, which is the limit for tax-free gifts. It will actually amount to more than that in six months for big things are in store for us I do believe. Please do not object to this because this would be part of your inheritance anyhow and there is no reason why you should not have it now rather than at my death which may not be for years. I repeat that you ought to do in life what you want to do, especially since you are a single man without as yet any of the compensations which marriage can give you, which, I must say, are very real compensations. You know, at the time I graduated from the State University I had an offer for a tryout with the St. Louis Cardinals which I did not take. I have regretted this many times. My only reason for saying this is that I don't want you to ever regret anything which you don't have to.

Affectionately,
FATHER

The letter which follows was written by me to the publishers of this book before the subject of my acting as an editor had been considered.

DEAR SIRS:

I assume from your letter that when you ask me the cause of Mr. Selleck's death you are not asking for a medical answer, for a medical answer is too easily given. Medically, he died of a secondary coronary occlusion suffered some six months after his first one, a history which is not uncommon. I take it that you want to know something more than medicine in this matter although outside the field of medicine I do not feel myself to be too reliable an observer.

But in a random way, here are my thoughts about Jeff Selleck. First of all, it has sometimes seemed to me that the men most subject to heart diseases are those least able to sustain them. Your coronary is frequently, but certainly not invariably, a hearty, robust, life-loving type, a hard-driving man who works hard and plays hard. Intemperate is probably the word, not your ulcer type at all, although naturally I am hesitant about making categories. Jeff Selleck was the type of man which I mention. Why did he die? A man who gets a heart attack is always likely to die, almost as likely to die from his first one as from his second, and in the case of Jeff, his second attack was caused by the same things as his first one, the attempt to juggle more things than a man is supposed to juggle. He insisted upon going back to the office for half days in April. He fooled himself into believing that since he was only a half day at the office he was only doing a half day's work. He was doing considerably more than a half day's work and he pardoned himself, when I took him to task, by saying that shortly George Manelle, his son-in-law, would be with him to do everything for him.

But there is always a question which arises for me in matters of this nature. Is it better for a man to live unhappily half alive

for a long time or completely and happily for a very short one?
I do not know the answer, and my profession dictates the pro-
longation of life at all costs. But of this I am sure, those last
months for Jeff were very happy. But happiness is not a medical
question.

Nonmedically, though, what did Jeff die of? Do you know anything about modern weed killers? There is one kind which kills
by causing a plant to grow, to live that is, too intensely. I think
that life, for Jeff, was some kind of spiritual Two-Four-D which
stimulated beyond endurance.

*From Miss Flanagan we have the following which is a descrip-
tion of the funeral service held for Mr. Selleck.*

It was a lovely service conducted by the American Legion.
Mrs. Selleck had wanted a simple Episcopalian one, but I remembered that he had often said to me that when he passed on
he wanted to be buried by the American Legion, for he was a
great patriot and a great Legionnaire. Mr. Zadina agreed with
me, and, since it was mostly Mr. Zadina and I who had to do the
planning, that was the way we had it.

I had never been in a Protestant church before, and I found
the Second Baptist Church a very strange one, more like what
I had always imagined a synagogue to be than a church. It was
octagonal in shape with organ pipes filling the front of it where
the Cross should have been. The choir loft ran all the way across
the front end, too, at right angles to the way you would have
expected it to be. Below it, on a raised platform, was the pulpit,
and the casket was below that on the floor of the auditorium,
for I think of it as an auditorium and cannot think of it as a
church.

Flowers were banked around the casket in a very lovely way,
and lights were so arranged below the casket as to throw deep
shadows up onto the domed ceiling.

There was nothing of religion in any of this, which I regretted,
for while Mr. Selleck always denied a religion, I have always felt
a deep spiritual force within him. There was nothing religious,

I have said, but otherwise everything was lovely, the flowers, the lights, and the stained-glass windows.

The service itself was very simple. The Legion Chaplain who gave it spoke very well and very aptly of Mr. Selleck and, in conclusion, read the poem "Abou Ben Adhem," which all of us learned as children and which was a very true thing to say over Mr. Selleck, for if any man ever loved his fellow men it was Mr. Selleck, and I wanted to cry when the Chaplain finished the poem with: "And lo! Ben Adhem's name led all the rest."

Mr. Selleck was buried in the Selleck family lot at Mt. Prospect Cemetery, and at the grave the American Legion guard of honor fired salutes above the casket and the bugler played Taps. And this was very appropriate, too, for a good soldier who had been fighting one battle or another all his life.

There was one thing about the service which I have not mentioned and which I would like to mention because it was the thing which most impressed and touched me. Before the casket was closed, those attending the service who wished to were permitted to file up to the front of the auditorium and look at Mr. Selleck for the last time. I did not do so, for I knew that if I did I would be too profoundly affected. But from where I sat I could see the shadows of the people who did cast on the ceiling of the front of the church as they crossed those lights shining from below on the casket. And those shadows of hundreds of people who had known and loved him, shadows of people I didn't even know, and I think that I did know more of his friends than anyone else did, were what affected me mostly.

2

There are anecdotes within the Selleck family which I have felt should be included in this book but for which there was no place in the main body of the work. The following taken from a letter from Tinker Selleck Manelle to me is of this nature.

. . . however there is one story about Father which I think should be included in his book somewhere because there is a

touch in it which I, at least, would never have expected to find
in Father. It happened about a week before my wedding, but
what went on before it I don't exactly know. You see, the story
I have to tell is just the ending of something else which I can
only imagine. The story, I have come to call for myself, is that
of Father and the Princess.

You see, as it is not very well brought out in Father's book,
Father wanted awfully to get into the Army during this last war.
I suppose that he wanted to go in with some important kind of
a commission, but I am very sure he would have enlisted as a
private if he could have been accepted that way and been sent
overseas. I don't know why, but more than anything else he
seemed to want to get into the fighting, which I do not understand because most of the boys I know who did get into the fighting do not seem to have liked it at all.

The Army would not take Father, but at the end of the war,
through some of his political friends, he was sent to accompany
the governor on a tour of Germany on some kind of a commission which was supposed to report on something. What Father
reported on I don't know, but what he did there this anecdote
suggests a little.

It was a week or so before my wedding, and Father, Mother,
all of us, were at home in the evening, which was fairly unusual because when there was nothing better to do, Father and
Mother usually went to the neighborhood movie in the evening.
And at the time, I, for I was so rushed right then, was somewhere
every evening. Anyway, we were all at home and all dead tired
and all in the living room together. As I remember, Mother was
working over her checkbook, and Father was reading the paper.
The telephone rang, and I went out in the front hall to answer.

The voice at the other end was a woman's voice and it had a
rich, wonderful foreign accent something like Marlene Dietrich,
and it asked for Father. I asked who was calling.

And this rich, foreign voice said, very much to my surprise:
"The Princess Wied-Neuwied."

And I have to confess, at first I took this as a joke of some
kind on Father. I had seen pictures of the Princess of Wied-
Neuwied in *Vogue* and *Harper's Bazaar* and places such as that,
and I could not see any connection between this fabulous (fabu-

lous to me anyway) woman and my father. And I couldn't see
any reason, even if there was a connection, why the Princess
should ever be in Gateway City. But if it was a joke, I decided,
I would not be one to spoil it.

I went into the living room again and said: "Father, the Princess of Wied-Neuwied is on the phone and wants to talk to you."

Well, my first surprise was Father's reaction. He put his paper
on the floor and smiled and got up. "By God," he said, "it's
Butch."

And Mother, looking up from her checkbook, said, "And who
is Butch?"

Father said: "Butch Braunsberg, the Princess of Wied-Neuwied."

"Yes, I know," said Mother very queerly.

Then Father said, "Just a kid I ran around with for a while
when the governor and I were in Munich."

"Well, do you want to talk to her?" I said.

"You bet I'll talk to her," Father said, striding toward the telephone in the front hallway. "I'll talk to Butch with pleasure."

He answered the phone and then took it into the little lavatory
under the front stairs where all of us took the phone when we
wanted to talk in private. I stood there and looked at Mother, and
then both of us shrugged our shoulders.

"It's Butch all right," Father said when he came out again and
joined us. "It's Butch and she's finally come around to get her
package."

"What package?" Mother and I both said together.

Father said, "Why, the one she gave me in Munich."

And then he sat down and told us the story. He had met
Butch, as he insisted on calling her, although her name was the
Princess Eliena Braunsberg, Princess of Wied-Neuwied, and
probably half a dozen more names and titles. He had met Butch
and, as he said, "run around with her a little." Then, at the moment of his departure, she had come to him before he boarded
the plane which would take him home and asked him if he would
take a package to the United States for her. He had agreed to
do that and to keep the package in a place of safety until a time
when she would either come to pick it up or send someone to pick
it up for her.

"And you did it?" Mother said in consternation.

"Sure," Father said. "Why not?"

"There might have been a bomb in it," said Mother.

"Nonsense," Father said. "It's been up in the attic for almost four years now."

"In our attic?" said Mother, in even more consternation.

"Sure," Father said. "It's under a floor board, and I'm going up to get it." He paused and said, "Butch said that she'd be right over."

Then he went off up the stairway.

Well, if we had been surprised so far, we were bowled over when we met the Princess. She was wearing the simplest, most expensive-looking mink coat I've ever seen, and a black turban. And the jewelry she wore you could tell right off didn't come from the ten-cent store or even maybe Cartier's, either. And then, as everyone knows who's ever seen her picture, she is beautiful if you care for that dark, nervous type of woman.

Father met her at the door and she threw her arms around him and kissed him and said, "Oh, Popsie, you're getting fatter."

And Father became embarrassed and tried to pull in his waistline and said: "Well, of course, Butch, we're all getting older."

Then she kissed him again and he said in greater embarrassment: "Now, Butch, remember I'm a married man with a family and a position."

Then Father introduced the Princess to us and with us she was very polite and formal.

We talked for a few minutes and then the Princess said: "Popsie, I've come to get my package."

Father simply pointed to the living room table where he had put it after he had come down from the attic. It was about twelve inches by five inches by five inches in size and it was wrapped in oiled silk, with lots of official-looking seals on it with the crests on them.

"Ah," said the Princess as she picked up her package, and by this time Mother and I were sitting on pins and needles.

"Perhaps, Popsie," the Princess said, "you would now like to see what you have been guarding."

"Yes, of course," said Father quite calmly.

The Princess was standing in front of the coffee table in front

of the sofa. She broke the seals on the package and then poured
. . . and I say poured because that's just the way it was . . .
poured out its contents.

"Oh, my God!" said Mother.

Well, what it was was jewelry. Of course it was jewelry. It
had to be jewelry, but it was the kind of jewelry you don't ever
see in store windows, things that made your mouth water, with
stones which seemed to light up our living room in a way that
nothing else could light it up either.

"Oh, my God," Mother said again. "And to think that for almost four years that's all been up in our attic under a floor
board."

"Popsie," the Princess then said, and made a royal gesture,
"you have just said that your daughter is to be married. I would
like to give her a little something."

She bent over the array of treasures on the coffee table and
looked at them intently. Then she picked out a small diamond
clip and, handing it to me, said: "May you make a happy marriage." And she did it so magnificently that without knowing it,
as she gave it to me, I curtsied.

And I had realized that she was really the real McCoy, too,
when she had studied those things for an instant, because the clip
she gave me was far and away the least expensive thing there
was there, but it was estimated at a thousand dollars when we
got the insurance on it.

Well, the Princess left a very dazed household behind her
when she left with her package a little later. Mother and I just
sat there stunned, and Father went back to his paper and pre-
tended to read the sports page.

Then Mother said suddenly, out of the silence: "Jeffrey, just
what was your relationship to the Princess when you were in
Munich?"

"Who? Butch?" Father said, and put down his paper.

"Yes, Butch!" Mother said, standing up and looking severely
at him.

And then happened one of the very few times which I have
ever witnessed in which Father conversationally got the better
of Mother. Instead of speaking, he just smiled and started singing: "You can easily tell she's not my mother. My mother's forty-

nine." He stood up and walked to the doorway into the hall and
went on: "You can easily tell she's not my sister. I wouldn't show
my sister such a whale of a time. You can easily tell she's not my
sweetie. My sweetie's not that kind." By this time he was at the
foot of the stairway. "She's just a peach of a kid. She didn't know
what she did. She's a personal friend of mine."

And without giving Mother a chance to answer he swung up
the stairway and on up to his room to bed.

I hope very much, Dr. Crocker, that you can get them to put
this into Father's book. Perhaps it's snobbishness on my part,
but I like to think that there was a secret part of Father's life
about which none of us knew anything at all. Whether he was
one of nature's gentlemen or not I like to think that he had had
more fun than we suspected.

*For the following letter I am indebted to both Tom and
Gertrude Selleck. It was written by Gertrude to Tom during the
time when the publication of this book had become something of
an issue within the Selleck family. In a sense this could have been
inserted in the chapter entitled "1915 and 1920," but although to
the point it seemed to be an interruption at that place. Mrs.
Selleck to Tom, who was most enthusiastic about publication,
says:*

DEAR TOM:
After reading this book of Jeffrey's which you have sent to
me I hardly know what to think. You know what my feelings
were about his memoirs while he was still alive.[1] Well, those
feelings have not changed since then.

As for my allowing these recollections to be published, I can't
forbid it because it was apparently Jeffrey's wish, but I can

---

[1] Tom Selleck says: "Mother was never in sympathy with Father's project.
And especially, she resented the recording machine itself for she felt that
he was telling secrets to it, secrets which he had no business telling. She
could not have been angrier, I think, had Father had a mistress, and I think
she considered the machine a kind of mistress to whom he told things he did
not tell her. She hated it more than she could have hated a mistress, for,
since it was mechanical, she could not compete with it as she could have
competed with a woman."

hardly give my approval, either. If it is a matter of suing which worries these publishers I will not sue because I don't know exactly who to sue in this case and because I would think it a rather undignified thing for me to do, especially when, as you say, I will be getting a share of the royalties from the sales. Therefore I can only appeal to your good taste which should tell you what to do.

But there are things in this book which I object to very strongly. I see no reason why his description of our wedding night should be included, especially in the very biased way in which he describes it. I also object to the way in which he consistently seems to draw me as a sort of child. Perhaps there was a child in our family, but with all due respect to Jeffrey, the child was not your mother.

He implies that I was extravagant and had no concept of money. Let me point out a few extravagances which he indulged in. Think of his guns which you now have. They, with all their accessories, must have represented well over a thousand dollars and, except for a week a year, he never used them. And the same thing is true to a lesser extent of all his fishing tackle. Think of the motion picture camera, the projector, and the still camera he had during the period when he decided that he would go in for photography. Those and the darkroom equipment and the enlarger were all expensive items also, and they were rarely ever used after the first six months of that enthusiasm. Think of the workshop he had for a while in the basement with all those expensive tools. Think of that and then remember that almost the only thing he ever built was the martin house which is in our back yard. I suppose that it is cruel of me to say these things about one whom I loved very dearly and who cannot now answer, but I want to point out that there are more ways than one in which a person can be childish.

He has mentioned our wedding night, as I have said. Well, if I cannot change what he has said, I can in all justice go on and describe the honeymoon which followed.

Can you imagine where we went? We went to Yellowstone Park. Yes, Yellowstone Park, my dear child. And do you know why? It was because your father had always wanted to see Old Faithful. And do you know how we went there? We went by

automobile. And traveling anywhere by automobile in 1920 was
not exactly what it is today. No, we did not wear linen dusters.
I may be aged, but I am not quite that aged. We didn't wear
linen dusters, but Jeffrey did have a pair of driving gloves with
gauntlets.

For a wedding gift, Jeffrey gave me a shiny, brand-new, big
black Oldsmobile which was very touching inasmuch as I had
not yet learned to drive in 1920. And it was in the Olds that we
made our trip. It was a touring car which meant that there was
nothing which you missed, especially the dust and the rain, for
the side curtains could keep out neither.

We had the back seat of the Olds loaded down with luggage.
Jeffrey had wanted to fasten a tent onto the running board because he had felt that it would be romantic if we slept out in the
open. However, I vetoed the tent, and if I had been sensible I
would have vetoed the whole trip also. He was disappointed and
said, in that hurt way of his which could be so maddening: "But
in a tent, dear, we could be like a couple of gypsies." I said:
"Gypsies, my foot! I suppose that while you are fixing tires I can
tell a few fortunes."

We spent our wedding night, as he has said, in that horrible
Gateway Hotel. The next day, after stopping in to see my father
and mother and his father and mother, we set off on our safari.
When we had gone for about ten miles we had our first puncture.

"Don't worry, dear," your father said, "I'll have it fixed in a
jiffy."

That jiffy lasted for one hour and a quarter.

After that we had a charming little lunch in one of those de-
lightful country bistros where the special luncheon is overcooked
pork chops and undercooked potatoes with lumpy cream gravy.
I had indigestion for the remainder of the journey.

After lunch, when we had gone a few miles farther, I asked
Jeffrey where we would spend the night.

And he said: "Anywhere you like, dear."

"You mean," I said, "that you have not written ahead anywhere for reservations? You mean that you don't know where
we're staying?"

And he looked hurt again and said: "Why dear, I thought
we could just gypsy along staying in the places which caught our

fancy. I thought that we could just adventure along together."

Lighthearted adventuring gypsies us. . . .

I hate to remember some of the places in which we stopped. Once, we asked for a room with a bath, and that was exactly what we got. The bath was right in the room with us. But that was wonderful compared to some of the places we stayed in some of those windswept towns in Nebraska and Wyoming. And to make everything just a little bit more delicious, in every one of those towns Jeffrey seemed to find someone who had "served" in that grand and glorious fighting unit, "the Old Forty-second Division." And every one of those noble yokels had to "come up and see the missus," the belle of the regiment, your mother.

Somehow, and I can't imagine how either, we finally reached the Yellowstone and the lodge at Old Faithful. And the first thing your father did was get out that enormous gold watch he used to carry, and time the geyser. "Yep," he said, "exactly every seventy minutes."

"In that case," I said, "are you ready to go home now?"

He looked surprised and hurt.

I said: "I don't know about you, but I'm on my way back to Gateway."

"But Gertrude," he said, "I was sort of hoping that we could roam around for a while in this he-man country and the wide-open spaces."

I said: "I've had enough he-man country and wide-open spaces. You can roam around if you want to, but I'm on my way home now, alone if that's the way you want it."

We got back into the Olds and turned around and began the homeward journey.

I shall not mention the horrors on the way back, but they were something comparable to the return trip of Robert Conway to Shangri-La in *Lost Horizon.*

All of this was unimportant and does not mean that we did not love each other, but I mention the trip, Tom, to show you, or anyone who might read Jeffrey's memoirs, that his descriptions of our life may have sometimes been one-sided. Jeffrey was a good man and he left me well provided for, but one must realize at the same time that he certainly was not perfect.

3

The last letter here is from Miss Florence Dinwiddie, who taught Latin to Jeff and me and all the rest of us way back in antediluvian days when we attended old Downtown High. Miss Dinwiddie, remarkably enough, is still alive and active although today she is in her eighties.

Of course, John, I remember Jeff Selleck very well. He was in my Latin 1–2 class in 1907 before the high school building was remodeled. He was about thirteen then and a very big, serious and enthusiastic boy with blond hair and a way of bumping into things in the classroom. We started out that year, as usual, by learning the conjugation of the verb *sum* and I shall never forget the method which he invented to help the class learn it. He made the whole thing into a football yell which I will give here as I recall it:

> *Sum! Es! Est! Sumus! Est's Sunt!*
> Gateway! Gateway! Block that punt.

The rhyme is unfortunate, but it was effective with the whole class yelling it together. The second verse of the yell naturally went into the past tense.

> *Eram! Eras! Erat! Eramus! Eratis! Erant!*
> Touchdown! Touchdown! Don't we want.

The final verse of the yell was the future indicative, as is to be expected.

> *Ero! Eris! Erit! Erimus! Eritis! Erunt!*
> Rack-'em-up! Sack-'em-up! Jiminy-gee!
> The conjugation of the verb "to be."

Jefferson was a very nice boy but not a particularly good student. He was slow, but once he learned a thing he had it forever, which is very well demonstrated in what I will now tell you.

Only a year or so before his death, I happened to meet him one day in the Gateway National Bank and he recognized me at once and spoke to me.

"Jefferson," I said, half joking, "what is a gerundive?"

And quick as a wink he answered: "Miss Dinwiddie, a gerundive is an adjective and is always in the passive."

It seems very strange to me that he should have written a book now. I will be curious to see it. I am,

Very respectfully,
FLORENCE DINWIDDIE

To conclude, I want to quote from Jack Morgan's column, "Just Us People" in the Gateway Times Examiner. *The passage quoted was published the same day that Jeff died. Jack, as the reader knows, was one of us — that is, one of the ones who knew Jeff and loved him. I think that Jack's remarks here made a fitting ending to Jeff's story.*

JUST US PEOPLE

BY

JACK MORGAN

Monday, May 22nd . . . Today, as it must to all men, death came to Jeff Selleck. He was a gentleman, a scholar, and a good judge of whisky. And, having written that, the pen stops, and the hand falters.

"He was a man, Horatio," I could say, "take him for all in all, I shall not look upon his like again." I could say that, for to me there was always something Shakespearean and gallant about him. But rather than say anything of my own here I would like to quote the last stanza of a favorite poem of Jeff's, a poem which all of us learned long ago when we were pupils at old Downtown High School:

> There in the twilight cold and gray,
> Lifeless, but beautiful, he lay,
> And from the sky, serene and far,
> A voice fell, like a falling star,
> Excelsior!

A youth who bore mid snow and ice a banner with the strange device, my friend, Jeff Selleck.